THE ART AND SCIENCE OF LOVE

The Art and Science of Love discusses the most intimate phases of love-making, and does so without false shame. You will find it a rich source of constructive information, an indispensable aid to happiness and fulfillment at every stage in your marriage.

The Art
and Science
of Love

by

Albert Ellis, Ph.D.

A LYLE STUART BOOK

To
the pioneer authorities
on love, sex, and marriage
who made the writing of this book possible;
especially to Iwan Bloch, Katharine B. Davis,
Robert L. Dickinson, Havelock Ellis,
Sandor Ferenczi, Henry T. Finck, J. C. Flugel,
August Forel, Sigmund Freud, Paul H. Gebhard,
Rene Guyon, Norman Haire, G. V. Hamilton,
Edwin W. Hirsch, Magnus Hirschfeld, Max Hodann,
G. Lombard Kelly, Alfred C. Kinsey,
Richard von Krafft-Ebing, Paolo Mantegazza,
Clyde E. Martin, William H. Masters,
Margaret Mead, Ovid, A. P. Pillay,
Wardell B. Pomeroy, W. F. Robie,
William J. Robinson, Margaret Sanger,
Eugene Steinach, Wilhelm Stekel, Hanna M. and
Abraham Stone, Lewis M. Terman,
Theodore Van de Velde, Vatsyayana, and
Edward Westermarck;
and
to the outstanding authorities
on love, sex, and marriage who read this book
when it was in manuscript and made valuable
comments and suggestions, but in no way are
responsible for its final version; especially to
Hugo G. Beigel, Harry Benjamin, LeMon Clark,
Lester W. Dearborn, Henry Guze, Robert A. Harper,
Hans Lehfeldt, and Robert Veit Sherwin.

Contents

Introduction:

Why Another Marriage Manual?

There are, heaven knows, many published marriage manuals. Why, then, another?

Because, although many of the existing books are excellent and have well served the patients and friends to whom I have recommended them, none quite seems to fill all the requirements which I am ungracious enough to demand of the ideal work in this area.

What are these requirements? Simply that a handbook of marital relationships be—

Objective rather than moralizing.

Practical rather than academic.

Psychosexual rather than merely sexual; psychobiological rather than only psychological or biological.

Honest and forthright rather than vague and defensive.

Modern rather than dated.

Complete as to essentials rather than irrelevantly all-inclusive.

Clear and interesting rather than profound and dull.

I have shaped this book to these requirements so that men and women may have the basic knowledge that they need of themselves and of each other.

I hope it will guide them toward experiencing the creative sex relationships that are the birthright of every human being.

ALBERT ELLIS

New York City

THE ART AND SCIENCE OF LOVE

1.

The Human Sexual Apparatus

Many human beings, in fact all too many, seem to think that our sexual apparatus largely consists of the genitals and associated structures. They are wrong.

The sexual apparatus consists of the entire human body, most of the essentials of which are not only necessary for the arousal of sex desire and the attainment of orgasm, but are also intimately involved in climactic release. As Kinsey and his associates (1953) most dramatically and convincingly have shown, so many parts of the body are directly related to sexual excitement and satisfaction that listing all of them is like outlining a textbook on human anatomy.

For purposes of simple classification, we may say that the main bodily parts which directly and indirectly affect sexuality are (a) the brain and the rest of the central nervous system; (b) the autonomic nervous system; (c) the sensory organs and the muscular system; (d) the hormone-producing glands; and (e) the external genitals and the internal reproductive system.

What are the major ways in which each of these parts of the body affect sex desire and fulfillment? Briefly, these:

The brain and central nervous system. The human brain, particularly the most highly developed part of it, which is called the cerebrum or forebrain, is largely instrumental, once it receives impulses from the sensory organs, in instigating or facilitating sexual arousal (Lastrucci,

13

1947). When the individual is aroused, his brain helps him reach orgasm and provides him with feelings of pleasure or satisfaction. With his brain severed from the lower part of his body (as occurs in some instances where the spinal cord is cut), a man may become genitally excited and may even have an ejaculation. But his excitement will come only through tactile stimulation of his genitals, not through thinking; and his pleasure will be nil.

The brain also serves as a controller or inhibitor of sex excitement or climax. Even when he receives direct genital stimulation a person may focus his attention on non-stimulating thoughts (such as thoughts of housecleaning or playing chess) and may prevent himself from becoming aroused or reaching a climax (Walker, 1946).

The central nervous system includes (a) the brain and (b) an elongated extension of the brain, consisting of the spinal cord and a number of large branchings (which ultimately connect with the numerous smaller branchings of the peripheral nervous system and the sensory organs). The central nervous system conducts ingoing sensations from the skin, limbs, muscles, eyes, ears, nose, tongue, etc., to the brain and outgoing sensations or impulses from the brain back to these organs again (Durand-Wever, 1952).

The part of the central nervous system that is specifically connected with sex sensations is the lower region (or sacro-lumbar area) of the spinal cord, situated in the small of the back. In this region important bundles of nerve cells are directly connected with the smaller nerve endings in the genital and pelvic areas. They control the stimuli to and from these areas.

If the nerves in the genitals are in good order and the nerve cells in the lower region of the spinal cord are also working properly, stimulation of a man's penis may lead to erection and orgasm even though (as in the case of some paraplegics) parts of the rest of his nervous system may be severely damaged. However, as noted above, a paraplegic will not receive any pleasure from his orgasm, since the nerves that would normally conduct sensations to his brain and back again to his genitals have been cut at some point in his spinal cord.

Where all parts of the central and peripheral nervous systems are working effectively, sex excitement and satisfaction are a two-way process: (a) Tactile stimulation of the genitals sets up nerve pathways to the lower region of the spinal cord and activates return arcs to the genitals. These sensations are also submitted, through the upper part of the spinal cord, to the brain. (b) The brain, when impinged upon by sensations from the lower part of the spinal cord and by sexual stimuli from other channels (such as the individual's seeing a desirable sex partner), returns nerve impulses to the lower region of the spinal cord, and thence to the genitals again.

By this two-way combination of local genital stimuli and brain-centered thoughts and signalings, the individual becomes maximally aroused and satisfied. With either of these two major nerve circuits working by itself, he is likely to achieve only partial sex arousal and/or satisfaction.

The autonomic nervous system. The autonomic nervous system is a special nerve network which tends to control involuntary actions (such as heart beating and breathing) while the central nervous system controls voluntary actions (such as running, knee-bending and throwing objects). Although it is not presently clear how the autonomic nervous system acts to produce or enhance sexual desire, it seems certain that it significantly causes or influences most of the bodily activity that occurs in conjunction with or immediately following orgasm. Thus, sexual responsiveness usually results in an increase in pulse rate, blood pressure, breathing rate, genital secretion, salivary secretion, and so on; and all these responses seem to depend upon nerve impulses flowing along the channels of the autonomic nervous system.

The sensory organs and the muscular system. The peripheral nervous system consists of the final branchings of the nervous system and the sense perceptors or receptors (taste buds, hot and cold receptors, pain spots, etc.) and the muscles to which the sensory branches lead. Without this sensory-motor system, humans would have no physical feelings, would be painless and joyless. Nor would they be able to move.

Sexually, the sensory nerves conduct sensation from the genitals, eyes, nose, mouth, fingers, and other organs of sensation to the spinal cord and brain; and, kinesthetically, from the pelvic, genital, and other muscles to the brain.

The central nervous system, in return, sends signals to the muscles that enable them to adjust in different ways so that sex (and other) movements are facilitated.

Because, at bottom, sexuality is intimately related to sensuality, or to touch sensations, both arousal and orgasmic release largely depend on the proper functioning of the senses and the muscles. If these are seriously impaired, much sexual excitement and fulfillment becomes non-existent.

The hormone-producing glands. Human beings have several important hormone-producing glands, including the gonads (testicles in the male and ovaries in the female), the adrenal, thyroid, parathyroid, and pituitary glands. The hormones produced by these glands are powerful chemical substances which, when released into the blood stream, often have dramatic sexual (as well as nonsexual) effects (Beach, 1947, 1948, 1956).

Although it was once believed that each of the major hormone-producing glands secreted its special hormone, it has recently been discovered that several of these glands give off more than one hormone. Sex hormones, for example, may be produced not only in the ovaries or testes but also in the adrenals and elsewhere. Moreover, the production of one hormone, such as thyroxin, may have significant effects on the production of other hormones.

It has also been found that hormonal effects on human desire and orgasmic release may be both direct and indirect. Thus, when hormones are released into the blood stream, they may (a) directly excite nerve centers leading to arousal; and (b) indirectly influence sex performance by directly affecting the individual's metabolism, general health, or reproductive cycle—which, in turn, influence his or her sexual proclivities. Hormonal influences on sexuality are therefore not only highly significant but enormously complex.

The genitals and reproductive system. Assuming that an individual's central nervous system, autonomic nervous system, sensory organs and muscular system, and hormone-producing glands are in good working order, the frequency, intensity, and duration of his sex activities will importantly depend upon the condition of his or her genitals and reproductive system. Thus, someone who has genitals which are injured or diseased may experience serious blockings in his sex arousal or performance. And a woman may find that her sex desires are considerably increased or decreased at different periods of her menstrual cycle.

In many major ways, then, the various parts and systems of the human body significantly affect our sexual inclinations and acts. Sexually speaking, we usually behave as total organisms rather than as specifically genital-oriented animals. Since this is a marriage handbook, we shall describe and discuss the sex organs and their functions at some length. But, in so doing, we shall never lose sight of the fact that a man or a woman is far more than a penis or a clitoris and that even the most sexual thoughts and feelings have important semi-sexual and non-sexual roots.

The male sex organs. The most prominent and important part of the male sex organs is the *penis,* which is employed for both urination and sex relations. In its unerect or flaccid state, the penis is usually three to four inches long; in its excited or erect state, generally five to seven inches. Both its length and diameter vary considerably in size with different individuals. It becomes distended or erect mainly through sexual arousal (and, secondarily, through other stimuli, such as non-sexual excitement). When stimulated, blood pumps into the hollow areas in its shaft and keeps it in an erect state until physical or mental stimuli have subsided, when it returns to a flaccid condition.

The penis contains a head (or glans); a rim (or corona) which divides the head from the shaft; a main shaft, which takes up most of its length; and a root or base where it is attached to the body, underneath the pubic bone. Through the penis runs a tube called the urethra, through which urine or semen are expelled from the slit (the meatus) at its front. The most sensitive parts of the penis are usually the head and the under-side about an inch behind the head.

Covering the head of the penis, in its original state, is a fold of skin called the foreskin (or prepuce). The foreskin is sometimes difficult to keep clean, as a secretion called smegma tends to accumulate under it. It is also sometimes too tight and causes irritation. It is frequently removed by being clipped off, or circumcised, soon after a male child is born. Although originally a religious rite of several peoples of the world, circumcision is now recommended by many medical authorities. Others, however, oppose it as a general practice (Duzet, 1957, Weiss, 1964).

The *scrotum* is a sac or bag underneath the penis which normally holds the *testicles* and *epididymis*. The testicles produce (a) spermatozoa or sperm, by which the male may impregnate the female; and (b) some of the sex hormones, especially androgens, that influence the development of maleness (beard growth, deep voice, male features, etc.) and contribute to the arousal of sex desire. A male's left testicle is usually a little lower than his right one. Sometimes one or both testicles may be missing or may fail to descend from the inguinal canal to the scrotum —in which case medical attention should be sought. If at least one testicle is properly descended and is in good order, the male will usually be fertile. He may be potent even if both testicles are undescended.

Inside the scrotum or groin are accessory male sex organs, including: the *epididymis,* an elongated structure springing from the testes, in which the sperms gradually mature; the *vas deferens,* a continuation of the epididymis, running from the testicles to the ejaculatory duct; the *seminal vesicles,* lying at the base of the bladder and connected with the vas deferens, which act as reservoirs for the semen, storing it until it is needed; the *prostate gland,* encircling the urethra in front of the mouth of the bladder, which forms a thick, milky fluid which makes up a large part of the liquid portion of the semen; special *ejaculatory ducts,* carrying secretions from the seminal vesicles, which mix with the spermatozoa from the vasa deferentia, and help expel it from the penis at the point of ejaculation; and *lubrication glands* (bulbo-urethral or Cowper's glands), which help the semen flow through the urethra to its opening or meatus.

The female organs. The female sex organs are somewhat more complicated than those of the male. They consist, firstly, of the *vulva* (a general term for the external female genitals). The vulva is an oval-shaped arrangement between a woman's thighs, extending from the mount of Venus (or mons Veneris), the fatty tissue above the pubic bone, to the region just above the opening of the rectum (anus). Covering the vulva when it is closed are the larger or outer lips (*labia majora*) and, inside these, the smaller or inner lips (*labia minora*), both of which consist of folds of skin. The larger lips are coarse and skin-colored and extend from the mount of Venus almost to the anus. They are generally covered with hair. The smaller lips are delicate and reddish and tend to become swollen, sensitive, and well lubricated when the female is sexually excited. According to Masters and Johnson (1961, 1962) they become bright red when a woman is about to attain an orgasm.

Inside the smaller or inner lips, from top to bottom, are (a) the *clitoris*, (b) the *urethral opening* (meatus), and (c) the *vaginal opening or orifice*. The clitoris, a small, exquisitely sensitive, penis-like structure, is usually (though not always) the main seat of sexual sensation in women. It has no passage for urine, as the penis does. Like the penis, it has a head and shaft, and its head (or glans) is covered by a small hood or foreskin, which has an underfold that should be kept free from accumulated secretions or smegma (otherwise an offensive odor may result). Occasionally, where the hood of the foreskin is too tight or irritating, circumcision of the clitoris may be necessary. More often, where secretions have accumulated and hardened underneath the hood or in its folds, cleaning by a gynecologist may be desirable.

Although the bulk of the clitoris normally is embedded in the female's flesh and consequently feels as if it were only peasize to the touch, the organ actually is about an inch and a half long. Like the penis, its head and shaft swell with blood during sexual excitement, stiffening the clitoris and making it tumescent or erectile; but, because of its small size, not so markedly erectile as is the male penis.

The urethral opening in the female is separate from both the clitoris and the vagina and is not, strictly speaking, a sex organ but is designed for urination. However, it tends to be sensitized and may sometimes be used for masturbatory or other sexual purposes.

The vaginal opening lies just above the anus. It has a small entrance or vestibule (part of which is called the introitus) which, like the smaller lips, is well supplied with nerve endings and is quite sensitive to tactile stimuli. In back of the vestibule and the vaginal opening is the vagina itself, which is a stretchable tube about three to four inches long.

Normally, the vaginal tube is in a collapsed state; but when the penis enters, it adjusts itself to the size of the penis and may become quite distended.

Different women's vaginas vary widely as to length, diameter, and the size of the opening; but, in the great majority of instances, because of the elasticity of the vagina, a woman is able to accommodate a penis of almost any size.

In a girl or woman who has never had intercourse, the entrance to the vagina is usually partly covered by a membrane of tissue called the *hymen* or maidenhead. The hymen may be thick or thin, strong or weak, elastic or rigid; or it may never exist at all, since a few girls are born without one. It may easily tear or stretch during initial intercourse; or, occasionally, it may block coitus completely and have to be surgically removed. It is often broken or stretched long before a girl has intercourse, by medical examination, sexual exploration, the use of tampons, etc.

The vagina leads to the cervix, or neck of the womb, which protrudes into it near its back end. It then extends a little beyond the cervix. During sexual excitement and coitus its walls are lubricated; and the glands of Bartholin, located near its entrance, may also be activated and provide lubrication (Masters and Johnson, 1961, 1962).

The vagina serves several important functions: (a) It is an outlet for menstruation, which usually occurs every twenty-eight days or so. (b) It stretches very widely to serve as a birth canal when a woman bears a child. (c) It opens and stretches to receive the male's penis during intercourse.

Though it appears to be, when it is in a state of rest, a rather small and narrow organ, it is amazingly distensible and is able to carry on all its functions adequately when there is no pathological condition.

Cases of sexual incompatibility stemming from lack of congruency between a man's penis and a woman's vagina most often are caused by the fact that, especially after a woman has had several children, the vagina may become too wide and muscularly lax for satisfactory coitus. Fortunately, modern surgery can usually correct such a condition.

The vaginal walls are ringed by powerful muscles at its lower end which may be active during intercourse and which are able to clasp the penis tightly. When coitus leads to climax, the muscles of the lower part of the vagina often contract spasmodically, thus inducing the woman to feel that she is having a special kind of "vaginal orgasm." Actually, the same contracture can be experienced, but may not be felt as keenly, when a woman receives a climax from massage of her clitoris or by other extra-genital means; so that it is doubtful whether a special "vaginal orgasm" exists.

Where a man generally has pubic hair around his penis and covering part of his lower abdomen, a woman's pubic hair usually stops short of her abdomen, mainly covers the top part of her vulva, and then comes down in triangular fashion over her outer genital lips.

Above the vagina, in the abdominal cavity of the female, is located the *womb* (uterus), with arm-like attachments (Fallopian tubes) close to which are situated, on either side, an ovary. Like the testicles of the male, the ovaries secrete both reproductive cells (which are called egg cells or *ova* in the case of the female) and hormones which influence menstruation and the growth of the woman's sex characteristics (hair, voice, appearance of genitals, etc.).

The womb, as noted above, has a neck (or cervix) which juts into the upper part of the vagina. During intercourse, the male ejaculates sperm at the entrance or mouth of the cervix and this sperm then enters the womb through the cervical canal and makes its way up to the female's Fallopian tubes.

Approximately once every 28 days, under usual conditions, an egg is released from one of a woman's two ovaries, passes through the tubes into the womb and, if it meets a sperm and becomes fertilized, imbeds itself into the lining of the womb, which has previously been prepared by hormonal influences to receive it.

If this egg does not become fertilized, the lining of the

womb which has been prepared to nourish it breaks down and passes out of the woman's body through the cervical canal and opening into the vagina. This periodic breakdown and hemorrhaging of the lining of the womb is called *menstruation* and usually lasts from three to five days.

2.

Sexual Performance in Males and Females

Sexual Performance in Males. The process of sexual arousal and satisfaction in the human male normally consists of several steps:

1. The entire body, and particularly its nervous and muscular tissue, achieves a sufficient amount of rest, oxygen, nutrition, etc., to bring it to a state of readiness for sexual activity.

2. The testes and the other hormone-producing glands secrete an adequate amount of sex hormones, particularly androgen, to pour into the blood stream and sensitize the genitals.

3. The whole organism is bombarded with physical and psychological stimuli of sufficient degree and intensity to excite the nerve centers in the brain and lower region of the spinal cord. The main stimuli which are usually effective in this connection are the sight, touch, and thought of a sexual object—particularly, of a member of the other sex (Dengrove, 1959; Kelly, 1957; Long, 1922; Moll, 1931).

4. When the nerve centers in the brain and spinal cord are stimulated, the head and shaft of the male's penis become engorged with blood, causing the shaft to become rigid or bone-like and the penis to rise or become erect, so that it stands out from the body.

5. At the same time, the precoital lubricating fluid is stimulated into flowing from the male's urethra onto the head of the penis, thus facilitating any intercourse and

ejaculation that may take place. This lubricating fluid may occasionally contain sperm; but it is largely a secretion from Cowper's glands. It may become reduced in quantity and finally absent as the male ages.

6. Urged on by his rising excitement, the male generally makes certain that some kind of steady friction is applied to the sensitive parts of his penis and he tends to focus his pelvic movements, particularly if he is having intercourse, so that they too, along with the steady penile sensations, send impulses to the nerve centers. Additionally, he may focus on movements of his lips, hands, shoulders, etc., which also send signals to his spinal cord and brain (Beach, 1956).

7. To and fro, back from the spinal cord and brain centers to the penis and other end organs of his body, and then back again from these peripheral organs to the central nerve centers, the impulses of excitement keep moving and mounting.

8. Finally, after a sufficient summation and intensity of neuromuscular impulses have been achieved by consistent penile and bodily movement and friction, the nerve centers send out impulses which trigger off orgasm, or what Kinsey and his associates (1953) term an "explosive discharge of neuromuscular tensions at the peak of sexual response."

Orgasm in the male is usually accompanied by an ejaculation from the penis; but it may also occur, especially in young boys or in older males who have recently had prior orgasm, without ejaculation.

Orgasm is normally associated with intense pleasurable sensations in the penis and other parts of the body and by several kinds of psychophysical sensations and spasms, including a marked increase in pulse rate, blood pressure, breathing rate, genital secretion, nasal and salivary secretion, pelvic congestion, and muscular movement in the pelvis, thighs, arms and legs, abdominal muscles, and almost all the other major muscle systems of the body.

Sexual performance in females. As far as can be presently determined, sexual arousal and climax in females is remarkably similar to that which occurs in males, except for some physiological changes in uniquely female organs. Thus, Masters and Johnson (1961) have recently found that during sexual excitement women's breasts and vaginas tend to expand considerably and the inner lips of their vulvas become, at the point of orgasm, bright red.

When a woman has an orgasm, a quantity of mucus may be expelled from her vaginal walls and from Bartholin's glands and she may therefore seem to be having the equivalent of a male ejaculation. Actually, however, she has nothing analogous to the male's expulsion of semen.

There is considerable talk in the popular sex literature about the significant sex differences between males and females; but there has been relatively little factual evidence to validate this talk (Bonaparte, 1953; P. and E. Krowhausen, 1964; Mead, 1949; Scheinfeld, 1947; Woodside, 1948; Zimmerman and Cervantes, 1956).

Careful consideration of clinical and experimental evidence would seem to warrant the following conclusions:

1. Most males are aroused more easily and quickly than females. There is a small minority of females who are instantaneously aroused by suitable sexual stimuli and are much more often sexually excited than are most men. But the average female in our society has to make more of an effort focusing on sexually exciting ideas than the average male; and she has to have a longer period of active physical stimulation of the erogenous parts of her body before she becomes sufficiently aroused to approach the point of sexual climax (Adams, 1953; Landis, 1942; Terman, 1951; Shuttleworth, 1959; Wright, 1949a, 1949b).

2. Most males in our society are able to attain orgasm more quickly than most females, although there again is a small minority of females who can have climax just as quickly or more quickly than the average male. When the average female is directly stimulated—which can usually be done more effectively by manipulation of her clitoris than by coital penetration—she seems to take about four or five minutes to reach climax, while the average male, under the same circumstances, takes from two to four minutes. When the female, however, is indirectly stimulated, as tends to happen during coitus, she often takes ten or twenty minutes to achieve orgasm, and frequently she cannot achieve it at all.

3. More females appear to be diffusely sensitive while more males are specifically genitally sensitive to sexual stimuli (Daniels, 1953; Davis, 1956; Kisch, 1926). Thus, males often tend to be interested primarily or exclusively

in genital contact, while females are equally or more interested in kissing, caressing, and other sexual preliminaries to genital contact. At the same time, there is no evidence to show that the average male's penis is more sensitive than the average female's clitoris, nor that the male's breast is less sensitive than the female's. Moreover, there are some females who are primarily interested in genital rather than in pre-genital contact and there are some males who are enormously interested in sexual foreplay as well as active copulation (de Beauvoir, 1953).

4. It has been shown, especially by the Kinsey researchers (1948, 1953), that females tend to be less psychologically responsive to many stimuli than are males—that they are less interested in the sex activities of others, show less preferences for particular types of sexual acts, and react to a smaller variety of sexual objects.

It is quite possible that some of the observed psychological sex differences between males and females in our society may result from their radically different kinds of training in regard to sex (Van Emde Boas, 1950). It is also possible, however, that there are innate psycho-physiological differences between the sexes which lead to the average male's greater responsiveness to a wider range of stimuli.

5. Once a female is aroused sexually and has a satisfactory orgasm, there is a good chance that she may be able, within a short period of time, to have another, and still another orgasm, until she has had about a half dozen full climaxes (Masters, 1961). A few women, moreover, are able to have ten, twenty, thirty, or more orgasms, or long strings of minor and major orgasms, within a half hour or an hour after they have had their first climax. In this respect, women tend to be sexually "superior" to men; since the latter normally require a resting period of a half hour or more between orgasms, and can rarely achieve more than three or four orgasms in a period of several hours.

6. Whereas the male's orgasm usually lasts but a few seconds, the female's frequently seems to last for a somewhat longer length of time. In some cases, particularly where it is not followed up by subsequent climaxes, it gradually rather than quickly subsides.

7. Although the male orgasm is generally quite intense and pleasurable it often covers quite a wide range of inten-

sity, since it is by no means always as pleasurable as it can be when it is at its best. The female orgasm also covers a very wide range of intensity, perhaps even wider than that of the male's. When it is at its best, it can be shatteringly intense and satisfying. Frequently, however, it is unintense and only mildly or moderately releasing (Adams, 1953; Knight, 1943).

Female orgasm can be somewhat vaguely classified into the two categories of minor and major climaxes, with only the latter being fully releasing and satisfying. Sometimes the minor female orgasm is equated with a so-called clitoral climax while the major one is equated with a so-called vaginal climax, but there is no evidence to support this equation. On the contrary, many women can only achieve their major climaxes through direct clitoral stimulation while penile-vaginal intromission provides them, at best, with minor orgasm (A. Ellis, 1953a, 1963a, 1963b, 1965a; Ellis and Harper, 1961a).

8. Whereas most males in our society reach their peak of sexual performance late in their teens, females tend to do so in their late twenties. How much of this slowness of full sexual maturity is the result of biological factors and how much is related to the sexual inhibitions which we especially place on females is not as yet clear. In any event, once the female reaches the peak of her sexual arousability, she tends to maintain a fairly steady level of arousal and satisfaction for the next twenty or thirty years or longer. Some women even show a higher state of sexual arousal after they have reached the menopause. In contrast, most males slowly but surely tend to decline in sex desire and performance after the age of twenty.

All told, then, there appear to be significant sexual differences between the average male and the average female, some of which are biologically based and some of which have probably been created or exaggerated by the different kinds of sex attitudes which we tend to give the two sexes in our civilization (Hardenberg, 1949; Zimmerman and Cervantes, 1956). As is true of all human traits, however, *average* figures regarding male and female sexuality have little meaning. Just as the average male is taller than the average female, but *some* females are considerably taller than *some* males, so may *some* females be considerably more highly sexed, quicker to become aroused, and easier to bring to orgasm than *some* males (Landis, 1940).

This is particularly true of those females who, because of their unusually high sex endowments, are prone to have many voluntary and non-prostitutional premarital affairs. Such females are frequently so easily aroused and satisfied sexually that their male partners receive the erroneous impression that all normal females are, or should be, the way this minority of females behaves. Consequently, when a male has an affair with or marries an *average* female he is shocked to discover that his sweetheart or wife is sexually "subnormal."

In regard to human sexuality as well as to other characteristics and traits, therefore, we must always realistically keep in mind the facts of both group *and* individual differences. Otherwise, unrealistic expectations will arise to sabotage our heterosexual relations.

3.

Kinds of Sexual Outlets

Biologically and biosocially human beings resort to many kinds of sex outlets. They may become sexually excited and come to orgasm in several major ways: (a) They may consciously or unconsciously think or daydream about sexually arousing persons or objects. (b) They may have sexual dreams. (c) They may masturbate. (d) They may have heterosexual coitus or non-coital sex relations. (e) They may engage in homosexual activities. (f) They may on occasion have sex relations with animals.

Since, under favorable conditions, all these forms of sex participation are exciting and may lead to climax, there is every reason to believe that if human beings were raised without any sexual prejudices or preconceptions they would, in the course of their lifetimes, engage in most of them, though to varying degrees (Freud, 1938).

Thus, under conditions of complete acceptance of all forms of sexuality, the average man or woman would probably participate in heterosexual intercourse or non-coital relations (heavy petting) for the great majority (perhaps 80 to 90 per cent) of his or her outlets, and would employ other forms of sex relations for the remainder of his or her activities.

In our own society, however, as well as in other parts of the world, distinct sexual attitudes are instilled (Seward, 1946); so that most people ultimately, particularly after marriage, end up by favoring one type of outlet—usually heterosexual intercourse—while a minority favor another type—such as homosexuality.

This channelizing of our plurisexual urges into one or two main outlets has several possible causes: (a) We are raised to feel that outlets other than the ones we favor are immoral or impermissible. (b) We become, because of emotional disturbances, compulsively attached to a certain outlet. (c) We become neurotically afraid of one mode of behavior (for example, afraid of rejection by members of the other sex) and therefore substitutively remain fixated or fetichistically attached to another outlet (such as homosexuality). (d) We openmindedly try several outlets (such as masturbation, heterosexual petting, and heterosexual intercourse) and decide, on the basis of our experience, that one of them (say, heterosexual coitus) is far more enjoyable than the others.

Even in our own sexually prejudiced and neurotic society, however, complete channelizing of the sex urge is hardly the invariant rule. Most people resort to several different kinds of behavior in their early life before they mainly become attached to one special kind; and many resort to plurisexual activities during all or most of their lives. Some of the major forms of sex participations prevalent today will now be discussed in more detail.

Sexual thoughts and fantasies. Virtually all normal males and females have considerable sex thoughts and fantasies (Ramsey, 1950). They think, usually, about meeting attractive members of the other sex, undressing them, petting with them, having coitus, etc. Such fantasies may range very widely over the imaginative spectrum and frequently include somewhat unusual, peculiar, or "bizarre" thoughts and fancies. It is only when such unusual sex ideas acquire an obsessive-compulsive element, or when they cannot ever be dispensed with in the process of arousal and fulfillment, that they can rightly bs labeled as being pathological. As Levine (1955) has noted, "A common misconception is that all unusual or bizarre thoughts indicate psychoses or abnormality."

In the great majority of instances, sex thoughts and fantasies are used for purposes of arousal and do not, unassistedly, lead to orgasm. In a minority of instances—probably no more than one per cent of females and an almost negligible per cent of males—thinking about sexual subjects may result in an individual's having a regular climax. Thinking about sexual objects and affairs will not itself bring on climax in most cases but will be of decided aid. Often it is indispensable for reaching orgasm during masturbation, petting, and coitus.

Sex dreams. According to the Kinsey findings, almost all males and about seventy per cent of the females who have been studied admit to having nocturnal sex dreams, with or without orgasm. In some cases, such sex dreams seem to increase when an individual's other sex outlets decrease; but in many other instances this is not true, especially for females. Even when sex dreams do increase as a result of a drop in other outlets, the number of orgasms thereby obtained does not seem to equal those otherwise missed.

Sex dreams, like thoughts and fantasies, are perfectly normal and expectable (Gutheil, 1950; C. Landis, 1940, 1942); it is unusual when they never occur. If either dreams or waking thoughts about sex assume unusual proportions, however, it is to be suspected that the individual does not have sufficient other outlets or that he is emotionally disturbed and is therefore obsessively concerned with sex. In the former instance, his acquiring more other outlets would usually be desirable; in the latter instance, psychological help should be sought to get at the root of the disturbance.

Masturbation. Originally, masturbation meant the manipulation of the genitals manually, usually until the point of orgasm had been attained. Today, the word is more loosely used to cover almost any kind of self-stimulation, manual or non-manual. It is also often applied to extracoital relations between two individuals, but then confusingly overlaps with the term petting, which for the sake of clarity should be used instead. For the purposes of the present discussion, the word "masturbation" will be applied only to autoerotism or self-stimulation—that is, to describe sexual arousal and satisfaction which occurs when a person is alone.

Through the ages, many objections to masturbation have been written and declaimed—in spite of the fact that at least ninety-five per cent of American males and seventy per cent of females seem, without apparent harm, to masturbate at some time during their lives (Finger, 1947;

Kinsey and associates, 1948, 1953; Peck and Wells, 1925; Ramsey, 1950). Today, there is no longer a tendency to claim that autoerotism results in mental illness, physical debilitation, genital injury, many diseases, etc., as was once erroneously claimed by many so-called authorities (Dearborn, 1947a; Lawrence, 1953; Spitz, 1949, 1952; Wettley, 1959). But several other objections to masturbation are still printed in most modern sex writings; and virtually all these objections, as I have shown in my books, *Sex Without Guilt* (1965a) and *Sex and the Single Man* (1963b), are groundless.

The main anti-masturbatory arguments and the answers to them are these:

1. It is held that masturbation is immature. Actually, however, unmarried men and women in our culture make it, in the majority of cases, their main sex outlet. Autoerotism becomes immature or deviant only when an individual who has the choice of several other forms of sex activity finds that he can *only* experience masturbatory satisfaction or when he employs masturbation fantasies and activities for anxiety reduction (Abramson, 1955; Faust, 1957). Such individuals are comparatively rare. Virtually all other males and females who masturbate, at whatever age, are in the normal sexual range.

2. It is objected that masturbation is asocial. But the idea that masturbation is a lonely, unsocial habit that will lead men and women to avoid the company of others is as ridiculous as the notion that going to a movie is socially healthier than viewing television at home or that individuals who read at home are poor lonely souls compared to the socially healthy persons who read in libraries.

A girl or fellow who is unsocial and who fears facing others may well masturbate instead of trying to achieve heterosexual relations; but rare indeed is the individual who becomes unsocial *because* of masturbating. About *guilt* over autoerotism, yes; but not over masturbation itself.

3. It is claimed that masturbation does not lead to full emotional gratification. But no sex act—including heterosexual coitus—can give full emotional gratification at all times to all persons. The concept that every sex act, in order to be considered a "good" or "beneficial" one, must be intensely emotionally satisfying, or that sex without

love is wickedness, is a non-scientific, basically puritanical notion (Ellis, 1965a). Sex without love or emotion, including masturbation, may be, under many conditions, less *preferable* to sex with love; but this hardly makes it wrong or bad.

4. It is contended that masturbation is sexually frustrating. However, although it may be *relatively* frustrating, when compared to sex relations between two human beings, it is rarely *absolutely* frustrating; otherwise, millions of people would hardly continually and repetitively keep resorting to it. A man or woman who has been reared with anti-masturbational attitudes will naturally find autoerotism relatively unsatisfactory. One who has been raised with pro-masturbational views will find it quite satisfying—though not, usually, as satisfactory as various forms of inter-human contact.

5. It is alleged that masturbation leads to impotence or frigidity. Actually, there is no evidence to support the belief that it causes impotence or premature ejaculation in males; and the Kinsey research group found that where approximately thirty-three per cent of females who did *not* masturbate before marriage were coitally unresponsive in the early years of marriage, about fifteen per cent of those who did masturbate were equally unresponsive. My own clinical findings, over a period of many years, also indicate that a large number of women are helped to achieve satisfactory marital relations if they first engage in some amount of masturbatory activity.

Dr. Robert A. Harper of Washington, D. C., in a letter to me states: "Masturbation is an excellent device to help women who are frigid to overcome their frigidity when it is accompanied by attitude reconditioning. Men, too, may be helped to overcome premature ejaculation if their masturbation is accompanied by rational attitude reconditioning."

6. It is held that masturbation may lead to sexual excess. But erotic response, in both males and females, depends upon a remarkably foolproof mechanism. When an individual reaches the limits of his or her physiological endurance, he or she no longer responds sexually. Under the circumstances, only a most abnormal person, such as a psychotic, would masturbate when he or she had no desire and only this kind of person might conceivably masturbate

xcess." Kirkendall (1958, 1961a, 1961b) has recently shown that young males often have much more sexual potential than they actually use.

7. It is sometimes contended that, because children in our culture often get the idea that masturbation is dangerous and consequently become guilty about it, parents should reassuringly ally themselves with the child's own conscience and, while assuring him that the practice is harmless, help him to find ways to grow out of it. This is a pernicious, defeatist doctrine: since children obviously get the idea that masturbation is dangerous from *someone;* and their parents should unceremoniously annihilate, instead of cowardly accepting, this idea.

No one would say that, because children fear breaking mirrors or passing in front of black cats, parents should help them grow out of breaking mirrors or walking by black cats. Rather, they should be helped to overcome their *fears* and not to stop the *actions* caused by such fears. So with masturbation: children should be helped to overcome their fears of autoerotism instead of to stop masturbating.

Altogether, then, the caviling attitudes on masturbation which still fill most of our sex manuals—attitudes which state or imply that autoerotism, while not completely harmful, is still not "good" or "desirable"—have no scientific foundation and constitute a modern carry-over of old antisexual moralizings (Brown and Kempton, 1950; Stekel, 1950). As LeMon Clark (1958a) notes: "Where self-relief in the male or the female brings release from tension, promotes repose and helps attain relaxation and sleep, it is not only harmless, but definitely beneficial. Aside from what slight recognition one should give to the problems of over-indulgence and methods which may cause injury, there need be no concern whatever about this natural practice, which goes back far into prehistoric times."

The fact is that the vast majority of Americans engage in a considerable amount of masturbation for some period during their lives. In view of our other restrictions on sexual activity, they would be abnormal if they did not.

Petting or non-coital sex relations. Like masturbatory activities, petting generally has a bad name in our society. It has been variously claimed that petting for its own sake or to the point of orgasm is abnormal, perverted, un-healthy, immature, frustrating, and frigidicizing. Except to a limited degree, these allegations appear to be groundless (Beigel, 1962; R. Harper, 1961b).

Petting for its own sake consists of tactile stimulation of the body, particularly of the genitals and the erogenous zones, of the sex partner. It is usually done through caress-ing, embracing, kissing, biting, massaging, etc. When confined to lip kissing, embracing, and stimulation of the breasts and other areas above the waist, it is sometimes called *necking*. When it includes mutual nudity and stim-ulation of the genitals, it is often called *heavy petting* or *non-coital sex* relations.

Prolonged petting that does not lead to orgasmic release may result, for some individuals, in states of tension, pains in the groin or testicular region, headaches, and other forms of physical discomfort. According to the findings of Dr. Abel J. Leader, a Houston urologist, a chronic disor-der of the male's prostate and seminal vesicles (known technically as vesiculoprostatitis) may result when the se-cretions produced by these glands are retained instead of being discharged—as would occur if a male pets or is otherwise aroused over an extended period of time with-out sexual satisfaction (Secor, 1959). According to Le-Mon Clark (personal communication), "Girls frequently acquire chronic pelvic congestion as a result of heavy pet-ting without reaching orgasm. Their pelvic capillaries be-come chronically dilated, leading to congestion and discom-fort. An occasional petting party without orgasm does lit-tle harm, but heavy petting two or three times a week for a year does."

On the other side of the ledger, it would appear that some persons are able to engage in prolonged petting ses-sions with little or no harm and with some amount of satisfaction and tension reduction. For these individuals, who may well be in the minority, petting for its own sake may be more fulfilling than not engaging in any form of sex relations whatever. At the same time, most of them would doubtlessly derive greater fulfillment and benefit from petting to climax.

Petting to orgasm, when it is not engaged in exclusively or invariantly, would appear to have no serious disadvan-tages whatever when compared to participation in actual coitus. It is frequently not as pleasurable an activity as is coitus, particularly for the male; but some persons, especially females, actually find it more satisfying than intercourse. It involves exactly the same kind of stimulation and response as does coitus in most respects; and, as far as can be presently determined, virtually all males and females experience quite the same kind of orgasm through petting as they do through copulation—provided that they do not have some significant psychological prejudice in favor of one of these two sex acts (Lindsey and Evans, 1925, 1929).

When it is practised exclusively as a means of achieving orgasm or is invariably preferred to all other forms of sex relations, petting may be part of the individual's system of sexual fetichism, compulsivity, or neurosis. Thus, it may be continually resorted to because the individual is afraid of intercourse, or would be guilty about technical loss of virginity, or is fetichistically attached to, say, breast manipulation. In a few instances, however, as where a male discovers that he very quickly has an orgasm in intercourse but has a more retarded and enjoyable climax if his wife caresses his penis, or where a female finds coitus but not non-coital relations physically painful, petting may be primarily or exclusively employed on a non-fetichistic and non-neurotic basis.

Petting to orgasm is particularly normal and healthy when it is resorted to because other forms of sex activities might result in real difficulties. Thus, if two young people or even two older married individuals want to have sex relations and have a legitimate fear of pregnancy, they can have virtually all the satisfaction they crave without taking any risks. Or if two people can only have sex relations in a semi-public place—such as a parked automobile—and wish to minimize the danger of detection, petting may well be a more practicable form of sex involvement than coitus. (Bromley and Britten, 1938; Reevy, 1960; Rockwood and Ford, 1945).

It is most surprising—as Dr. Alex Comfort (1950) has pointed out—that a society such as our own, which frowns so heavily on premarital sex relations and which stresses the dangers of illegitimate pregnancy and abortion should also disapprove of petting to orgasm. For if young people tend to have strong sex desires—which they do—

KINDS OF SEXUAL OUTLETS 37

and if they are going to have some kind of sex participation—which they evidently are—it would seem far
wiser to encourage them to pet to climax than, say, to
have premarital coitus or to engage in homosexual
activity.

Our own society, unfortunately, is neither perceptive
nor wise in this connection. It frowns upon premarital intercourse—as well as on the thoroughly undangerous sex
acts, masturbation and petting. In so doing, it virtually
ensures that there will be considerable copulation on the
part of young people who, if they had been more rationally educated in sexual areas, would probably be petting to orgasm in most instances. A most peculiar
paradox!

In any event, petting would seem to be relatively harmless for many individuals when it is carried on in its own
right and absolutely harmless when it is continued to the
point of mutual orgasm. The vast majority of males and
females can easily come to climax through various types
of petting; and there seems to be absolutely no good reason why, when they want to do so and are released from
the belief that sex equals sin, they should not.

Premarital sex relations. According to the findings of
Hamilton (1929), Davis (1929), Bromley and Britten
(1938), Dickinson and Beam (1934), Terman (1938),
Hohmann and Schaffner (1947), Kinsey and his associates (1948, 1953), Gebhard, Pomeroy, Martin, and
Christenson (1958), Ehrmann (1960), Ellis (1965c),
Reiss (1960), Brown (1964), Locke (1951), and other
investigators, premarital coitus, although almost universally condemned in this country, is practiced by perhaps
half the females and eighty to ninety per cent of the males.
Most studies also tend to show that the rates of participation in this type of sex activity have been increasing in
recent years, particularly in the case of females (Chesser,
1956; L. Fink, 1950; Lanval, 1950a, 1950b; Maddock,
1962).

Virtually all marriage manuals, if they discuss the matter at all, devote considerable space to the disadvantages
and virtually no space to the possible advantages of premarital coitus.

The usual contentions are that people who engage in
prenuptial sex relations risk venereal disease, illegitimate

pregnancy and abortion, guilt and anxiety, loss of reputation, frigidity or impotence, emotional disturbance, ex-
ploitation of one's sex partner, sabotaging of family life,
sordidness, lack of responsibility, lack of happiness in marriage, promiscuity, etc. (Blood, 1955; Butterfield, 1953; S.
Duvall, 1952; Christensen, 1959; Duvall and Hill, 1952;
E. M. Duvall, 1963; Fromme, 1950; Mace, 1958, 1960;
Sorokin, 1956; Unwin, 1933, 1934).

These objections to premarital intercourse have been
considered in detail in my book, *Sex Without Guilt*
(1965a). Suffice it to say here that, although most of the
so-called disadvantages of premarital intercourse may well
apply to ignorant, stupid, or seriously disturbed individuals, they hardly apply today to the intelligent and in-
formed adult who has some degree of emotional stability
and maturity. Such an individual can easily eliminate the
dangers of venereal disease, illegitimate pregnancy, and
abortion; will not become unduly guilty, irresponsible,
frigid or impotent, exploitative, or neurotically promiscuous; and will frequently tend, because of his or her premarital sex experience, to have a happier and healthier
sexual and general life after marriage.

At the same time, premarital sex affairs have many distinct advantages. They provide sexual and psychological
release for those who need sex outlets; they enhance sex
competence and self-confidence; they provide adventure
and experience; they serve to prevent the development of
sexual abnormality and deviation; they limit prostitution
and sex offenses; they provide variety and pleasure; etc.

As Dr. Louis Berg, one of the leading psychoanalysts
and sexologists of the last few decades has said in regard
to a male's truly understanding the differences between
himself and a female, unless he "has had a personal experience broad enough to enable him to discover them for
himself, he is bound to make mistakes either of omission
or commission. . . . It is obvious that no man with three
or four isolated premarital affairs, or even a single extended one, is in a position to acquire more than a bare
fundamental knowledge of the complicated and varying
sexual nature that is a woman's" (Berg and Street, 1953).

This is not to say that all individuals under all circumstances should engage in premarital coitus. Indeed they
should not. Many people, because of stupidity, ignorance,

chronological immaturity, emotional instability, or other traits will get into more difficulties by having than by not having antenuptial intercourse. But probably just as many or more, because of their high sex drives, their physical and emotional maturity, and their desires for adventure and experience, will get into more difficulties by not having some form of premarital heterosexual contacts. If, as previously noted, actual coitus is considered too risky or too little enjoyable to be practiced premaritally, then it makes sense for certain individuals to pet to orgasm and thereby, with maximum safety, satisfy their urgent sex desires.

Chastity and virginity. It has frequently been claimed in the sex literature that there are no real or major hazards or disadvantages to an individual's being strictly chaste or virginal before marriage. Such individuals, it is pointed out, can fairly easily sublimate their sex needs by engaging in other forms of activity, such as athletics or social engagements, and can thereby forego sex participations.

Although the theory of sublimation of sex outlets was first presented by no less an authority than Sigmund Freud (1938), it still appears largely to be mistaken. Individuals can apparently only healthfully sublimate one kind of activity by substituting another when the substitute act is closely related to the one that is eliminated (Gallichan, 1916, 1939; A. Hamilton, 1955; Leuba, 1948). Thus, a woman who greatly desires to be a mother, but who can have no children of her own, may adequately sublimate her mothering desires by becoming a nurse, a nursery school teacher, or in some other occupation where most of her time and energies are devoted to caring for children.

Sex activities, however, cannot easily be sublimated into anything but other sex activities. An individual may remain healthfully virginal—providing that he or she masturbates or pets to orgasm. But, as Taylor (1933) showed in a classic monograph and as the Kinsey research team (1948, 1953) has more recently affirmed, human beings, and especially males, rarely eliminate all their sex outlets for non-sexual interests. Instead, they generally substitute one form of sexual behavior for another.

Particularly for many highly sexed men and women almost any kind of true sex sublimation is virtually impossible. Such individuals rarely remain literally chaste; and when they force themselves, for any period of time, to refrain from all forms of sex behavior, they usually become tense and disturbed (Arlington, 1958; Guyon, 1934, 1951, 1963; Fielding, 1961; Russell, 1929; Stokes and Mace, 1953). In addition to extreme nervousness and irritability, they often develop physical symptoms, including headaches, gastric upsets, congestion of the pelvic region, and high blood pressure (Robinson, 1930).

Complete chastity, or refraining from all forms of sex outlet, is impractical or harmful for many or most humans (Beigel, 1961; Briffault, 1931; Brown and Kempton, 1950; Frumkin, 1960; Hiltner, 1953; Kronhausen and Kronhausen, 1959, 1964; Langdon-Davies, 1954; Nystrom, 1919; Wile, 1934; Wood, 1960b; Wylie, 1947; Young, 1964). Technical chastity or virginity—by which is meant abstinence from certain forms of sex relations, notably coitus—is both possible and harmless, as long as sufficient other outlets are utilized. There are a few individuals who can obtain orgasmic release from literally no other method than vaginal-penile copulation; and such individuals might not even be able healthfully to tolerate technical chastity. But this would not be true for the great majority of males and females. Absolute continence or abstinence, however, has never been practiced by any sizable proportion of healthy young men and women, and there is no reason to believe that it ever will be (A. Ellis, 1965c; Haire, 1948, 1951; Wood, 1960a).

Extra-marital relations. Extra-marital relations or adultery arise when an individual who is legally married has sex relations with another individual who may or may not be married. In other words, both partners to an adulterous affair may be married; or only one may be. Most human societies—but by no means all—have condemned adultery, largely because it raises paternity issues and tends to disrupt family life (Ford and Beach, 1951; Hambly, 1959; Kardiner, 1944; Westermarck, 1922; Wood, 1960b).

Our own society has always roundly condemned and penalized adulterers on moral, religious, social, and other grounds (Drummond, 1953; Murdoch, 1949; Pilpel and Zavin, 1952; Ploscowe, 1951). Most of the objections that have been raised against extramarital affairs, however, are of dubious validity today, although they may have been quite valid a century or more ago (Dearborn, 1947a; A. Ellis, 1965a; R. Harper, 1961b).

An intelligent, well-informed, emotionally mature individual who presently engages in adulterous relations will not consider himself to be intrinsically wicked and sinful and will therefore not suffer intense guilt. He will normally employ proper contraceptive technique to avoid the dangers of illegitimate pregnancy and abortion. He will take suitable measures against venereal infection. He will rarely worry about loss of reputation and will tend to be quite honest with his extramarital partners and avoid exploiting them. He will usually arrange to commit adultery on an affectional basis, under non-sordid conditions. And, by being discreet about his extramarital involvements, he will avoid any penalties that may accrue from detection.

Instead of being highly inconvenienced by his adulterous participations, the intelligent adulterer today will frequently gain considerable advantages—that is, the same kind of advantages of adventure, experience, varietism, and pleasure that the mature participant in premarital relations tends to gain today. Why, then, should anyone refrain from committing adultery? For several reasons:

1. Because we (perhaps illogically) insist that an adulterer does not love his mate and places his marriage in jeopardy when he engages in extramarital affairs, we, by this very insistence, *make* adultery a marriage destroying act when it is (as it often is) discovered. Under these conditions, adultery often does sabotage even good marriages.

2. Because people in our society *believe* adultery to be inimical to marriage, husbands and wives who engage in extramarital affairs usually have to do so secretly and furtively. This means that they must be dishonest with their mates. And although their adultery, in itself, might not harm their marriage, their dishonesty about it (as about any other major issue) may well be harmful.

3. Because, in our civilization, married couples are supposed to achieve sex satisfaction only with each other, if one mate is an adulterer he may have less sex interest in the other mate (though the reverse is also sometimes rue); and, in consequence, this other mate may become exually deprived and maritally discontent. Similarly, the ne, energy, financial resources, etc., that are often re-

quired to carry on an adulterous affair may detract from those available to the legal mate.

4. Because, under our system of raising males and females, adultery generally (though not always) will to some degree interfere with and jeopardize a marital relationship, if an individual has a good all-around marriage, and if his mate might be unhappy if he were discovered in adultery, he would be rather foolish to risk the break-up of his good relationship for additional sex pleasures. On the other hand, single persons (who are committing adultery with a partner who is married) or married persons who are living in a hopelessly poor relationship might not be taking serious risks in committing adultery.

In view of these reasons, even a non-moralizing individual who wants to retain the many advantages (along with the disadvantages) of monogamous marriage would do well to refrain from adultery. If, perchance, he and his wife honestly and mutually believe that extramarital affairs are beneficial and are not disturbed by the knowledge of each other's infidelities, they may sanely participate in occasional or frequent extramarital affairs.

In Dudley, England, for example, in February, 1959, the city council, after first forcing Joseph New and his wife Margaret and his mistress Sadie and their ten children (seven by Margaret and three by Sadie) to vacate a city-owned apartment because of their living in an adulterous menâge à trois, relented and provided a house for this family. Sadie, according to a story in the New York *World-Telegram,* became Joseph's mistress several years ago. After they had had a child he took her home to meet his wife. After talking it over, Margaret agreed that Sadie and her baby should move in with the family; and Joseph and his wife and mistress and children have lived amicably together ever since.

This unusual situation, where the husband's adultery is fully accepted by the wife, also sometimes exists in other parts of the world, especially Latin countries, where a husband's adultery with a paid mistress or prostitute is often condoned, while his having a love relationship with a non-prostitute is highly objected to by the wife. As Dr. Harry Benjamin (personal communication) points out, it is a love or marital *rival* who is feared; but a paid prostitute c a woman who is accepted by the wife (as in the case of Joseph New) is not considered to be a serious rival.

Be that as it may, the chances of an American wife or husband's fully and openly accepting an adulterous relationship on the part of his or her mate are exceedingly slim. Therefore, even though adulterous *desires* are quite strong and completely normal on the part of most husbands and wives, extramarital *actions* are usually impractical and immature.

If and when extramarital relations do occur and are discovered by the non-adulterous mate, they need not be taken as a sure sign that marital love is dead and a divorce must immediately be arranged. In most instances the marriage may be salvaged, and sometimes even improved, if the non-adulterous partner will (a) remain calm and refuse to catastrophize about the situation which has occurred; (b) refrain from blaming the adulterous partner for his or her immature but very human behavior; (c) put aside all ideas of revenge or retribution; (d) look into his or her own heart to discover what he or she may possibly have done to encourage the mate's adultery; (e) make every possible effort, in line with the methods about to be discussed in the rest of this book, to improve sex-love relations with the mate; and (f) if necessary, seek the counsel of an impartial and objective marriage counselor or psychotherapist who will help get at and correct the underlying attitudes and emotions which lie at the source of the adultery that has been committed (Ellis, 1963a).

4.

Psychological Methods of
Arousing a Sex Partner

Sexual arousability in human beings is an importantly psychological as well as physical process (Lastrucci, 1947; Maslow, 1955). Males and females not only may be sexually excited by several of their senses—particularly those of touch and of sight—but also may become aroused by thoughts and feelings. That is to say, they may achieve a state of tumescence or erection, begin to secrete precoital fluid, and at times even attain orgasm when they remember past sex experiences, think about present involvements, or imagine a future adventure.

If, therefore, you would maximally arouse a member of the other sex, so that he or she fully desires to have sex relations, you had best employ both physical and psychic avenues of excitability (Bibby, 1961; Malla, 1964; Reik, 1958; Stekel, 1926; Stokes, 1948; Vatsyayana). The main psychological avenues and techniques which may serve you in this connection are the following.

Love-sex appreciation. People usually enjoy being enjoyed. If you are enthusiastic about your mate's looks, personality, sex techniques, and so on, your enthusiasm will tend to make him or her more interested in you and your attributes.

No matter how good-looking, bright, talented, or sexually adept we may be, we all like to be concretely and specifically appreciated by our *particular* love partner. We want, at least at fairly frequent intervals, to be *told* that we are nice, enjoyable, pleasing. And sometimes, more importantly, we want our beloved to back up his or her words with convincing actions—with special consideration, occasional gifts, remembrances of anniversaries, surprise theater tickets, or just a glow of real pleasure from sitting over dinner together.

Especially in regard to sex relations, if you can show your mate that you are greatly looking forward to having contact that night, that you consider physical intimacy an important part but still only a part of a complete relationship, and that there is no one else in the world with whom you can imagine having equal love-sex satisfaction, it is likely that your eagerness and ardor will excite reciprocal ideas and feelings (Fromm, 1956; Mace, 1945, 1958; Robinson, 1962).

Particularly if your partner has, or thinks he or she has, some physical or other defects (if she thinks that her nose is too large or he thinks he breathes too heavily), it is important that you be kind and accepting and that you go a little out of your way to emphasize his or her good qualities.

Any critical or non-accepting attitude you may take toward his or her "defects" will most likely kill or neutralize desire. Conversely, full acceptance of your mate, including flaws and failings, encourages him to become most aroused and let go sexually.

If being with your partner excites you, your excitement will often enhance his or hers. By all means show, then, whatever sex and love interest you have in your mate. Don't hide it away in the dark where it can't possibly be catching.

Demonstration of love. Love tends to increase emotional security and release inhibitions. When we are sure that we are accepted and approved, we do not *fear* what others will think of us—including what they will think of us sexually. We let ourselves go with those who love us, rather than with others who may disapprove. And we try things with those who care for us that we would be afraid to try, for fear of failing or being laughed at, with others. Conversely, if we are afraid we are not loved or will not continue to be loved, we may fear to make any move that might shock our sex partner and alienate him or her (Grant, 1957; Levy and Munroe, 1938).

Especially to females in our society, love is an important requisite of uninhibited sex relations. Perhaps there is something biological in this: since females do take greater risks, such as the risks of pregnancy, in having coitus; and love reduces risk. However that may be, Western women are certainly raised to hold back sexually until they feel perfectly secure with their mate—until they are sure of love.

Western males, too, are often raised to find sex relatively worthless, meaningless unless it is accompanied by feelings of love; so that they may hold themselves back in a non-loving sex relationship.

Be apprised, then: The more love you give, in sexual affairs, the more you are likely to arouse your mate to the highest peaks of excitement and create an eagerness for him or her to satisfy you in return. Love not only begets love—it also begets greater sexual responsiveness.

Self-confidence and initiative. Although, as noted in the previous section, most humans are less inhibited when they are accepted and approved than when they are unloved, lack of inhibition is primarily related to self-approval and self-confidence rather than to acceptance by others. Sexual inhibition is nothing but a high-class word for *fear* or *anxiety;* and most human anxiety, as I point out in my book, *How to Live With a Neurotic* (1957a), stems from an individual's exaggerating the significance of what others think of him and not having the courage of his own convictions.

To gain self-confidence and reduce anxiety, one must stop blaming oneself for one's mistakes, accept oneself fully with one's weaknesses and fallibilities, and stop trying to win the love and approval of virtually everyone one encounters.

In being self-confident, one gains sexually in several ways. In the first place, one takes the attitude that one will succeed; and, having this attitude, generally does succeed. Or, if first attempts to arouse a sex partner fail, one confidently continues these attempts until, in many instances, one succeeds.

Secondly, by being confident and taking the sexual initiative, one instills confidence in oneself in the other person. Most women, as Caprio (1952) points out, react badly to sexual shyness in their husbands, partly because they feel that he will be sexually inadequate. A self-confident partner, on the other hand, gives his mate the idea that he will be able to perform competently; and consequently she will tend to let herself go to her own greatest degree.

Thirdly, self-confidence in one mate tends to serve as a good model for the other partner. If a husband or wife acts as if he or she is sexually adequate and is almost certainly going to have a good time in bed, the spouse will tend to believe that he or she can also have an equally good time, and will follow through in a relatively relaxed manner.

Fourthly, if one mate takes real sexual initiative, the other mate will normally believe that he or she is greatly desired and loved. Particularly, as Mozes (1959) observes, "Nothing can heighten the excitement of the husband more than his realization that his wife is participating fully in the act by taking the initiative, or at least encouraging him. Consequently, the wife should take an active role in all parts of love-play."

Self-confidence and taking the sexual initiative, then, are important requisites for arousing one's sex partner; and, if more people were concerned about how much they respected themselves, rather than how much *others* approved them, their sex techniques would improve enormously.

Talking things out. No man or woman is a mindreader. Even individuals who are passionately in love frequently misunderstand each other; and husbands and wives certainly do. Your sex proclivities are necessarily so personal and unique that it is difficult for another member of the same sex to understand them. A member of the other sex, who is bound to be startlingly different in many ways, has even greater difficulty. The only sane way, therefore, to know what sexually arouses and satisfies your mate is, in unvarnished English, to ask him or her; and the only sane way to get your mate to understand what sexually arouses and satisfies you is to tell him or her (R. Harper, 1958; Katz, 1956).

Shame, in this connection, is utterly silly—just as silly as a husband's being ashamed to tell his wife that he likes eggs scrambled instead of sunnyside-up, and then becoming angry because, somehow, she does not fathom this. Why the devil should she? And why on earth should he be ashamed to tell her?

If, then, you like your sex with the lights on, with music playing, in front of mirrors, rolling on the floor, slow or fast, orally or manually, by land or by sea, for heaven's sake *say* so. And do your very best to discover, by *words* as well as deeds, what your mate likes, too.

If either you or your parner cannot talk about sex and let the other know what your likes and dislikes are, then disturbed, needlessly guilty attitudes exist between you, and professional help may be indicated. But before you open the directory to look for a psychologist, open your mouth and speak up!

Bed manners. Although over-politeness and fear-inspired etiquette have little place in sex relations, normal politeness and good manners are often important adjuncts to arousing your mate. Only in Utopia do two partners desire exactly the same approach at precisely the same time. Usually, one takes a little longer than the other to become aroused; or requires different kinds of exciting techniques; or acts differently when sexually desirous.

Under these circumstances, it will often be necessary for you to be unhurried or patient when you would rather rush ahead; or to be impetuous when you would rather wait. Similarly, you may have to slow up your caresses when you would prefer to go faster; be gentle when you would rather be more vigorous; use a monotonous rhythm when you feel like caressing in a less regular fashion; and otherwise inconvenience yourself to some degree for the greatest arousal and satisfaction of your mate.

The main point to note here is that not merely your physical technique but your *attitude* should be considerate and kind. If you are doing exactly what your mate would prefer you to do, but you are obviously clenching your teeth and champing at the bit while doing it, you cannot expect him or her to be relaxed and content and to be most aroused.

If you indicate, however, that you *want* to be sexually pleasing, that you *enjoy* being patient, your mate will deeply appreciate your attitude and tend to let himself or herself go to a maximum degree.

It is often erroneously thought that someone who is, as the vernacular saying goes, "good in bed" is one who thoroughly enjoys sex relations himself or herself and who consequently is adept at satisfying the sex partner. This is only partly true; and sometimes it is wholly false. Individuals who thoroughly enjoy themselves in bed are often so intent on their own pleasures that they are hardly considerate of their mates and are therefore rather poor bed partners.

What is perhaps more important than self-enjoyment, in some respects, is a deep-seated feeling of *empathy* with the other individual and an intense desire to discover what pleases the other and to perform such pleasing acts. The deeply empathic individual not only passively notes what his or her bed mate requires but actively *looks for, seeks out* this mate's requirements, and then caters to them.

Sex skill, in other words, is part and parcel of a highly creative, active, experimental, love-motivated outlook. It is prophylactic considerateness: an absorbed attempt to discover not merely what *is* but what *might be* satisfying to the partner.

Sex skill is not masochistic or self-sacrificial, in the sense that the good lover totally neglects his or her own desires in order to fulfill the other's needs; but is self-participating as well as other-directed, in the sense that the lover *enjoys* the pleasurable reactions of his or her mate and *wants* to discover new and better means of arousing and fulfilling this mate (Rhoda Winter Russell, personal communication).

Good lovers, in this fullest sense of the term, are rare in our society and when they do exist and give full play to their creative love-making with their mates they tend to be exceptionally appreciated, even though they themselves may not be the most highly-sexed, youngest, or most beautiful or handsome individuals.

Using arousing materials. As a result of his biological tendencies as well as his being raised in a society where certain things are considered to be unusually stimulating, the average person becomes conditioned to various stimuli, such as romantic stories, pictures of nudes, risque limericks, etc. If this is so, then it is ridiculous to pretend that it is not or to be ashamed that it is.

If there is any problem in arousing your mate sexually, do not hesitate frankly and openly to make use of whatever materials may serve you best. Discover, by conversation and experimentation, if there are any such stimulating materials and be sure that you are well provided with them at the proper time and place.

This may not be too easy to do since, as Maddock (1959) and Kronhausen and Kronhausen (1959b) have pointed out, the kind of stimulating sex material that tends to be available in this country is cheap pornography which is not too exciting to many intelligent and cultured individuals. But if there are stories, recordings, or films which help arouse your mate they may be worth obtaining and employing.

Sometimes the only materials needed for purposes of sex arousal will be your own voice or actions; but at times props may be desirable. Kelly (1953) highly recommends that husbands and wives place a fairly large mirror at the foot of their bed and watch themselves having intercourse by using this mirror in conjunction with a hand mirror held by the mate who is surmounting the other. In this manner, the partners can see and be additionally excited by the exact state of their intromission and movements. Other arrangements may be profitably employed by different couples.

Sexual focusing. As far as your own arousal is concerned, it may be sometimes necessary to focus your thoughts on sexually exciting topics. This is not so unusual as it may sound: for actors, public speakers, writers, and musicians—to name but a few examples—find it impossible to give excellent performances if they do not, while acting, speaking, writing, or playing, force themselves to focus on the subject matter at hand.

Suppose, for instance, a great violinist were thinking of cabbages and kings while he was playing a Beethoven or a Mozart concerto. Would he ever be able to convey deep-seated feeling for the work to his audience? Hardly. Why, then, should you be able to convey a deep-seated sexual interest in having sex relations with your husband or wife if, while so engaged, you are thinking of your job or your housework?

If you have amy difficulty, then, becoming sexually aroused or reaching a climax, focus, and keep focusing, on something sexually exciting—whatever that may be. Your mate's body; the time you copulated in the woods; the sexy story you read yesterday; the girl you saw in the bus;

—anything, as long as it gets you more interested in your current relations.

Is your imagery bizarre? Is it fixated on one certain kind of thing? Does it tend to be "perverse"? No matter— as long as it is just imagery and it works in your relations with your mate. If it ceases working or if it requires some special kind of sex activity as an accompaniment, then (as we shall discuss later) you may be in more serious trouble and may require psychological help. But, in general, do not be afraid to let your imagination reign. Sex, in many instances, needs freely placed imagery for its highest achievements. Don't be afraid to give it its ideological gun.

As for your partner, if he or she is difficult to arouse because of lack of proper sex focusing, you can encourage and help him or her to focus more specifically and adequately on arousing stimuli by being yourself objective about his or her doing so.

That is to say, if you convince yourself that it is insulting for your mate to focus on sexually exciting people or things while you are having relations, naturally he or she will feel guilty about doing so and will be seriously inhibited. But if you realistically accept the fact that your partner's thoughts and actions in connection with you, and you alone, may not be sufficient to arouse him or her to sexual peaks, this partner will have maximum leeway to think about whatever is most exciting; and, peculiarly enough, by first thinking of someone or something else, is more likely to end up by thoroughly satisfying himself or herself with you.

The use of novelty. In some cases lack of sex desire may result from over-familiarity and the continual irritations and pressures of everyday living. In such instances, it may be desirable for husband and wife temporarily to cut down the frequency of intercourse; or to take a vacation together and free themselves from many of their ordinary cares and responsibilities. During such a vacation, which may be a kind of second honeymoon, sex urges that have been becoming dormant may quickly rise again and even reach previously unattained heights.

If loss of sex desire results from over-familiarity between the partners, it may sometimes be resuscitated by their taking separate bedrooms; or, occasionally, by their taking periods of vacation from each other (Benjamin,

1939b). Most marriage counselors, however, seriously doubt that any kind of togetherness can be achieved by a couple's being apart, and would advocate working through a sex problem rather than even temporarily running away from it.

More practical in most instances is the use of physical and psychological novelties. Using, at times, the floor instead of the bed; having sex relations in the middle of the day rather than at night; reenacting dramatic scenes, which the partners create themselves or read from a book; using forms of sex practices which the couple does not usually favor but which occasionally may be exciting;— all these and many other forms of variety can easily be invented and employed by mates who are a bit too used to the old routines.

Although it is often believed that the male of the species craves variety and novelty more than the female, this is not always true. Precisely because most males are so easily aroused and satisfied, they can often go through the same monotonous sex procedures and not complain. But many females, with their less imperious sex urges and their greater sensitivity to the romantic aspects of life, have much greater need for unusual surroundings and situations.

Have you, with your mate, tried spending a night on the beach? Or swimming in the nude? Or a bed of pine needles in the deep woods? Or making love to the sounds of a recorded version of Tristan and Isolde? You might be gratified at the way your spouse responds.

One of my patients was so delighted when the man she married twelve years before carted her off from their four children one Sunday evening and, for the first time since courtship days, took her for some heavy necking in a car parked by the waterfront, that she felt certain, for a change, that he *really* loved her, and she experienced more sex satisfaction than she had felt on many a night in bed.

Can you see this woman's—and many other woman's—point? Or, if it is your husband who enjoys novel, exciting, romantic sex backgrounds, can you take a gentle hint? Sex variety may be the splice of love as well as the spice of life.

This does not mean, now, that *every* couple must practice considerable sex varietism within marriage, nor that novelty is an absolute necessity for continued satisfaction. Some husbands and wives, as Clark Vincent (1956b, 1957) shows, find that they can get along perfectly well with the same old matter of fact foreplay and a pattern of one or two coital positions; and it is foolhardy for such couples to think that they *must* copulate in nine feet of water or swing from the proverbial chandelier. Indeed, an insistence on sex novelty may actually help create frigidity in some wives and impotence in some husbands who think that they are incompetent if they do *not* crave unusual settings and coital positions.

Be that as it may, where arousal is somewhat difficult, novelty and adventure in sexual relations may well have their place. Giving them an honest try is not likely to do any harm and sometimes may work wonders.

Special conditioning procedures. It is sometimes happens that one or both sex partners have been conditioned, by prior experience or training, to become more easily aroused or to inhibit arousal under certain specific conditions. Thus, a woman may have had most of her early sexual participations under conditions where her lover slowly undressed her; and this kind of a situation may induce her to become quickly aroused, where dissimilar situations (or, rather, her attitude toward them) make it difficult for her to become excited. Under these circumstances, it is well for this woman's partner to go along, at least at the beginning, with the conditions that she believes she requires for easy arousal and to make use of her prior conditioning.

Similarly, as Berg and Street (1953) sagely indicate, an individual may have grown up in an atmosphere of parental squabbling and may consequently not be able to become sexually desirous when he or she is arguing or fighting with his or her mate. Under such conditions, it would be well for the mate to discover those situations which are repelling and to avoid sex contact under these circumstances.

Summary. Sex arousal, as we have indicated in the previous chapter, is only partly mediated through nerve pathways that are set in motion through physical or bodily stimulation. It is most importantly, in addition, the result of brain processes: of thinking and emoting. The art of sex is therefore, as Ovid properly called it many centuries ago, the art of love—that is, the art of being considerate, kind, loving, interested, self-confident, communicative, imaginative, permissive, and experimental. In the last analysis, the head and the heart rather than the lips, fingers, arms, and genitals are the main organs of arousing and satisfying one's mate.

5.

Physical Methods of Arousing a Sex Partner

Erogenous zones. The chief physical methods of arousing someone sexually consist of touching, stroking, caressing, massaging, manipulating, squeezing, pressing, kissing, or biting the genitals themselves and some of the so-called erogenous zones. The erogenous zones are those parts of the person's body which are well supplied with nerve endings that respond to touch or pressure and which easily communicate their nervous responses to the centers of sexual arousal in the spinal cord and brain.

In most individuals the genitals themselves are the primary erogenous zones. The majority of males are most sensitive genitally at the head of the penis and the underside of the shaft about an inch in back of the head. The rest of their genitals, including the shaft of the penis and the scrotum, are also likely to be rather sensitive, though not nearly so much as the head and underside of the shaft.

Most females are exquisitely sensitive at the clitoris, inner lips, and vestibule of the vagina and are secondarily sensitive at the rest of their genitals. The vagina itself is not particularly sensitive to touch but may respond to pressure (Guze, 1961; Krantz, 1958). In many women the upper wall of the lower part of the vagina, where the roots of the clitoris are located, is quite susceptible to stimulation.

The non-genital erogenous zones in both sexes are probably more numerous than has generally been previously indicated in sex manuals and may include the lips, ear lobes, scalp, neck, armpits, breasts (especially the nipples), buttocks, anus, thighs, small of the back, spinal column, and shoulders. As in most aspects of sexual technique, the watchword in regard to locating and stimulating any individual's erogenous zones is: Be alert to individual differences! Also: experiment!

Many men and women, either because of their peculiar physical makeup or because of the influence of some early instilled prejudices, are insensitive or irritable in some regions where, theoretically, they should react the most. Thus, a minority of women have little or no breast excitability; many shy away from all anal stimulation; and many are over-sensitive or insensitive in their clitoral regions and balk at any direct contact with the clitoris (which may be because adhesions between the prepuce and clitoris, with clumps of cells beneath, make clitoral stimulation irritating instead of pleasurable; but which may also be because these women just do not enjoy clitoral contact or are overly-sensitive to it). At the same time, a considerable number of males, because of psychological prejudice or insensitive nerve endings, are not particularly aroused by caressing or kissing of their ear lobes, breasts, or scrotum.

On the other hand, a good many individuals may go into paroxysms of sexual joy when they are stimulated in regions which, according to the textbooks, should leave them as cold as a cucumber. W. E. Parkhurst (personal communication) indicates that light and delicate stroking motions on the inside of the forearm, directly above the wrist, will significantly arouse many women.

Other experimenters have found other out-of-the-way spots that work wonders in different individuals (Grafenberg, 1950). Unless, therefore, you venture widely in this respect with your own sex partner, you may easily overlook his or her most vitally alive potentialities for sexual arousal.

Another word of caution here: In practically all matters of sex it is foolish to take an initial No for a final answer. If human beings only tried something once and for all and never repeated their original trial unless they immediately derived enormous joy, many of the most intensely pleasurable delights—such as eating oysters, imbibing Martinis, and going skiing—would hardly exist. Therefore: if your mate, at first blush, doesn't seem to become aroused by a certain kind of caress or kiss, by all means try, try again—until you are fully convinced that that maneuver is just not his or her cup of tea. Do not *force* any sexual issue; but neither should you be too easily discouraged.

Patience, as Katz (1956) stresses, "will insure your success. A calm, confident attitude is reassuring to your mate and will keep her from feeling frustrated and upset. It takes time to learn techniques, and it takes time to achieve a satisfactory sexual relationship. If you can accept occasional failures and disappointments as normal, you will find most of your sexual relations to be very satisfactory." Berg and Street (1953) endorse this position and note that kissing and caressing of a woman's erogenous zones should usually take fifteen minutes before intercourse is attempted even though she may be sufficiently aroused in less than five minutes. The other ten minutes properly utilized can stimulate her to even greater heights of excitement.

It should be remembered, at the same time, that some women and many men begin to become bored and to cool off sexually if foreplay is continued for too long a period of time. Such individuals may have to be given a resting period before they can satisfactorily continue to have relations; or else they can be brought to the point of orgasm by the other partner, who can later be satisfied after the first mate has achieved climax.

As long as there is no arbitrary insistence that both partners *must* be fully aroused and have their orgasms at exactly the same time, spouses with widely differing periods of arousability should have little difficulty in satisfying each other. Preferably, however, the mate who is aroused more easily can learn to hold back full participation, especially by avoiding genital contact with the other mate, until his or her partner is also fully aroused and actively desires intercourse or other orgasm-producing contact.

Caressing techniques. The two main methods of arousing a sex partner to a peak of excitement are caressing and kissing, the details of which have often been sadly neglected in Western texts on lovemaking. Eastern works on erotology have been more explicit; and the earliest of these works which has survived, Vatsyayana's *Kama Sutra* (which dates back at least to the sixth century A. D.) details numerous ways of eight major methods of pressing, marking, or scratching with the nails, and eight different modes of biting.

The sense of touch, as Van de Velde (1926) indicates, is the most important of all the senses in sexual matters; and the primary organ for arousing a member of the other sex is not a male's penis or a woman's vagina but the former's forefinger and the latter's hand. The possibilities of caressing, touching, and stroking your partner's erogenous zones are infinitely varied and should be approached with considerable imagination, experimentation, and curiosity.

Most individuals are more easily aroused by light, deft, painless, often rhythmic strokes and manipulations. But a considerable minority finds this kind of caressing annoying and teasing and desires, instead, firmer, more rapid, sometimes rather forceful and painful strokings. Still other individuals respond best to a combination of light and slow caresses followed or alternated with heavier and more rapid ones. Which class of individuals your own partner will be in has to be experientially determined and should never be assumed or predicted in advance.

The technique of caressing your mate's clitoris or penis should be given special attention. Usually it is important to maintain steady and fairly prolonged clitoral contact, since many women complain that their husbands keep losing contact with their clitorises and that they are therefore continually frustrated and brought back to scratch after they have once begun to become aroused. In some instances, however, the clitoris may be intermittently plucked, somewhat in the manner that a banjo string is plucked, or firmly pushed from side to side, again and again, until the female reaches her heights of excitement (and perhaps achieves a new orgasm with each plucking or pushing).

The clitoris or the clitoral region may be slowly or quickly massaged in a circular motion; or it may be rubbed or kneaded from top to bottom or from side to side. Berg and Street (1953) point out that the tip of the clitoris tends to be particularly sensitive and that contact with it may result in body twitching on the part of the female which is inimical rather than helpful to sexual arousal. They therefore recommend that massaging of the clitoris often be done around its side and top, following a U-shape curve, and that contact with its head be avoided. Parkhurst (personal communication) recommends intensely rapid friction or vibration on the clitoris and the upper end of the vulva. Other authorities favor slow, deep, and regular strokes, ranging from the clitoris to the vaginal opening (Masters and Johnson, 1962).

Individual differences among women are so wide-ranging that only considerable practice and experimentation are likely to lead to the proper technique—or, for that matter, varying techniques—which will be effective with any particular female.

Caressing of the male's penis can also be an art and a science rather than a hit-and-miss affair. Usually, it has a quite sensitive spot, on the underside of the glans or an inch or so behind the head, where finger massage will be unusually arousing. As is true of manipulating the clitoris, soft strokings of the tender parts of the penis may be much more effective than rough grasping and rubbing (which may at times even be painful). As always, however, some males do require unusual pressure, rubbing, clasping, and even pinching or biting for penile arousal.

It is often erroneously assumed that, once a male or female has had an orgasm, all manipulation of his or her genitals should immediately cease, since these organs tend to be supersensitive after climax. However, gentle and mild caresses of the clitoris or penis or their surrounding parts (such as the female's outer lips or the male's scrotum) may be most satisfying after orgasm has taken place, and may sometimes lead to re-arousal and further capacity for orgasm.

It is also often assumed that, just because no arousal takes place at first when a male's penis or a woman's clitoris is manipulated, the individual cannot be aroused at this time. Frequently, however, especially in the case of the female, ten or fifteen minutes of persistent, comfortable massaging are necessary to stimulate sensation; and then, after sensation develops, a considerable further period of time may be needed to arouse the partner to heights of real arousal.

Although the fingers, and especially their tips, are most useful as a means of caressing and massaging the genitals and other erogenous zones of your partner, you should not hesitate to use other parts of your body as well for manipulative purposes. Thus, you may felicitously employ your knuckles, finger nails, palm of your hand, forearms, fist, elbow, and so on.

You can also, at times, effectively utilize your toes, foot, knee, leg, thighs, and various other parts of your body for caressive purposes. Even the head and face can be used surprisingly well in this connection. Virtually any part of your body which you can voluntarily move can be imaginatively employed.

The penis, although mainly an organ for the male's own satisfaction, can also be used for caressive purposes. It can be used to stimulate a female's breasts or other erogenous zones; and it can be employed for delightful contact with the woman's external sex organs as well as for vaginal intromission. Thus, in the Truk Islands the natives practice a special mode of sex relations which is called "Trukese striking." This involves the male's manipulating his penis against the female's clitoris, as he sits with his legs in front of him and the woman sits on his legs. The Trukese natives think so highly of this sexual pastime that they largely reserve its use to highly involved sweetheart-lover rather than more routine and less loving husband-wife relations (Swartz, 1958).

Caressive movements, as is implied in what we have just been saying, do not merely consist of strokings or one-dimensional fondlings. They may also include clutching, kneading, massaging, grasping, manipulating, pinching, clasping, and so on. Embracing, or pressing your partner closely to you, is also included in caressive technique. Also: clasping, hugging, and cuddling various parts of your mate's body, from his or her head to toes.

Techniques of kissing. Kissing, of course, is a highly favored kind of caressive technique and also includes a wide range of activities, such as pressing with closed lips, using an open-mouthed approach, nipping, licking, sucking, biting, etc. Like other caresses, it may be done mildly or intensely, in a wet or dry manner, for a long or short period of time, by itself or interspersed with other caresses. Van de Velde (1926) recommends that "three senses are blended in the kiss: touch, taste, and smell.

Sound should be conspicuous by its absence." There are, however, some individuals who actually enjoy the noisy mutual smacking of lips together.

Like many other caressive measures, but especially so, kissing often has to be practiced for a period of time before it becomes thoroughly enjoyable. Thus, many men and women who, at first, are rather revolted by "soul kisses"—or kisses that are deep and wet and where the participants insert their tongues into each other's mouths for long periods of mutual exploration (*Maraichinage* or *Kataglossism*)—eventually come to enjoy this kind of kissing immensely. Some degree of persistence and experimentation in kissing, as in other sex practices, is often necessary for the achievement of maximum satisfaction and arousal.

It is commonly assumed that, in the case of civilized women, caressing and kissing must largely be devoted to the non-genital erogenous zones before any attempt is made to stimulate their genitals. This assumption may be, in many instances, mistaken: as some women are quickly arousable after only the most meagre non-genital preliminaries and prefer to be directly aroused by genital kissing more than by any other form of contact.

Oral-genital stimulation has traditionally been considered to be taboo in our society but there appears to be no good reason why this taboo should be continued. The main reason for the existence of a negative attitude toward genital kissing is probably the concept of "dirtiness" that for centuries has been attached to the genitals. Part of this concept, in turn, stems from ancient confusions of genital and anal functions, which may have arisen because the anus and the genitals are in such close physical proximity (H. Ellis, 1936; Robie, 1925). The female vagina is also close to the urethra, while the male's sex organ, the penis, also serves as his urinary outlet.

But where the anus is, at least to some extent, a "dirty," malodorous, and unhygienic organ, the genitals are hardly in the same class. Moreover, it is relatively easy to keep them scrupulously clean. Consequently, individuals who may have a legitimate objection to direct contacts with the anus of their partners may over-generalize their objection to include oral-genital relations as well. If they unprejudicedly tried passive or active genital kissing, they might well find it unobjectionable and enjoyable (Thornton and Thornton, 1939).

Although most modern marriage manuals have something to say about positions of coitus, they rarely point out that positions of caressing and kissing may be equally important. The "normal" tendency of men and women who engage in precoital play is to lie side by side. Actually, this position is a rather limiting one and makes many of the most interesting and exciting kisses and caresses almost impossible.

In general, caressive and kissing positions, especially those that involve genital manipulation, are somewhat the same as copulative positions which are described in detail in a later chapter. They involve the partners' lying face to face, face to back, sitting, kneeling, or standing.

In genital kissing or caressing the active partner may lie below the more passive partner; or alongside but facing in the opposite direction; or sitting or kneeling on the floor while the mate is lying with his or her genitals at the edge of a bed or chair; or, when both partners are active in genital kissing or caressing, the so-called *sixty-nine* position may be employed, with one mate surmounting the other in a face to face position but facing in opposite directions.

Non-genital foreplay. Most foreplay, or non-genital caressing and kissing which takes place prior to coitus, is a stimulating and enjoyable part of sex relations. It is particularly appropriate when the male is trying to arouse a virginal or near-virginal female who is somewhat afraid of sex participation and who therefore has to be slowly led up to it. This type of foreplay, however, is not necessarily suited for mates who are not fearful and who know perfectly well that they are going to wind up by having intercourse.

Some spouses enjoy non-genital foreplay immensely and often have it for hours on end; but others can easily dispense with it on most occasions and should not prolong foreplay because they *once* found it useful and delightful. When taken beyond a certain appropriate point it may lead to sexual cooling.

Recently one of my marriage counseling clients complained that her husband insisted on engaging in non-genital foreplay for at least an hour before intercourse, even though they frequently lost needed sleep thereby. Sometimes, she said, she enjoyed this kind of activity immensely —when sufficient time was available. At other times, however, it detracted from her fulfillment and resulted in her having an unintense climax.

When I spoke to her husband about her complaint, he quickly saw that he was insisting on prolonged foreplay largely because that is how he had proved himself to be a "real man" and a good lover in his premarital affairs and that he, too, could easily dispense with this amount of foreplay on most occasions.

If one mate finds non-genital foreplay eminently desirable, the other mate should normally try to please in this respect—provided that the first partner's demands are not too onerous or time-consuming.

The matter of one mate's being inconvenienced in regard to foreplay goes both ways: so that the irritation caused, say, by a wife's *not* having lengthy foreplay can be mirrored by a husband's annoyance at his *having* to engage in it.

Where couples differ significantly in their desires, a compromise solution based on good sense and fair play is probably best—as it is in most aspects of sexuality where distinct differences exist between two partners.

Just as many individuals find extragenital play relatively unexciting and annoying, others find that it is more stimulating than direct genital involvement. Particularly after a male or a female has had one orgasm, he or she may feel that direct genital contact is irritating. But, when in this very condition, he or she may be surprised to find that light or strong kissing or stroking of other parts of the body, such as the thighs, buttocks, or back, may lead to a renewed state of complete arousal.

Non-genital stimulation, though usually referred to as "foreplay," may be misleadingly named in many instances. In the first place, it may never lead to genital play or to coitus, but may be resorted to as an end in itself, since some individuals find it eminently satisfying. In the second place, when used as an end in itself it may result in full orgasmic release, especially in the female. Thus, many women are brought to complete climax by lip kissing, close embracing, or caressing of the nipples of their breasts.

There is nothing unusual, abnormal, or perverted in achievement of orgasm by non-genital stimulation and there is no reason whatever why spouses who are able to achieve climax in this manner should not do so—as long as they make certain that their partners are also brought to the point of orgasm by some non-genital or genital technique.

Genital stimulation. Although, as ever, it is difficult to speak in average or general terms, direct stimulation of the genitals themselves tends to be the easiest and best arousing techniques for most males and females. Massaging the penis of the male or the clitoris or other regions of the vulva of the female is usually most effective in this connection. Here, as previously indicated, experimentation is the main keyword; since some people respond enormously to light stimulation, some to heavy; some to manual, some to oral methods; some to rhythm, some to intermittent massage; and so on.

Here again, lack of sexual inhibition and shame is the crux of the matter of excellent technique. People who feel that sex, in any of its aspects, is sinful, wicked, shameful, evil, or immoral will inevitably be reluctant to resort to the kinds and quality of genital stimulation that is often necessary for maximum arousal of their mates. Those who have sane sex attitudes and are relatively ininhibited will make the best arousers of themselves and their spouses.

As in most forms of sex behavior, genital stimulation should normally be varied. There are some individuals who become easily aroused over and over again by the use of exactly the same kind of genital kisses or caresses. But there are others who, even when they enjoy a given type of act, become relatively inured to it after awhile, and sometimes are arousable by some other mode of genital contact.

Self-arousal. It is too often erroneously believed that an unaroused sex partner can only be brought to a pitch of sexual excitement if the other partner works very hard to encourage and contribute to his or her arousal. In point of fact, as we noted in the previous chapter, the unaroused partner can often stimulate himself or herself by focusing on arousing stimuli. Physically, too, the non-aroused partner can frequently bring himself or herself to a peak of excitement by concentrating on stimulating the other mate.

Take, for example, a male who is somewhat tired and uninterested in sex relations when he goes to bed with his wife. I have seen many psychotherapy patients who had this complaint about themselves or their spouses. When I induced them, once they were in bed, literally to force themselves to make sexual overtures toward their mates— to try to arouse and satisfy their wives rather than themselves—almost all these individuals found, to their surprise, that in the process of actively trying to stimulate their spouses they themselves ferquently became quite interested and wound up by having fully pleasurable relations. Physical self-arousal may take place, then, as a result of deliberately engaging in sex activity, even though onc originally seems to have no interest in it.

Coitus as a sexual excitant. A tremendous to-do is often raised in marriage manuals about patience, particularly on the male's part, in the course of sex preliminaries. Balzac's famous dictum in his *Pysiology of Marriage* is often quoted: "Never begin marriage with a rape." Some of this concern is well taken: since some males do try to have intercourse too quickly with their unaroused wives; and the results may be disastrous.

At the same time, there are instances in which the best prelude to coitus is coitus itself: where almost nothing short of this will stimulate one or both partners to a high state of excitement. Thus, there are husbands and wives who are cool, lukewarm, or neutral after they have engaged in considerable preliminary play. But once copulation has been effected and some powerful thrusts have been made by themselves and their mates, their sexual parts may begin to warm up and become well lubricated and they may have thoroughly satisfying relations. Experimentation in this respect, especially with lubricants (such as saliva or K-Y jelly) which may be necessary to make the onset of copulation possible when there is little initial desire, may prove to be quite rewarding.

The use of stimulants. In addition to the psychological stimulants discussed in the previous chapter, there are various psychophysical excitants which sometimes may be effective in arousing yourself or your mate. The following possibilities may be considered in this connection.

1. One of the best sexual stimulants is the sight and smell of the partner's body. To this end, if you want to arouse your mate sexually you should try to keep in good physical condition and particularly try to avoid extremes of fatness, thinness, poor complexion, etc. (except where, in a few cases, these physical extremes are specifically and perhaps fetichistically stimulating to your mate).

Cleanliness, notably of the genitals, is usually important, as the female clitoris and the male foreskin may, if not kept clean, accumulate secretions (smegma) which produce a strong odor and interfere with the partner's arousal. Male and female organs should be washed regularly with soap and water, with the individual taking care to get at the folds of tissue under which secretions may adhere. In some instances, males (and very occasionally females) should be circumcised to aid cleanliness and avoid irritations and infections.

If a female employs douching for purposes of cleanliness it should only be done under a physician's direction; since, by washing away the normal protective vaginal secretions, douching is likely to do more harm than good.

Attractive bedtime clothing, especially on the part of the female, may aid in the stimulation of the spouse; and, in accordance with the tastes of the individuals concerned, semi-nudity or complete nudity is often highly desirable.

Although the demand for their wives to wear sheer negligees or other provoking underthings does not seem to be half so great today as it was with husbands of previous generations, (Ellis, Doorbar, Guze, and Clark, 1952) I still receive occasional complaints from males who feel that their spouses make no effort whatever to attract them physically and that, therefore, they are semi-impotent in their bedrooms.

More often, however, I receive wifely complaints to the effect that their husbands do not bathe or shave frequently enough or that their breaths too often reek of alcohol.

Greve (1957) points out with unusual candor that "there are a hundred different subtle points, along the same line, usually disregarded by women. Unattractive, soiled, or torn nightgowns, bed-sheeting not overly clean, body hair (many men are repelled by hair on the female body) and offensive breath (due often to eating foods such as onions or garlic, or odor due to defective teeth, etc.) very often subconsciously kill the desire of many otherwise normal men."

In both sexes, then, there is much that often can be done if one partner is to increase his or her sexual attractiveness to the other. Better looking and sweeter tasting and smelling mates are almost unbeatable sexual stimulants.

2. Various foods have for ages been recommended as aphrodisiacs or sex arousers. Most of these—such as oysters, fish, honey, asparagus, and spices—are of no proven value as specific sex excitants. What does seem to be clear is that low protein diets tend to inhibit sexuality and semi-starvation diets (as shown in a famous experiment at the University of Minnesota) (Keys and others, 1950) eventually lead to sexual indifference. A good nourishing diet, on the other hand, including sufficient amounts of protein and a well-rounded supply of vitamins, tends to lay the foundation for maximum sexual arousability. Both obesity and undernourishment are inimical to sexual arousal and satisfaction.

It is possible that there will someday be discovered some food that is truly an aphrodisiac. As yet, however, all reports of such foods have proven, upon scientific investigation, to be entirely groundless. Although many exquisitely flavored and highly spiced foods, as MacDougald (1961) shows, may have symbolic significance or may for psychological reasons make those who ingest them feel as if they have been sexually stimulated, none is presently known that has true aphrodisiacal qualities.

3. Sex desire is easily extinguished or impeded by fatigue, low resistance, illness, and general tension. Conversely, adequate rest, exercise, interesting work, and relaxation are most important in laying the groundwork for sex arousability. A warm bath or shower just before having sex relations will sometimes be relaxing or properly invigorating and will consequently aid sexual arousal in some individuals.

4. There are several drugs which, if taken in sufficient but not over-sufficient quantities, will encourage sex desire in some persons. These include:

a) Alchohol, taken in moderate quantities, often acts as a sex stimulant because it tends temporarily to allay anxiety and reduce inhibitions. It may also tend to deaden nerve sensitivity and thereby enable individuals who normally have a quick orgasm to have a slower-timed reaction. W. Horsley Gantt (Himwich, 1958) has presented clear-cut experimental evidence to show that this is true in dogs; and there is much clinical data to show that it is equally true in humans.

The slower timing that results from imbibing alcohol may, in some instances, increase the individual's (particularly the male's) confidence in his own prowess and consequently lead him to look more favorably on sex participation. If taken in large quantities, however, alcohol usually deadens sexual excitability and ultimately leads to complete anesthesia and impotence.

b) Opium and its derivatives (such as morphine, heroin, Dilaudid, and codeine) and the newer synthetic analgesics (such as Demerol and methadone) may at first enhance sex excitement by allaying fear and anxiety. But addiction usually kills sex interest in the long run. According to Mauer and Vogel (1954) "in both males and females, opiates have a general tendency to reduce or obliterate sexual desire, although there may be individual exceptions to this." Dr. Marie Nyswander, in her book on *The Drug Addict as a Patient* (1958), shows that morphine makes the addict feel as satisfied as if he had performed a sex act and makes him more interested in searching for his next shot than in looking for sexual fulfillment.

As in the case of morphine and its derivatives, the taking of bromides, barbiturates, marihuana, mescaline, and cocaine sometimes has an initially sex-exciting effect, partly because of the reduction of anxiety and inhibition. Eventually, dependency on such drugs has direct and side effects that are antagonistic to sex desire and fulfillment.

c) There are several substances, such as strychnine, cantharides ("Spanish fly"), and yohimbine, which sometimes lead to sexual arousal through irritating the urinary tract or nervous system. Virtually all these drugs, however, are exceptionally dangerous, will frequently do considerable damage to the individual, and should under no circumstances be employed except under strict medical supervision. Kelly (1957) is one of the few outstanding sexologists who believes that considerably more research in relation to drugs such as strychnine and yohimbine should be done and that they may sometimes be used effectively with individuals who have nonpsychogenic cases of impotence. As yet, however, the research that Kelly calls for has not been done, and great caution must be taken in the use of these drugs.

d) Several tranquilizers which temporarily allay anxiety and may thereby encourage sex desire and participation have recently been discovered; and many experiments with these kinds of drugs are now going on. Drugs of this type should, again, only be used under medical direction, since they frequently have dangerous side effects.

e) The use of sex hormones and other hormones is sometimes dramatically effective in stimulating sex urges. Thus, women who are treated with the male hormone, testosterone, because they are afflicted with cancer frequently become much more interested in sex relations than they ever previously were (Kupperman, 1959). There is also a possibility that in some instances where males have a real hormonal deficiency the administration of testosterone (or androgen) may be helpful in relieving some of their symptoms of impotence (Clark, 1959a).

The effects of sex hormones on different individuals vary widely, however; and it is often difficult to tell whether it is actually the administration of the hormone, or the suggestion given to the patient as a result of this administration, which leads to some of the obtained beneficial results. Hormones, moreover, can have serious side effects; and they, like other drugs, should only be individually prescribed and taken under medical supervision.

f) Perfumes are often found to be sexually exciting, particularly to males in our society. Ointments, unguents, perfume sticks, bath salts, toilet water, etc., all of which are highly scented with various kinds of aromatic substances, are sometimes efficacious in this respect. At the same time, there are some individuals who, usually for psychological reasons, are prejudiced against most perfumes and who tend to lose rather than gain desire when they are used by the sex partner.

Summary. There are many psychophysical techniques of arousing a sex partner, some of which (such as caressing and kissing) are harmless and effective, and others of which (such as the employment of alcohol and drugs) are dangerous and of dubious effectiveness.

All physical methods of sex arousal depend, in the last analysis, upon the psychological groundwork which underlies their use; since if a person is psychologically prejudiced against sex or against a particular partner, it is doubtful whether almost any technique will serve to arouse him or her.

Even powerful "truth-compelling" drugs, such as sodium amytal, it must be remembered, will not work on many persons who are determined not to surrender certain information. Similarly, powerful sexual excitants will not work with those who are determined not to let themselves become aroused.

Your best bet, therefore, in bringing your mate to a point where he or she ardently desires sex relations and may fairly easily be brought to climactic heights is to employ the kinds of psychological influences and methods outlined in the chapter prior to this. Used in conjunction with the best kinds of physical techniques, which are described in this chapter, this dual approach to arousal will usually be effective and sometimes work wonders.

If all the foregoing physical and psychological measures to arouse your mate (or yourself) are honestly and persistently tried and found wanting, then there is a good possibility that some biological or mental block exists. Advice and examination should be sought, first, with a qualified physician or medical specialist, to see if a physical disability or disorder can be discovered; and consultation should also be sought with a psychologist, psychiatrist, or marriage counselor, to investigate the possibility of a psychological disturbance.

Many instances of lack of sex arousability are traceable to irrational thoughts and feelings which, once they are uncovered, faced, and combatted, can be eradicated as causative factors (A. Ellis, 1953b, 1954c, 1957a, 1962a, 1963a, 1963c, 1965a). Where selfhelp, therefore, does not work, competent professional aid should promptly be sought.

6.

Sexual Intercourse: First Steps

If anything comes naturally to man without any prior learning and experience, it is *not* sexual intercourse. Most lower animals copulate instinctively and are directly driven to do so by impulses from within. Man, in contradistinction, often becomes instinctively *aroused*—or, more accurately, a considerable part of his sex arousal is instinctive or innate—but even in this respect much learning and conditioning are also involved in his excitability.

As for the specific method he will employ to reach a climax once he is aroused, man (as we saw in Chapter 2) largely relies on socially-inculcated and experimentally-acquired rather than on instinctive tendencies.

Theoretically, he has a wide-ranging choice of sexual outlets. Actually, which of these possible outlets he will specifically employ for orgasmic purposes depends on many factors in his early and later life experiences.

The individual, therefore, who has had relatively little heterosexual intercourse has much to learn about coital technique. Some of the pointers which may be helpful in this connection will now be delineated.

Signs of readiness. Sexual intercourse should normally occur only when both partners are sufficiently ready for it; otherwise, difficulty may well ensue. In the male, readiness for coitus is presumably easy to determine: since it largely consists of an adequate or stiff erection of the penis. Actually, however, males may sometimes experience formidable erections when they are not particularly aroused sexually and when having intercourse would lead to pain, discomfort, or indifference. Similarly, a female may have a distinctly tumescent or erect clitoris without truly being desirous of and ready for copulation.

True sexual excitement in the male or female is usually accompanied by several discernible symptoms. In addition to swelling of the genitals, various other parts of the body, particularly the lips, breasts, and nipples, may become enlarged and swollen. Blood pressure and pulse rates generally rise, the individual becomes restless and tense, the rate of breathing increases, goose pimples may appear, the skin may seem flushed and hot, tremor may develop, an odor may emanate from the mouth, and (perhaps most frequently) the precoital secretions of the male and female begin to flow, sometimes in copious amounts.

In the case of the female, as Masters and Johnson (1961, 1962) have recently discovered, the fact that a woman is highly excited sexually and is well on the way to having an orgasm is invariably mirrored in the state of her inner vulval lips, which begin to turn bright red.

In spite of these overt signs of sexual arousal, many spouses, particularly when they are focusing upon their own excitement and reactions, cannot accurately judge just when their mates are ready for actual coitus. This is because some persons—usually females—not only have to be aroused to desire penetration, but have to be *sufficiently* excited, often for a considerable period of time, before they want intromission. It is almost impossible for anyone but themselves, in some instances, to tell when this sufficient degree of excitement has been achieved.

In consequence, couples who have intercourse regularly should normally agree upon some set of predetermined signals for beginning copulation. The one who usually takes longer to achieve an urgent desire for intromission should, when he or she finally reaches this point, tap the other, say "Now!" or otherwise signal the partner that he or she is ready. Here again, as previously stressed, it should be realized that neither mate is a mind-reader and that plain, unvarnished English is often the most nearly ideal means of sexual communication.

Initial intercourse. The very first time an individual has coitus is likely to present some difficulties, not merely in the case of the woman but the man as well. For the virgin male simply does not know what to do; what is more, he is often afraid that he will do it badly or incompetently. As Mozes (1959b) indicates, because of the difficulties of defloration, authorities estimate that about one out of twenty of all brides is still a "married virgin" at the end of the first year and one out of every hundred, at the end of the second year of marriage.

Where the virgin female may be afraid that she will be hurt or may not enjoy intercourse, the male is afraid that he will not *succeed*. Even when she herself receives no orgasm, the female need not fail her partner: since, no matter how ineffective she is, the male, particularly if he is easily excited and satisfied, will in all probability obtain an orgasm.

But if the male fails the female she will not be able to attain satisfaction—at least, not coitally. So it is the male who primarily bears the brunt of feeling that he has completely failed; and his anxiety about failing (that is, his defining himself as being worthless because of failure) may well make initial intercourse, or even the first dozen times, something of an emotional nightmare.

It is most desirable, therefore, that the female be especially kind and forgiving if she knows that her partner has had little or no prior sex relations. She should show him that although she would like him to succeed, for the sake of his pleasure as well as her own, this is not a vital necessity to her; and she should indicate that she does not measure his essential *manhood* or *value* in terms of his sexual competence.

The man, of course, should do likewise with the virgin female: let her see that he *wants* her to experience satisfaction but that this is no dire *need* of his. As in all other aspects of human living, it is important to view sex relations, especially the first sexual contact between a couple, as a matter of personal or total involvement rather than of purely sexual involvement with the other partner.

A sex partnership is hardly different from any other partnership in its essence. If you want your new business partner to be effective and to work well with you, you must understand and accept him as a human being, rather than just as a business man. If you want to get the most out of your associates on a committee, a fraternal organization, or an athletic group, you must again see them as human beings rather than mere associates. Certainly, then, if you want to make the most of your sex relations with your mate, you should see him or her as a person rather than a sex machine.

In seeing your sex mate as a person in the course of initial coitus, you should particularly understand that he or she probably has distinct fears—such as the fear of appearing ugly or deformed, the fear of being inept and incompetent, the fear of having poor or low sex capacities, etc. Let him or her know that you do not *expect* flawlessness or perfect technique; that it is not success but the person that is important to you; that you do not care if it takes him or her a long time to become sexually adept; that you are more interested, in some ways, in his or her satisfaction than in your own; that you are certain that, eventually, he or she will enjoy sex immensely; that you are looking forward to a long term relationship, and not merely this one night.

Technical pointers regarding sex relations leading to initial intercourse include the following:

1. The first night you have the opportunity for intercourse with your sex partner need not be the first night you take advantage of this opportunity (Kling, 1957). For one or several nights there may merely be heavy petting, including mutual orgasm, but no actual penile-vaginal penetration.

This may enable either or both mates to get used to the idea of coitus; to approach it slowly; to get to know each other thoroughly before they actually have it; and to convince themselves that intercourse is not an all-important act, but is merely one of the several kinds of interesting possibilities for mutual enjoyment. Especially where your partner is quite young, nervous, ignorant, inhibited, or seriously disturbed it may be best to defer penetration for one or more times.

2. Although, as we shall discuss later in this book, having coitus while the female is menstruating is feasible in many instances, it is probably preferable not to complicate initial intercourse with the factor of menstruation. Consequently, wedding or other plans should be made so that the first few nights the mates expect to spend together do not include days on which the bride is having her period. If menstruation is taking place, and especially if there is a

heavy flow during the first days a couple are together, it may be well for the partners to limit themselves to non-coital relations, up to and including orgasm, until menstruation has ceased or the flow is slight.

3. Actual penetration may at first be made with the male's fingers instead of his penis. The average male, especially when he is a novice at coitus, often does not know how to handle his penis well or control its movements adequately; therefore, he is likely to be inept at penetrating a virgin partner's vagina with his penis. Instead, he may gradually expose the vagina with his fingers, and stretch, break, or push aside the female's hymen by digital manipulation. In this manner, he can best allay his partner's fears and doubts—as well, often, as his own.

4. When penile-vaginal penetration is finally attempted, it may be well for the male to try to enter his partner's vagina at its upper (or anterior) side, where the opening left by the hymen is likely to be larger. Penetration and the stretching of the hymen can often be made more conveniently in this manner. However, as Dr. Hans Lehfeldt (personal communication) points out, the anterior wall of the vagina also is near the nerve endings from the underside of the clitoris as well as the female's urethra; consequently penile penetration toward this area may arouse feelings of tenderness or pain in some virgins.

It should not be thought that defloration is always or even usually a very painful procedure and that extremely careful precautions invariably have to be taken to make it tolerable. In the majority of instances, even where relatively little care is taken, initial intercourse is almost painless and a large loss of blood or other traumatic effects are unusual. Nonetheless, a male has to make certain that his particular partner is not one of the minority with whom difficulties may ensue; and some amount of caution and care on his part will enable him to see if his mate is unduly sensitive about initial coitus.

5. Although gentleness, patience, reassurance, and prolonged precoital play are generally best employed by the male who is having initial intercourse with a frightened or skittish female, in some instances the bold stroke, or let's get-this-over-quickly technique may prove to be preferable. Since the woman knows her own sensations of pain better than does her mate, she should be the one in some

instances literally to break or stretch the hymen herself, by sharply and quickly bearing down on her partner's penis when she feels that it is properly contacting her hymen.

Where the female for some reason cannot or does not wish to do this, the male may sometimes make a quick pelvic thrust that rather painlessly passes by the hymen and effects complete penetration. Where the hymen is very thick or inelastic or the vaginal entrance narrow, the quick thrust approach may be too painful and unwise, and gradual stretching, sometimes over a period of many days or weeks, may be the best method.

If the partners prefer, or if entry is quite difficult, the hymen may be stretched or broken by the woman herself, using her fingers. Cauldwell (1958), quoting from information in the British Medical Journal, gives some informative details in this respect: The female may cut her nails short and wash her hands thoroughly. With the help of a lubricant, she can insert one finger tip into the vagina and exert steady pressure around the circumference of the hymen. After repeating this procedure for several days, she then can insert the tips of two fingers and finally three into the vagina without any discomfort. Usually, she will find it best to carry out this procedure in a squatting position, during or after a hot bath.

The male, too, can gradually stretch his partner's hymen by using his fingers or his penis. It is best that he use adequate lubrication, such as saliva or surgical lubricating jelly (e.g., K-Y jelly) when he is doing this kind of stretching.

Another possibility is for the male to stretch or break the female's hymen by using an analgesic ointment, such as Nupercainal ointment or creme, which may be applied to the hymen and vaginal orifice several minutes before penetration is attempted and then removed before coitus so as not to affect the husband's organ.

6. If a woman is highly nervous, or real trouble is expected in the breaking of the hymen, or some attempts have been made at defloration and have ended in failure, it may be advisable for her to see a physician and have her hymen clipped or incised under local anesthesia.

In some cases, where the vaginal entrance or the vagina itself is quite narrow, it may be necessary for the physician to provide the wife with a series of graduated cylinders, which she may wear until a wider vaginal entrance or canal is effected. In other extreme cases, especially where a woman is upset at the prospect of being surgically deflorated, the cutting of the hymen (hymenectomy) may have to be done under general anesthesia.

In the great majority of instances, however, husbands and wives can handle the matter of defloration themselves and surgical treatment will not be necessary. Initial coitus, as the British Medical Journal points out, is just as well effected without surgical intervention, since the fact that an anesthetic is required for hymenectomy sometimes helps the woman believe that defloration and intercourse itself must be a painful process; and, in consequence, she may psychologically acquire painful spasms of the vaginal muscles (vaginismus) when she attempts coitus.

If resort to a medical specialist is employed, the wife should normally visit him two or three weeks or more before initial intercourse, thus allowing some time for her sore tissues to heal. Besides alleviating fear and pain, having the hymen surgically stretched or incised also has the advantage of enabling the woman to be fitted with a contraceptive diaphragm before initial intercourse, so that proper birth control measures can, if desired, be employed from the start and coitus can take place without the use of a condom. A cervical cap or a diaphragm can sometimes, but not usually, be inserted in spite of an intact hymen.

7. If a woman is sufficiently aroused before initial intercourse, she may sometimes lose herself completely in the heat of passion and not mind the tearing of her hymen even if it causes her some amount of discomfort. Some women may become so aroused that they do not even realize that they have had intercourse until it is virtually over and they are no longer virgins.

8. Normally, there will be a slight amount of bleeding when a woman is deflorated. If, when bleeding occurs, she will rest on her back with her thighs together it will usually stop in a few minutes. If bleeding appears to be excessive and does not stop after a while—which is very unusual but does occasionally occur—it may be necessary for the woman to see a physician.

9. No issue should be made, of course, if your female partner seems to have no hymen at first intercourse or if there is no trouble or pain in stretching whatever vestiges

she does have. Many women are born without hymens or lose them in the course of physical examinations, masturbation, petting, etc. Making an issue over a hymen is one of the best ways to show a girl that you are interested in her only as a piece of useful sex apparatus. It also indicates that you are a highly critical individual who will probably jump on her for other minor aspects of her behavior.

10. Whether or not a woman has an intact hymen, the use of sexual lubricants during initial intercourse is usually highly desirable. Because she may be tense and nervous, or has had little prior experience, or is vaginally tight, penetration is likely to be somewhat difficult and the female precoital and coital secretions which normally facilitate copulation may be sparse or lacking. Consequently, adequate lubricants, such as saliva or water-soluble surgical jelly (K-Y jelly) should be on hand. The use of these lubricants is outlined in detail in Chapter 9.

11. Frequently initial intercourse is not especially enjoyable for either mate, though in some instances it is unusually satisfying. It is therefore best not to have unrealistically high hopes about it. For some women it may be painful; and for some males it may result in a quick ejaculation or a relatively unpleasurable orgasm. So be it. Its main function is to serve as a prelude to future coitus, not necessarily to be ecstatically enjoyable in its own right.

12. Initial intercourse should usually be had in the face to face position, with the male surmounting the female, and the female's legs raised quite high, sometimes over the male's shoulder, so that the vaginal opening is as wide as possible. Penetration should generally be slow, so that the hymen may be stretched rather than broken. At the point where real resistance is met, it may be advisable for the male to make a quick, penetrating thrust and for the female to meet him in a similar thrust.

Until the male knows the female partner quite well in intercourse, and is certain about the width and depth of her vagina and how deep and intense penetration she can take, he should proceed slowly and carefully with intromission. It is often advisable for him to explore the vaginal vault with his fingers first, to see just how wide and long it is.

When he does enter the vagina with his penis, he should

at first penetrate only an inch or so, and then carefully go deeper and deeper. Not only the length but the circumference of his penis may be somewhat too large for his mate's vagina at first; and he may have to allow her some period of time to adjust to his organ.

If his wife is an older woman who has had a good deal of prior sex experience or has already borne children, no unusual precautions may be necessary; but even in these instances it is possible that, for all her prior experience and childbearing, she has a vaginal vault that cannot easily accommodate his penis at the beginning of their relations.

13. After initial intercourse has ended, it is often most important to see that your partner is made to feel as psychologically comfortable as possible. No regrets should be voiced, even if they are inwardly felt, about the loss of virginity, lack of pleasure in the encounter, or pain of defloration. Every effort should be made to show your partner that he or she is a worthwhile human being in your eyes—indeed, that you love him or her more than ever precisely because the relatively difficult task of initial intercourse has been completed and both of you can go on to even better sex satisfactions.

7.

Sexual Intercourse: Psychological Foundations

Assuming that initial intercourse has been completed and that you are having regular coitus with your partner, there are several attitudes which are important as a foundation for maximum fulfillment. We shall now review some of the main attitudinal prerequisites for having regular intercourse in a manner that is mutually satisfying.

Absence of coital fetiches. The first and foremost philosophy that it is advisable for you to adopt if you are intent on having fine coital relations is the belief that there is nothing sacred about intercourse itself and that it is only *one* of the main ways by which couples may enjoy themselves and come to climax. As soon as you conceive copulation as the *only* or even *indubitably* best mode of achieving satisfaction, you make of it (as we shall later explain in more detail) a fetich or a sex deviation.

Husbands and wives, it must be acknowledged, do not *owe* each other intercourse, even though some of our marriage laws state or imply that they do. What they do owe each other, if anything, as part of the marital *partnership,* is *some* form of sex satisfaction, usually leading to orgasm. That is, assuming that one mate desires to achieve climax and that his or her demands are not unreasonable, the other mate should then go out of his or her way to satisfy these desires. Otherwise, monogamy does not make much sense and becomes an onerous restriction on the unsatisfied mate's sex urges.

Satisfying one's mate, however, does not *necessarily*

mean fulfilling oneself at the same time; nor does it mean pleasing the mate through *coitus*. Thus, a wife may legitimately ask her husband to gratify her sexually when she is aroused; but it is silly, and often pernicious, for her to demand that *he also* receive simultaneous gratification. If he is not in an aroused mood, he can still bring her—but hardly himself—to climax.

Similarly: a husband may legitimately ask his wife to help him achieve orgasm—but not necessarily in intercourse. If, for the moment, she is indifferent or averse to coitus, it will usually become too directly-involving an act to request of her.

By the same token, if she has serious objections, temporarily or permanently, to oral-genital relations, then this becomes too directly-involving an act to demand. But, out of several possible ways in which the husband may (if he is not deviated or abnormal) achieve a climax, it is hardly unreasonable for him to expect his wife to help him achieve it in *one* of these ways—such as, for example, by massaging his penis with her hands, which (unless she is abnormally inhibited) will be a relatively uninvolving method for her to employ when she herself is not aroused.

Otherwise, if the wife does not satisfy her husband in *some* manner (and, of course, *vice versa*) continuous frustration will result, usually leading to poor marital relations and ultimately to extramarital affairs.

If and when intercourse is seen not as a fetich or a necessity but as *one* of the possible satisfying sex acts, even low-sexed or inhibited partners often become aroused quite spontaneously in the course of extragenitally satisfying their mates. Under these circumstances, coitus is likely to become more frequent.

Under other circumstances, where only coitus is conceived of as the "proper" or "good" means of sex relations, lack of desire on the part of one of the mates will lead to frustration, anger, and anxiety in most instances; sex will become more and more laden with negative emotion; both the desiring and the desireless partner will tend to avoid irritation-provoking sex relations or even sex talks; and in a fairly short period of time active copulation may easily diminish to near-zero proportions.

Differentiating sex competence from worthiness. A second psychological rule concerning intercourse is that it

should never be taken as proof of masculinity or femininity and that sexual competence should never be confused
with an individual's essential worth or value. The fully
masculine man is *not* necessarily the one who can last
indefinitely at intercourse, or who easily gets an erection,
or who is gymnastically adept at many coital positions.

On the contrary, many of the most masculine men are
rather poor at intercourse, for the simple reason that they
are so easily aroused that they quickly ejaculate and never
learn to be too coitally adept. Also: many other men, who
are masculine in the best possible sense of the word—that
is, are strong individuals, with self-confidence and a
powerful belief in themselves—just happen to be physically deficient and to be inept at intercourse.

Moreover: a man who is not, for one reason or another,
the best coital partner may still be one of the best *sex*
partners. For intercourse, as we just pointed out in the
previous section of this chapter, is only *one* way to satisfy
the average female; and frequently, one of the *lesser* ways.

The main sources of sexual sensitivity in the female are
not usually deep within the vagina, but in the clitoral region, the inner lips and the vestibule of the vagina, all of
which are well supplied with nerve endings, while the vaginal canal itself usually is not.

A man may therefore be an excellent *lover* without necessarily being an excellent *copulator,* since it is easy for
him to stimulate a woman's most sensitive parts with his
fingers, lips, tongue, or other parts of his anatomy, if his
penis is not adequate for the job. Indeed, as I often tell
my marriage counseling and psychotherapy clients, a man
who had no penis whatever could be an excellent lover,
just as a woman who had no vagina could be a perfectly
satisfactory sex partner for the average man—if he and
she did not have overpowering pro-coital prejudices. And
a woman with a perfectly normal vagina can be relatively
inept at or disinterested in copulation and still be an excellent lover—since, like the man, she has hands, lips, and
other organs which are in many ways capable of giving
exquisite pleasure.

Once again: assuming that a male or female is distinctly
below par in terms of enjoying and giving enjoyment
through penile-vaginal coitus, this has nothing whatever to
do with this individual's worth *as a person.* Many of us are

inadequate at playing basketball, bridge, or the stock-market; but that inadequacy hardly makes us a blackguard, a fool, or a lout. We may still be quite adequate in many other respects; and even if we are not, we may still be perfectly kind, nice, and lovable.

If, therefore, your marital partner is not a good coital bedmate and you happen to enjoy copulation immensely, that is certainly too bad, and you are hardly in the best of luck. But this does not prove that your mate is worthless, is doing you in, or is a thoroughly poor spouse. You may still, if you stop viewing his or her coital limitations as criminal, be able to have a remarkably good relationship, including even a good sex relationship, with this mate.

Deifying the coital act, or making it appear that your partner is weak, incompetent, or worthless because he or she is not a most enthusiastic and adept practitioner of this particular mode of human sexuality, will tend to sabotage rather than encourage coitus. For once a male or female begins to *worry* about how good he or she is in intercourse, his or her abilities to perform almost immediately tend to become impaired. This is not necessarily because of profound unconscious psychological reasons—such as unconscious hatred of the mate—but more often because of what I have called simple psychological distraction (A. Ellis, 1957a, 1959b, 1960, 1962a).

Human beings are the kind of animals who usually find it impossible to concentrate or focus on two things at exactly the same time. Even if they are reading a book and listening to music simultaneously, they are not able to pay as much attention to either the book or the music as they would be if they were doing either act separately, and they actually keep shifting their main attention first from one to the other of these occupations.

This is especially true when people are doing two similar things at once—such as two kinds of thinking. If you concentrate on thinking about a math problem, you will find it almost impossible to figure out the solution to a business or love problem at the same time. Similarly, if you focus on *how* you are doing at a given problem you will find it most difficult to focus, at the same time, on *what* you are doing. Thus, if you are worrying about how well you are reading a paragraph, or how much time it is taking you to read it, or whether you remember most of what you read, you will find your reading rate noticeably slower and you may actually read the entire paragraph without comprehending what you are reading.

Similarly with intercourse. If you concentrate on how well you are doing at coitus; or on how long you may last at it; or on whether you are going to have an orgasm; or anything else of this sort, you cannot help detracting, by this kind of focusing, from your concentrating on the real problem at hand: which is simply the act of intercourse and your enjoyment of it. The more you worry about the *degree of success* you are having, the less you will be able to focus on the coitus itself. In consequence, it will hardly be surprising if you lose your excitement or achieve a nonsatisfying orgasm.

Worry, fear, or panic—all of which are created by convincing yourself that it is terrible, horrible, and awful to fail at anything—will make a public speaker forget his speech, stutter, or say sheer nonsense. Why, then, should it not make a sex partner perform at a much worse level than he would without this handicap?

The more, then, you *demand* that your mate be good at intercourse, the more you look upon him or her as weak, incompetent, or worthless for not being coitally adept, the less likely is he or she to perform satisfactorily. And the more you let your partner feel at ease, feel that it would be nice, but not absolutely necessary, for coitus to be energetic or prolonged, the more he or she is likely to fulfill your fondest hopes (Bibby, 1961).

A very high percentage of the cases where one mate fails to perform intercourse adequately may be laid at the door of the other's unreasonable expectations, unconscious and conscious pressures, and critical disapproval.

When someone is, in your eyes, forcing, pressing you to do something, then, even if you yourself would like to do this thing for your own satisfaction, you are humanly prone to do it poorly because (a) you have little faith in your own ability to do it well and (b) you want to resist the pressure that you think is unfairly being placed on you.

A word to the wise, then: Do not exaggerate the importance of your mate's being competent at coitus, even though you would like him or her to be. As a result of your non-pressuring attitudes, your partner is likely to be maximally eager and competent to perform.

Interest in the partner. A third attitudinal rule for successful intercourse is: Be vitally concerned about your partner's succeeding for his or her sake rather than merely for your own. This is the same kind of rule you might well apply in all your relations with close associates.

No matter how strongly you *tell* people that you want to do something for their good, if they become convinced, in their own minds, that you really want them to do this thing for *your* good, they often despise you and (albeit often unconsciously) decide that this is the *last* thing they will do. But, if you can actually convince the same people, *because it is true,* that you are out for *their* good, and that you want them to do something because you honestly feel that *both* of you will benefit from doing it, then you have a good chance of inducing them to do this thing.

This means that you should want your mate to succeed at intercourse because you *love* him or her and, through love, want his or her good. By love, here, we do not necessarily mean romantic, obsessive-compulsive devotion— which often is a mask for the unconscious dire need *to be loved*—but the mature wish for another individual's growth and development for *his* sake, even when his desires do not precisely jibe with yours.

Although this kind of love is not absolutely necessary for the achievement of satisfactory coital relations between a man and a woman, it distinctly helps—especially where their relations are on a long-time rather than a sporadic basis.

In any event, as we pointed out in the previous chapter on sexual arousal, a person who feels that he is loved and approved by his mate, and that he or she will continue to be even if his or her coital performance is not super-excellent, will tend to have more confidence in his or her ability to perform, will not over-exaggerate the significance of possible failure, and will focus more adequately on the act of copulation rather than the supposed horror of failing at it. Under these circumstances, coitus will tend to be maximally proficient and enjoyable.

De-emphasizing simultaneous orgasm. A fourth psychological requisite for having successful intercourse is a lack of emphasis on the achievement of simultaneous orgasm. It is all very well when husband and wife, in coitus or extracoital play, are able to have exactly as many orgasms as each other and to have these precisely at the same instant. This, however, is a goal that relatively few can achieve because of the enormous range of orgasm capacity among different normal individuals.

Thus, a man or woman may be capable of having one climax every two or three weeks; or may be able to have three to four every day (in the case of a man) or twenty to thirty a day (in the case of a woman).

An individual may usually have an orgasm after a few seconds of active copulation or manipulation; or may only have one after a solid hour of active sex participation.

One person may have one climax and then be totally disinterested in sex for anywhere from a few minutes to several weeks later; while another (especially a female) may have strings of climaxes, or multiple orgasms, which may continue for many minutes at a time.

Under these circumstances, with individuals differing so widely in their sex desires and capacities, it is most unusual for a husband and wife to be so perfectly matched that at all or most times they have simultaneous orgasms. Moreover, even if they experience such simultaneity in the early years of their relationship, there is an excellent chance that later on they may change in their sexual proclivities, so that their old timing is no longer easy or possible to achieve.

It should also be realized in this connection that, even when a couple successfully makes an effort to achieve orgasm at the same moment, their achievement may detract from rather than add to their pleasure. For each partner may be concentrating so mightily on hastening or holding back his or her climax that orgasm is never properly focused on and enjoyed.

A more realistic goal, then, is *mutual* rather than *simultaneous* orgasm—with each partner trying to satisfy the other in *some* way at *some* time during the sex act. Even this goal should never be over-strictly sought, as many partners do not desire a climax at a given time but are most willing (as loving mates should be) to help their husbands or wives attain one or more climaxes.

In any event, the false ideal of two spouses always

achieving simultaneous orgasm will frequently result in distraction, frustration, disappointment, self-blame, hostility, and other unfavorable thoughts and feelings. A greater saboteur than this concept of coital "fulfillment" can hardly be imagined; and the sooner this ideal is realistically toned down and relegated to the realm of mild preference rather than obsessive demand the more likely are husbands and wives to have the kinds of satisfactory coitus of which most of them are quite capable.

Effective intercommunication. A fifth psychological rule for achieving successful intercourse is one which we referred to in our chapter on psychological methods of arousal—namely, that of down to earth and no-nonsense-about-it talking and signalling between the married pair. When intercourse is about to start, the partners should signal or tell each other that they are ready. Similarly, after coitus has ended, the mate who wants to break apart first should signal the other to this effect.

If one mate wishes to remain united for several minutes after intercourse, the other should cooperate to maintain the interlocking position. But this maintaining of the coital position for a long period of time can also become onerous to one of the mates—especially the one who may be lying under the other. Or other aspects of coital positions—such as the manner in which one's arms or legs are uncomfortably bent—may tend to be irritating to one of the mates if such positions are held too long.

If for any reason either of the partners feels physically uncomfortable before, during, or after coitus, he or she should speak up and induce the other to change to a more comfortable position.

Sometimes one mate desires sex or love talk before, during, or after coitus; and the other should make a point of saying the necessary words. Here again, however, the super-romantic or sexually fetishistic demands of one partner may become onerous and should be held in check or psychologically investigated if they seem to be unduly imposing on the reasonable preferences of the other mate.

Coitus as part of a whole relationship. Still another psychological rule relating to intercourse is that coitus cannot be isolated from the rest of a couple's life, but is part and parcel of the pair's whole relationship.

Occasionally, I see husbands and wives who have nothing in common except sex attraction and who manage to keep having excellent coital relations in spite of the fact that there is no love between them. These, however, tend to be the exceptions rather than the rule. Usually, if no love exists between a couple, or either or both mates are shirking their financial, companionable, parental, or other major responsibilities, their sex life will seriously suffer.

In cases where one or both mates are sexually unenthusiastic because of general marital difficulties, the basic causes of their incompatibility should be squarely faced and met—often with the help of a trained marriage counselor or psychologist.

The husband who is puzzled about his wife's sexual unresponsiveness should first ask himself whether he is *generally* a good partner; and the wife who feels sexually unsatisfied should try to discover whether she and her husband have a specific sex problem or whether it is part of a broader setting. Only when the total relationship of two mates is honestly faced and straightened out is it sometimes possible to see whether an actual *sexual* difficulty exists.

The setting for intercourse. Although some individuals, particularly males, are able to enjoy coitus almost under any conditions—in a semi-public place, for instance, or a cold room or on an uncomfortable sofa—others are more sensitive and require a proper setting for their maximum coital enjoyment. Even though you yourself may be rather insensitive in this connection, it is well to discover the preferences and sensitivities of your mate and to try to cater to them to any reasonable extent, in order that he or she may feel fully relaxed and released when having intercourse (Beigel, 1953).

It is often better to have coitus in a lighted or semi-lit room rather than in complete darkness. For one thing, nudity that can be seen is often arousing to one or both the partners; and certain coital positions require sight as well as touch for their successful completion. It should be pointed out, however, that if one of the mates, even for silly or neurotic reasons, has serious objections to having sex relations in a well-lit room, the other should, at least temporarily, willingly accept these objections, while gradually trying to re-educate the mate so that they are finally overcome.

In all instances where one mate has strong prejudices in favor of or against certain sex practices, the other partner should try to be unusually understanding and uncritical, even if the practices that are favored or disfavored seem to be outlandish. If the presumably more reasonable mate will at least give the "outlandish" procedures an honest try, he or she may find that they are really not as bad as they seem to be. Or, if they are found to be unsatisfactory, the more "normal" mate will then have a more objective basis for refusing to participate further in this kind of "peculiar" behavior.

If a very clearcut difference exists in this respect, with one mate insisting upon sex practices that the other mate finds completely distasteful, it is usually best for the first mate to drop his or her insistence and to seek for alternative outlets with the mate who finds particular acts most unpleasing.

In extreme cases of disagreement, professional help should be sought fairly early during married life; since one or both of the spouses may have a serious psychological problem that, if it were cleared up, would remove the existing sexual incompatibility.

8.

Sexual Intercourse: Physical Aspects

Even though the psychological foundations of satisfactory intercourse between a husband and wife may be well established, there are several important physical aspects of coitus which must usually be considered. We shall now discuss some of these physical problems.

Physical receptivity. As previously noted, intercourse should normally be engaged in only when both partners are sufficiently aroused and ready for it. Signs of readiness have been discussed in Chapter 7.

Receptivity for intercourse may sometimes be associated with an individual's physical condition at certain times of the day or month. Thus, some women are periodic in their sex desires and capacities and are much more ready for coitus on certain days—such as the days before, during, or immediately after their menstrual periods—than at other times.

Some men also have periodic cycles during the month, which may possibly be correlated with their production of sex hormones.

In individual cases, you and your partner's cyclical variations have to be determined by experience and observation and intercourse should be had, as much as possible, in relation to such cycles.

Many husbands and wives are not particularly periodic on a month to month or day to day basis, but are much more ready for intercourse at one time of the day than another. Some prefer nighttime and some the morning hours for coitus; while some may even prefer midday hours. There is no reason why such personal preferences cannot be discovered and, at least to some extent, conformed to as the daily schedule of living allows.

Because of convention, most people in our society seem to have their coital relations almost exclusively late at night, just before they go to sleep. This time, however, has distinct disadvantages for many persons who are fairly tired and lacking in energy by the end of the day. It is likely that a good many couples should select some more suitable time.

Intercourse can also sometimes be more satisfactorily bunched at a given time—such as at weekends, when conditions for it may be better—than had more regularly. Whatever is more convenient and comfortable for the partners can and should be arranged in this respect.

Sexual mechanics. The matter of human mechanics should be seriously considered in having intercourse. A human being can drive a car only because his body is able to execute certain motions (bending, pushing, holding, stretching, etc.) and because the car parts (steering wheel, brake, ignition switch, and so on) are designed so that they can be manipulated by the kind of body he possesses. Put a radically different kind of person (such as a midget) in a regular car or a regularly-built person in an unusually constructed car (such as one where the steering wheel is far to the right of its usual position) and difficulties will immediately arise. Or put a normal person in a regular car and let him try to steer with his feet instead of his hands and—watch out!

So with intercourse. People have to be somewhat designed for effective coitus; and, granting that they are well designed for the purpose (which, fortunately, most of them are) they have to do the right kind of mechanical things with their physical apparatus. This means, at the start, that they must accept the fact that, like cars, people are different.

You would not try to drive a mighty Buick in exactly the same way as you would try to drive a tiny Austin. In many instances, you would not even try to drive one Buick exactly as you would drive another. Why, then, should you try to have intercourse with one individual exactly as you may have had it with quite a differently constructed person? Why *need* you do the same sexual things with one that you might do with another?

One couple, for example, may consist of two wiry, supple, athletic-type individuals who can easily perform, and highly enjoy, all kinds of sex acrobatics. Another couple may consist of two rather obese, sedentary individuals who can just about achieve and enjoy one or two coital positions—or who even find coitus itself, in almost any position, too mechanically difficult and who therefore normally resort to extracoital means of satisfaction. As long as each of these couples does what *it* wants and *it* enjoys, why should it try to ape the coital technique of others?

Sex adeptness, particularly when coitus is carried on for a fairly long period of time on a given occasion, requires not only penile-vaginal but general mechanical aptitude. The fact that a given position, such as the usual one with the male mounting the female in a face to face position, is easy to *enter* by no means proves that it is just as easy to *maintain*.

A male, for example, may have no difficulties with his penis but may have great trouble with his back; and arching it over his partner for fifteen minutes or more may be the last thing he needs to keep in good physical condition.

Or a female may have an easy time getting into a good copulatory position when her husband is on top; but then, because of rectal trouble, sensitivity of the pubic bone region, or some other non-sexual difficulty, she may become uncomfortable after a few minutes of intercourse in this position.

Under these circumstances, experimentation is necessary to discover what is the most generally comfortable, and not merely the most sexually effective, positions for each couple to assume. At times, in spite of physical discomfort, sex partners may deviate from the coital positions they find satisfactory. But most of the time they will find it better to maintain comfortable positions, even when they find that these have some *sexual* disadvantages.

Favoring the partner with the greater difficulty. It is usually advisable to give special favor and attention to the general and sexual requirements of the partner who has the greater difficulties having satisfaction. Thus, a man may find it most enjoyable to have sex relations in the usual face to face position, surmounting his mate. But he may also find this position *so* enjoyable that he has an orgasm quickly and thus makes it difficult for his wife to have maximum satisfaction. Under the circumstances, it might be advisable for this couple usually to employ some other coital position where the man's orgasm tends to be retarded.

By the same token, a husband and wife may find that having intercourse in a certain way—say, through entering the vagina from the rear instead of the front—may be mechanically efficient and enjoyable but that it tends to lead to intercourse that is prolonged indefinitely without climax by one of the partners. This couple may therefore try using another position that, in some respects, may be less enjoyable but that enables both mates to reach climax more quickly.

Since one partner will frequently be adequately arousable and will be able to come to orgasm in neither an overly-rapid nor an overly-retarded manner, this partner can usually enjoy any number of sex positions and modes of behavior. If the other mate, however, is either very quick or slow to attain climax, certain positions and modes of action will tend to help this mate overcome his or her handicap; and these are the patterns of sexuality that should usually, though not necessarily always, be employed.

Patience and relaxation. Haste often makes waste in sexual intercourse as in many other facets of living. Although the male in particular may be imperious in his urges when fully aroused and may feel that he will lose his erection if he does not immediately copulate, it will usually be found that if he takes things easier, and slowly gets into the most comfortable coital position, he enjoys himself more thoroughly than if he effects hasty connection (Hamilton, 1961).

Imperiousness may be exciting for some; but for those who do not need such excitement, it may lead to muscle tension, awkward positions, or rough play, which detract from coital enjoyment.

When penile-vaginal penetration has been effected, there is perhaps a normal tendency for most males to want to get to the root of the matter as quickly as possible and to bring about orgasm in short order. They assume that this is the most enjoyable way to have coitus; and, in terms of short-range hedonism, they are probably correct. It is likely, however, that if they experimented with slower pacing, they would often experience longer-range satisfactions. What is more, by paying more attention to the slower-timed needs that their female companions frequently have, they would tend to arouse these partners to a higher pitch of desire and release that, in turn, would make their own enjoyments greater. This is not to say that more slowly paced and relaxed coital thrusts are best for *everyone* under *all* conditions; for this is not true. But, as part of the general sexual armamentarium, they have their definite place.

Coital varietism. Variety may or may not be the spice of coital life. Many people read the same story or poem over and over with unabated enjoyment; others cannot stand re-reading something they have recently perused. Similarly, many couples find that engaging in coitus in almost exactly the same way each time gives them maximum pleasure; while others find that repetition leads to boredom and disinterest.

The main rule in regard to variety is to give things a real try—and thereby discover whether you like them or not. By a real try we mean an honest attempt, on at least a few occasions, to enjoy a certain kind of coitus. Take, by way of illustration, something like rear-entry copulation. Normally, if the male lies behind the female and enters her vagina from the rear, he may at first have more difficulty than if he enters in a face to face position. Until he learns to adapt his body and movements to his partner's, this position may be less enjoyable than alternative methods. But often, if a couple persists in experimenting several times the mates will finally discover how to perform rear-entry coitus smoothly and efficiently and may then decide that it is one of the least energy-consuming and most enjoyable of all coital techniques.

The rule is, then, that if at first you don't succeed at any particular variety of coitus, try at least a few more times before you abandon it and assume that it is just not for you. If you give it a real chance and finally desist from trying, that may be perfectly legitimate; for not every kind of sex behavior is everone's oyster. But, if you refuse to try certain coital positions and abjure them without giving them any chance whatever, that begins to border (as we shall show in a subsequent chapter on sex deviation) on the pathological.

As we shall also note in more detail when we discuss deviation, the general rule in regard to intercourse is: No act is abnormal or perverted unless it becomes exclusive, fixated, fear-driven, or compulsive.

The individual who is not satisfied with so-called normal face to face coitus but insists on attempting every position in the books, including positions so bizarre that most people would never prefer them—that individual is not necessarily sexually disturbed. He only becomes abnormal or deviant when he engages in these modes of intercourse out of some irrational fear or compulsiveness; when he *exclusively* becomes addicted to one position and under no circumstances can find any enjoyment in any other kind of copulation.

By the same token, the individual who insists on trying *no* position other than one of the more usual ones, and who under *no* circumstance will give any other coital technique a chance—he is just as fixated and fetichistic, and hence as deviated in his sexuality, as is the compulsive and fearful varietist.

Human *preferences,* either for a variety of copulative methods or for a single one, are perfectly healthy; but *dire* needs for either performing or abstaining from sex varietism result from neurotically (or psychotically) exaggerating the significance of one kind of sex behavior and needlessly catastrophizing its effects (A. Ellis, 1957a, 1962a, 1963a, 1963d).

Clitorial contact during coitus. Although the importance of clitoral stimulation has been known for many centuries, its significance has only recently been acknowledged in English-speaking nations by leading sex authorities (Clark, 1949; A. Ellis, 1953a, 1961, 1963a, 1963c, 1965a; Hegelet, 1963; Hirsch, 1951, 1957, 1962; Kelly, 1953, 1957, 1961; Kinsey, Pomeroy, Martin, and Gebhard, 1953; Masters and Johnson, 1962). While Kelly, Hirsch, and others recommend that, during intercourse, the man "ride high" against his wife's vulva, so that the shaft of his penis is bent over against her clitoris and pressure against this organ is thus maintained during coitus, this is not an easy method to assume and sustain during active copulation. In fact, for many couples it is downright impossible. Moreover, this technique requires that the partners always assume the face-to-face, man surmounting the female position; and this position may not be satisfactory to all couples.

Other techniques of achieving maximum clitoral contact during coitus include the man's rocking against the woman so that the shaft of his penis maintains maximum contact with her clitoris and his pressing his pubic bone against her clitoral area. But these measures may not be easy for him to attain while he is intent on having a coital act that will be fully satisfying to himself.

More to the point, as Greenblatt (1957) notes, is the husband's pressing the head of his penis against his wife's clitoris prior to intercourse; and withdrawing his penis entirely from time to time and reapplying it to the clitoris. This, too, has limitations, however, as many couples do not want to interrupt penile-vaginal contact and a woman's clitoris often needs prolonged and intensive friction if she is to achieve a climax.

One of the best solutions to the problem of having coitus and simultaneously effecting sufficient clitoral friction is for the male to manipulate the female's clitoris with his fingers or knuckles during intromission. He can most readily do this, usually, *not* in the man-surmounting-woman position, since he then needs his hands to hold himself up, but in the woman-on-top-of-man or the face-to-face sitting or standing-sitting positions (which we describe in detail in the following chapter). Perhaps best of all, if the man lies behind the woman, while each of them is largely in a side position, and achieves vaginal entry from the rear, he can easily put his arm around her and manipulate her clitoris in almost any desired manner.

In women who have other parts of their genitals which are sensitive (such as their inner lips, vaginal vestibule, or some spots within the vagina) it may also be important for the male to try to reach and massage these parts, either with his penis or with some other part of his anatomy. Questioning and experimentation will be most helpful in this respect.

Although the male usually does not require special penile or genital manipulation while he is having coitus, this may sometimes be desirable. In these instances, coital positions (such as the rear entry position or the face to face position with the woman putting her legs together after entry has been effected) may be employed to shorten and narrow the vaginal canal, thus making for additional pressure on the penis. Also: in some positions, such as the male-surmounting face to face technique, the woman can fondle the man's scrotum or base of his penis while they are engaging in intercourse, thus heightening his pleasure, if he likes this sort of thing.

Effecting penetration. Starting intercourse may occasionally be something of a problem, since the woman's vaginal orifice may, long after she has lost her virginity, be small, oddly situated, or may lead to a narrow or (in rare cases) peculiarly slanted vaginal canal. The woman, even though sufficiently aroused and desirous of intercourse, may also be poorly lubricated.

Consequently, as noted in the case of virgins, one of the best methods for penetration of the vagina is to have the female lie on her back with her legs well raised, preferably over the man's shoulders, and her buttocks elevated with a pillow. The man, who is kneeling facing her, can then usually make easy entry. In general, the face to face positions, including the sitting or the sitting-standing ones (which are described in the next chapter) are desirable where penetration is difficult.

Because the penis has no sense of direction and literally does not know where it is going, the woman should not hesitate to guide it into the vagina with her hand. Otherwise, there may have to be considerable blind threshing around until the male finds the right spot for entry—and even then cases have been known where anal entry was effected when the male believed that his penis was penetrating his wife's vagina.

Coital stroking. Once entry has been effected, the male's thrusts and the female's parries may be gradual or sudden, shallow or deep, depending on the desires of the two partners. Often, it is best to employ short strokes and slow movements at the beginning and later to make the strokes longer and the movements more rapid. Powerful, penetrating thrusts usually are more exciting to the partners but can also be painful for one or both mates. As Berg and Street (1953) note, where the male's penis is reasonably large and the female's vagina is only of moderate length "it is unwise to batter as with a ram upon the vaginal vault and the tip of the womb. Eventually this will create pain and tenderness, and accomplish nothing other than to develop in the wife an aversion to the sex act." Powerful thrusts can also be too exciting—inducing the male or the female to come to climax too quickly.

Quick-climaxing men may find it desirable to slow down their thrusts or even rest completely for awhile immediately after entering the woman's vagina or after each series of thrusts. Women, too, may become overly-excited or exhausted by highly active copulation and may have to take rests.

By learning to tilt the pelvis instead of the whole body, one or both partners can remain relatively passive and wait for the other partner to approach orgasm. Or the more easily excited partner may do very little thrusting and may let the less easily excited one do most of the active pelvic movements. Where, for example, the male (as is usually the case) is easily excitable and prone to have an orgasm after few vaginal thrusts, it will usually be found that if the wife assumes the surmounting face to face position and does most of the thrusting herself a double purpose may well be served: since she may bring on her orgasm more quickly while the husband is better able to control his own.

On the other hand, where one or both partners have some difficulty reaching climax, quite active thrusting and parrying, on the part of the female as well as the male, may be desirable. Similarly, special juxtapositions of the sex organs, with the male or female resorting to riding high or riding low, to deep or short thrusts, to circular, side to side, or rocking movements during coitus, and so on, may be advantageous, so that the most sensitive parts of the genitals of the partners are thoroughly and consistently stimulated.

Some couples, then, want to give or receive no quarter in connection with powerful, violent thrusts and parries and enjoy fierce, quick penetration and invigorating pelvic lunges. Still other couples find that slow-timed or prolonged copulation results in the greatest heights and depths of enjoyment.

Some husbands and wives suffer physical pain from vigorous coital stroking and others become bored and disinterested with slower rhythmic motions. As ever, considerable individual experimentation is called for to provide maximum satisfaction in each case.

Extragenital stimulation during coitus. While intercourse is going on, there is no reason why other related activities must stop. Many couples thoroughly enjoy the continuation of kissing and caressing while copulating and some find difficulty coming to orgasm unless they can give or receive extragenital stimulation during coitus.

If one of the mates normally does most of the active kissing and caressing during intercourse, then it is usually best that he or she maintain a relatively passive position—such as lying on the back or side—so that his or her hands are free to engage in caressive activities. If both mates are relatively active in this respect, then the side by side or sitting positions are often most desirable.

Extragenital play during coitus is not only often useful in helping one or both partners to enhance their pleasure or come to climax, it can also sometimes be used for the opposite effect. Thus, a husband who is highly excitable and tends to reach an orgasm after only a few moments of intromission may find that if he focuses on kissing his wife or playing with her breasts or other parts of her body during intercourse he may be able to distract himself sufficiently from his own genital sensations to retard his climax and to prolong coitus.

Adequate lubrication. Adequate lubrication of the genitals is an important part of normal intercourse. Usually, the sex organs need no special lubrication because, when the participants are sufficiently aroused, their built-in lubricating glands do a good job. Indeed, sometimes they do too good a job and somewhat unpleasant slipperiness results. For the most part, if artificial lubrication has to be consistently employed, it may well mean that the female partner is not being sufficiently stimulated before intercourse takes place and that more attention and time should be given to getting her in a receptive mood.

There are, however, instances where the use of special lubricants is desirable. Thus, a woman's vagina may be unusually small and narrow; or she may only become well libricated after she has had intercourse for a period of time; or she may have a natural librication deficiency, especially as she grows older. In such instances, the most easily available lubricant that may be employed is the saliva of either or both partners. This will usually suffice, although there is a tendency for it to be quick drying and not to be as effective after several minutes of intercourse as it was when first applied.

The best artificial lubricant for most purposes is surgical jelly, such as K-Y jelly, which is greaseless, water-soluble, non-straining, economical, and suitabe for use with condoms.

Other kinds of lubricants, such as petroleum jelly (Vaseline), hand lotions, cold creams, spermicidal creams, and soap, may all be used in cases of necessity but have distinct disadvantages and are not recommended for general usage. All lubricants tend to be absorbed and to dry up if intercourse is quite prolonged and may have to be reapplied, on occasion, in the midst of coitus.

When a condom is employed, lubrication (particularly with a suitable spermicidal jelly or creme) is advisable on the outside of the condom. If the inside of the condom is also slightly lubricated with saliva, water, or some other suitable substance, it may help to restore some of the penile sensitivity which condoms often are accused of impeding. At the same time, lubricating the inside of a condom, unless it is carefully done, has the disadvantage of sometimes making it more likely to slip off the penis during the sex act or upon withdrawal.

Lubrication is often essential in extracoital play as well as in intercourse. If the wife is massaging the husband's penis or the husband his wife's clitoris it may be desirable to apply some lubrication, such as saliva or surgical jelly, so that friction will be pleasurable rather than irritating.

A pathological lack of lubrication, especially in older individuals or (occasionally) in those who have hypothyroidism, may occur and can usually be compensated for by the use of artificial lubricants. Medical examination and correction may sometimes be advisable in these cases.

Frequency of copulation. The frequency of copulation should normally vary widely according to the physical and psychological makeup of different individuals. Although rules about the frequency of coitus would seem to fall in the area of the physical aspects of sex, they often actually fall in the psychological sphere, largely because most of us have been raised with so many superstitions in this connection. Just as in the case of our ideas on masturbation, where we have been raised to think that autoerotism itself may be all right but that "excessive" or "too much" masturbation is harmful, so in the case of coitus many of us have been led to believe that it is a great thing in itself but must not be done "too frequently."

From a physical standpoint, this is largely bosh. As far as the male is concerned, it is almost impossible for a normal man to have "excessive" or "weakening" intercourse because he simply will not be able to obtain and maintain an erection if he does so. The female, on the contrary, easily can have intercourse more often than she desires; but if she does have it on this "excessive" basis, it seems to do little or no physical harm (unless she goes to unusual extremes, as in the case of some prostitutes who have ten or more lovers a day).

The main physical injury that may result from "excessive" copulation probably is the loss of sleep people are likely to experience when they are highly active sexually. The sex act itself is not overly energy-consuming in most instances. But if you lose an hour or so of needed sleep regularly because of extended foreplay and coitus you can easily become debilitated over a period of time. The moral is: the more frequent and prolonged your sex relations are, the earlier you'd better get to bed!

The other main physical harm that may result from frequent coitus is irritation of one or both partners' genitals. Particularly where sex relations are engaged in without sufficient lubrication, or coital strokes are too powerful, or when the partners' organs fit too tightly, or when there is some injury or pathology previously present in the genitals, irritation and soreness may occur.

In such instances, remedial measures, including medical examination and treatment, should be taken immediately; and, on occasion, coitus may have to be temporarily suspended or engaged in less frequently. If so, it usually will be quite feasible for the spouses to augment their extracoital relations to compensate for the coitus they are missing.

As noted in a later chapter, it may sometimes be necessary to decrease the frequency of some or all kinds of sex relations when one or both of the partners are physically run-down, injured, or ill. But even in many of these instances it is only necessary to stop certain highly active forms of coitus rather than all manners, shapes, and forms of sex activity.

In spite of the exceptions just noted, the general rule still stands: husbands and wives should have intercourse as often as they distinctly enjoy having it. They may often find that they enjoy it more by having it less often; but not necessarily—particularly in the case of females, who sometimes more greatly enjoy coitus the more often they have it.

Frequency may also vary with periodic and other factors. Some women, for instance, want coitus more often around their menstrual periods and less often in between; others may actually reverse this tendency. Both men and women usually desire coitus less frequently during periods of illness, fatigue, and emotional stress; but, as ever, there are notable exceptions.

The most common problem concerning the frequency of intercourse between a married pair arises when one enjoys it considerably more than the other. This can usually *not* be solved by the one who desires it less often forcing himself or herself to have it more frequently.

The male cannot easily force himself to copulate more often than he wishes to do so; and though the female can copulate far beyond her actual desires, it is neither physically nor psychologically preferable that she do this to any considerable extent, as her genitals themselves are necessarily involved in coitus and she is thereby forcing herself to have the most intimate kind of sex relations when she is not in the mood for them. This will often lead her, sooner or later, to become hostile toward her mate for wanting coitus so often.

Both males and females, however, can fairly easily satisfy their more desirous mates in quasi-coital or non-coital ways. Thus, the female who is not eager to have intercourse can engage in hand-genital, oral-genital, thigh-genital, or anal-genital relations with her husband—and particularly hand-genital relations, which tend to be less personally involving than other kinds of sex acts. And the male who is less desirous than his wife of having intercourse can satisfy her by manual or oral manipulation.

This is not to say that non-coital sex participations are just the same as or exactly as satisfactory as coital acts in all instances. They aren't. The vagina is an organ ideally suited to male pleasure and orgasm; and the penis has certain unique qualities for satisfying many females.

Ideally, therefore, it would be nice if each marital partner wanted intercourse precisely the same number of times as did his or her mate. Nothing, however, is ideal in human relations, including sex relations. And second-best, though not perfect, is often quite satisfactory.

If men and women would be unprejudiced about copulation and realistic in their sexual expectations, the great majority would be able to get just about as many and as few orgasms in marriage as they would prefer.

The frequency of marital intercourse, then, should largely be a matter of personal choice and should be expected to range, with different couples, all the way from a few dozen to a few hundred copulations a year. Anything within this range is perfectly normal in most instances—as long as the couple concerned thinks that it is.

Usually, the frequency of intercourse steadily but slowly decreases with the age of the individual. According to the Kinsey figures, teen-age couples, on the average, are likely to have coitus about three times a week, thirty-year-old couples about twice, and fifty-year-old couples about once a week. A small percentage of married individuals, however, have coitus five or more times a week until they are quite on in years; and another small percentage have it even during their younger years only once every two or three weeks. Each couple must therefore find its own level and unashamedly follow its own bents.

Post-coital relations. As in the case of intercourse itself, there are no unalterable or invariant rules for what to do after coitus has ended. Many individuals, as we noted previously, prefer to remain united for a period of time after intercourse; but others prefer to break apart quickly. Good communication and good sense about this issue should be the general rule.

A great many men and women are exhausted or sleepy after intercourse and prefer to doze off. Some of their tiredness, however, would appear to be related to the fact that most people have coitus late at night, when they are generally ready for sleep. Those who have it in the morning or in the middle of the day frequently find that they are refreshed immediately afterwards and prefer to get up and begin some activity.

Even among those who engage in coitus late at night, some are refreshed by it and prefer to stay up and talk, or eat, or do something else for awhile. Others, far from being tired, want to repeat intercourse fairly soon after their first attempt. Again, mutual cooperation and good sense should prevail in this connection.

There is an old notion that after coitus one is sad—*post coitum omne animal triste.* Although this probably applies to some individuals, and particularly to those who are guilty about sex relations, it is more likely that guiltless individuals generally experience a sense of relaxation, fulfillment, and peace. It is the *lack* of satisfying sex relations that is far more likely to lead to a feeling of irritation, annoyance, and sadness (Beigel, 1961).

9.

Sexual Intercourse: Main Positions

It is theoretically possible to outline scores of positions for intercourse, but there are actually only a few basic ones and all others are minor variations on these few fundamental themes. Most couples, moreover, will usually find it convenient, after a while, to employ one or two coital positions most of the time and to vary these with other positions from time to time.

Particularly where one of the partners has difficulty becoming sufficiently aroused or achieving an orgasm, it will usually be found that this partner is helped by the couple's assuming one or two regular positions after they have first experimented with a good many others.

It will also usually be discovered that the main positions favored by a given couple can be attained more easily in some instances by this couple's first assuming quite a different position and then, while the partners are still interlocked, shifting or rolling into the desired one. Thus, entry can be achieved in a face to face position, with either the male or female on top; and then, by shifting or rolling, a side by side position can be effected.

Some of the main coital positions and their advantages and disadvantages will now be discussed.

Face to face, man on top. Vaginal-penile contact is quite easily achieved in the face to face, man on top position—especially if the woman spreads her legs and flexes her knees or raises her feet. Sometimes, her feet may be placed on the male partner's shoulders and remain there during part or all of intercourse. If necessary, her buttocks may also be raised by putting a pillow under them.

It is usually important, in this position, that the man not lie directly upon the woman, thus limiting her freedom of action and often becoming onerously heavy on her. He should, instead, support the weight of his own body on his hands or elbows.

It is sometimes also important, especially in the case of a woman who has some difficulty in getting an orgasm, that the male "ride high" or otherwise rock or press against the clitoris during intercourse (although, as noted in the previous chapter, the "riding high" technique has distinct limitations in many instances).

It is sometimes also desirable, after entry has been effected, for the woman to close her legs, arch her back (sometimes with a pillow underneath it), and constrict her vaginal opening and walls, thus achieving more friction of the penis against her vulva and vagina. This may also be an excellent position if the male has a small penis and requires additional friction for his own pleasure. Pressure against the base of a man's penis in this position may likewise help him maintain erection if he finds it difficult to attain and sustain full erectile power.

Additional variations on the face to face, man on top position may include (a) the wife's keeping her legs apart and flat; (b) keeping them between her husband's knees; (c) putting one of her legs between his legs; (d) bending her thighs back toward her chest; (e) raising one of her legs while keeping the other flat; (f) wrapping one or both legs around her husband's and (g) wrapping her legs around his waist.

Some of the chief advantages of the face to face, man on top position are:

1. It usually makes for easy entry if the woman's thighs are parted and raised.

2. It allows the male to set the pace and to slow or hasten his own orgasm.

3. It facilitates great intimacy between the two partners, including mutual kissing.

4. The male can sometimes continue intercourse even after he has had an orgasm.

5. It is a good position for impregnation, since after

intercourse the woman can keep her knees raised and prevent the sperm from leaving her vagina.

6. It is most convenient for couples who enjoy the male's making vigorous pelvic thrusts.

7. If the woman flexes her knees or places her feet on the man's shoulders she will thereby narrow her vagina and intensify her and her partner's satisfaction if she tends to be vaginally wide and slack.

Some of the chief disadvantages of the face to face, man on top position are:

1. It tends to restrict the female's movements and thrusts.

2. It sometimes leads to too deep penetration and to pain on the part of the woman.

3. It is not easy for the male to resort to manual friction on the woman's clitoris in this position.

4. It is often too stimulating for the male and induces him to achieve climax too quickly.

5. It may be too acrobatic, when the extreme flexion position is used, for some couples, particularly for older and stouter mates; and in this position face to face intimacy is reduced.

6. If the male or female is obese it may become rather uncomfortable for the woman to have to bear the weight of her mate.

7. It may be uncomfortable and inadvisable for women in the later stages of pregnancy.

Face to face, woman on top. In this position the male lies on his back and the woman squats over him and guides his penis into her vagina; or she sits down in an astride position on his erect penis and loins, resting her back against his flexed knees and raised thighs. Or else the husband and wife can achieve penetration in some other position, such as the man on top position, and then gently roll around until the woman is on top.

Once entry has been effected, the woman can keep squatting, or can sit astride, or straighten out her legs and lie between or outside her husband's. The man can lie prone, or can raise himself on his hands or elbows, or raise his knees on the side of or in back of his wife.

Advantages of the face to face, woman on top position include:

1. The woman often has maximum freedom of action

and can move her loins so that her clitoris or other sensitive parts of her vulva directly rub against the male's genitals. The female can also, if she is athletically inclined, learn to make circular or powerful forward and backward rhythmic pelvic movements which may be most satisfying to her and her husband.

2. Because he can rest relatively quietly, without too much movement on his part, the quick-triggered man may often last longer in this position.

3. If a woman has a short vagina or has sensitive organs she may be able to regulate the depth of penetration and prevent any pain or injury to herself.

4. If a woman enjoys deep penetration or contact of the penis with her cervix, this position allows for such maximum penetration.

5. The easily tired or relatively unathletic male can maintain this position for a long period of time, until his mate achieves climax.

6. Where a woman has a long vagina or a male a fairly short penis, this position, because of its facilitating maximum penetration, may be more satisfying.

7. Some women are aroused by their own pelvic thrusts, which can be made satisfactorily in the woman on top position.

8. The female surmounting position frees a man's hands so that he can caress his partner satisfactorily and manipulate her clitoris if this is desirable. Although fully embracing the female is impossible when she is sitting astride, the partners have a full view of each other and may be inordinately pleased and excited by watching each other's movements and physique.

9. As Van de Velde (1926) points out, "There can be no doubt that coitus astride really can afford the summit in both excitement and response, the acme of specific physical sexual pleasure, to both man and woman."

10. In instances where one or both partners, particularly the male, is obese, this position is practical and comfortable for many individuals.

Some of the disadvantages of the face to face, woman on top, position are these:

1. The male's freedom of movement and of making pelvic thrusts may be impaired and he many consequently lose his erection.

2. Many women are not athletic or acrobatic enough to master this technique and feel uncomfortable when engaging in it. The very acrobatics of the position may detract from these women's pleasure.

3. Where the woman's vagina is short, penetration may be too deep and uncomfortable.

4. Where the woman's cervix is sensitive or vulnerable, penetration may be too deep.

5. The man's penis may keep slipping out of the vagina as copulation proceeds.

6. Van de Velde believes that, because it offers many possibilities for high sex tension, mobility, stimulation, and excitement, the woman astride position is too wearing and should only be occasionally used by older individuals but not necessarily avoided by younger and more vigorous ones.

7. The position is a poor one for impregnation, as some of the male's sperm is likely to seep from the female's vagina during and after intercourse.

8. When a woman is pregnant, this position may be uncomfortable for her.

Face to face, side by side. In this position, the partners lie side by side, facing each other. They may both have their lower legs on the bed and the woman's upper leg over both the man's legs; or the woman's lower leg may rest on the man's lower leg and his upper leg may rest between her legs, so that they are interlocked.

As Hirsch (1951) points out, the "side" positions are not exactly what their name implies—as the man is often largely on his back and the woman, resting on him, is partly supported on his chest; or else the wife may largely be on her back, supported by a pillow. The side by side positions may sometimes be achieved by the partners' beginning in another position, then rolling on their sides.

Advantages of the face to face, side by side position are:

1. It is quite restful for both partners in many instances and throws less strain on them.

2. In the interlocking position, maximum contact between the male's genitals and the woman's clitoris is sometimes achieved.

3. The position, because of its restful aspects, is particu-

larly helpful where one or both partners are fatigued, ill, invalided, weak, or old.

4. In cases of obesity and where one of the mates is considerably taller than the other, the side by side positions are quite useful, since the partners can adapt to each other and there is not too much pressure by one against the other.

5. In this position, the partners can sometimes go to sleep after coitus while still remaining sexually interlocked.

6. An easily excitable male can usually regulate his thrusts and last longer in this position.

7. Both partners have relative freedom of movement and a steady coital rhythm may easily be attained.

8. Withdrawal and reinsertion can often be done without a drastic change in the position of the partners.

9. The female can make sure that penetration is not too deep if she is vaginally sensitive or short.

10. There is little inconvenience to the woman when coitus is engaged in during the last months of pregnancy.

Disadvantages of the face to face, side by side position include:

1. It is not easy for some individuals to achieve entry in this position.

2. It is not comfortable for certain individuals. There may be too great a restriction or pressure on the woman's leg and on the male's freedom of action.

3. It is not sufficiently exciting in those instances where the partners require deep pelvic thrusts.

4. Penis penetration tends to be rather shallow for the preferences of some individuals.

5. In the interlocking position coital movements may be difficult without the partners' putting painful pressures on various other parts of their bodies.

Rear entry, man's face to woman's back. In the rear entry (or averse) positions, there are several main possibilities. (a) The man may lie on his side behind the woman's back (she too, being on her side), with her buttocks somewhat above his penis and her body slightly curved inwardly, her legs bent at her hips. The man enters the woman's vagina between her legs and his scrotum presses up against her buttocks. After intromission she may press her thighs together, providing additional friction for the penis and preventing it from slipping out of her vagina.

(b) The woman may kneel on her hands and knees, with her head and breast almost on the bed or sofa, with the man kneeling behind her. He again enters the vagina between her legs and presses his scrotum against her buttocks.

(c) The woman may lie on her stomach with her pelvis raised and the man lying on top of her. This is an awkward and not too useful position for most couples.

(d) The man may sit on the edge of a bed or a chair, while the woman, with her back to him, sits down on his penis and his lap (or lower part of his stomach). The man opens his thigh somewhat and leans back while the woman opens her thighs as wide as possible and leans forward.

Advantages of the rear entry positions include the following:

1. The male may be able to feel the woman's gluteal region with his legs, scrotum, and pubic area; and this may be stimulating to him and her.

2. The male can easily put his hands around the woman during copulation and play with her breasts or clitoris.

3. The rear entry position with both partners lying on their sides may be very restful, particularly for the male, and require even less exertion than the face to face, side, or the woman astride positions.

4. The rear entry lying-on-side position enables the man to insert his penis only to the degree that he and his wife desire.

5. Where either or both partners are fatigued, weakened, older, or convalescent, this position is easy and relaxing to employ.

6. The kneeling rear entry position may provide quite vigorous activity, particularly on the part of the male, if this is found to be desirable.

7. In rear entry positions the female's vagina is foreshortened—which may be advantageous if she has a wide and slack vagina or her partner a relatively small penis and closer vaginal-penile friction is desired.

8. When a woman's meatus or clitoral region or other parts of her vulva are inflamed or over-sensitive, rear entry positions bypass these sensitive spots.

9. The rear entry position is often excellent for impregnation, particularly when the male squats behind the female, since the cervix tends to be bathed directly in se-

men. If the male is lying on his side behind the female, however, entry may not be deep enough to aid conception; and the seminal fluid, in rear entry positions, may quickly trickle out of the vagina.

10. The averse position is a comfortable one for many couples when the wife is in the last months of pregnancy, particularly when both mates lie on their sides.

11. The kneeling rear entry position proves to be psychologically exciting to some individuals who seem to feel that its dog-like nature is more novel and unusual than face to face positions.

Disadvantages of the rear entry positions include:

1. Entry is often not easy, especially in the side positions or where the male has a large penis or the female a small vaginal opening.

2. Because the female's vagina is foreshortened in the rear entry position, the male's penis tends to keep falling out of the vagina, particularly after the male has had an orgasm.

3. The penis does not contact the clitoris during intercourse. However, it does press on the upper wall of the vagina, underneath the clitoris, which in some women is a sensitive region.

4. Because the vagina is foreshortened and penetration may be deep, there may be danger to the female organs in some instances if the male's thrusts are too vigorous.

5. Some partners object to the lack of face to face intimacy in the rear entry positions.

6. For stout partners or where the male has a small penis it is especially difficult for many individuals to effect copulation in the rear entry position.

Sitting positions. There are several major sitting positions of coitus, some of which will now be described:

(a) The man sits on a chair or on the edge of a bed and the woman faces him, her legs astride his. With his legs apart and the female's legs around his waist, the male can pull her toward and away from him, and raise and lower her pelvis, thus effecting copulatory movements.

(b) If the chair or bed which the partners are using is suitably high, the man can sit on it while the woman, facing him with her legs somewhat apart, can stand. He can pull her hips back and forth to him, in between his spread thighs.

(c) The man can squat between a woman's thighs, while she is lying on her back facing him, with her legs on his hips. He can then make pelvic thrusts or pull her pelvis back and forth toward him. Or the woman can squat between the man's thighs, while he is lying on his back with his legs apart, and she can move her pelvis in a circular fashion, making churning movements around his penis (Haire, 1951; Malinowski, 1929; Robinson, 1936).

(d) The man can sit on a bed or chair, while the woman bends over, in a doubled-up position, with her back to him. He can then, using the rear entry position, pull her pelvis back and forth over his penis.

Some advantages of the sitting positions may be:

1. In the face to face sitting position both partners may have maximum freedom of movement with their hands.

2. In the face to face sitting posture very close bodily contact may be achieved, with considerable freedom of movement still being maintained.

3. If the woman leans backward in the face to face position where both partners are sitting she may be able to achieve good clitoral stimulation while having intercourse. Indeed, better clitoral contact can sometimes be obtained in this than in any other copulative position.

4. The face to face sitting position is often quite restful and relatively free from exertion for both partners, particularly the male.

5. The male can sometimes retard his orgasm more easily, especially if he pulls the female to and from himself, rather than using sharp pelvic thrusts in his own right.

6. For those who enjoy it, deep penetration may often be effected, with contact between the penis and the cervix. For those who want less penetration, it is easy to control the depths of the male and female thrusts.

7. For purposes of impregnation the deep penetration that is possible with face to face sitting positions may be helpful.

8. During the last months of pregnancy the sitting positions can be relaxing and safe for the female.

Disadvantages of the sitting positions include:

1. Sexual thrusting may not be vigorous enough for either or both partners to achieve maximum satisfaction.

2. The deep penetration that is often facilitated by sit-

ting positions may involve a danger of injury to the female genitals.

3. The standing-sitting positions are easily tiring, especially for the male.

4. Impregnation may not be facilitated because the semen can easily seep from the vagina after the male's ejaculation if the sitting position is maintained.

Standing positions. If the woman has long enough legs or the man sufficiently short ones both partners may sometimes stand and face each other and thus have intercourse. Or the woman can lie with her legs dangling over the edge of a table or bed while the man stands between her legs. Or the man can stand while the woman, with her arms around his neck, clasps his hips between her thighs.

Some advantages of the standing or standing-lying positions include:

1. They may be varied and exciting at times just because they are not routine.

2. They usually leave one or both partners' hands free for caresses.

3. They can be combined with dancing, taking showers together, and similar standing pursuits.

Major disadvantages of the standing or standing-lying positions are these:

1. Entry may be quite difficult, particularly when both partners are standing facing each other.

2. Sustaining intercourse may become uncomfortable after awhile.

3. It is not easy for either of the mates to control his or her orgasm in most of the standing positions.

4. There may not be a sufficient amount of pelvic thrusting and parrying when either or both partners are standing.

5. If the woman stands, it will be relatively difficult for her to become impregnated.

6. If the woman is in her last months of pregnancy, standing positions, particularly when both partners are standing face to face, will become difficult or impossible.

10.

The Causes of Sexual Inadequacy

Sexual anesthesia or incompetence are usually termed *impotence* when experienced by the male and *frigidity* when known by the female. We shall try to avoid using these terms since they are not accurately descriptive of the various forms of disability that afflict either sex. Instead, we shall refer to sexual inadequacy or difficulty in the male and female.

Sexual inadequacy exists when an individual has little or no desire for sex relations, experiences little pleasure when stimulated, has poor ability to commence or sustain coitus, is unable to reach orgasm, or experiences little or no satisfaction when achieving a climax (A. Ellis, 1952a, 1961, 1963a, 1965a).

The average young male or female desires sex relations at least several times a month, considerably enjoys foreplay and coitus, is ready for copulation after no more than twenty to thirty minutes of preliminary activity, remains interested in coitus until orgasm has been experienced, achieves climax in some form of sex activity in a good percentage of the times, and distinctly enjoys his or her climaxes.

A middle-aged or older individual, naturally, is often much less sexually arousable or capable. Even young people sometimes have no desire or ability to participate in satisfying sex relations. But when a young and physically healthy person *consistently* has little or no sex interests, competence, or satisfaction, sexual inadequacy is to be strongly suspected.

There are many causes of sexual inadequacy, including organic, relationship, and psychological causes. We shall now discuss some of the major causes.

Organic causes of sexual inadequacy. Although sexual insensitivity and incompetence usually have no organic basis, they *sometimes* do. Physical reasons for these disabilities may include sex hormone deficiencies; inborn defects of or injuries to the sex organs; infection or inflammation of the penis or vagina, prostate gland, seminal ducts, ovary, cervix, or other accessory sex organs; serious nutritional lacks; lesions or defects of the central nervous system; circulatory defects; irritations or pathological conditions of parts of the body located near the sex organs; general organic ailments and diseases, such as diabetes, myxedema, heart disorder, anemia, or leukemia; fatigue and low vitality; overindulgence in alcohol or drugs; and normal aging processes (Abraham, 1950; Dengrove, 1959; Hirsch, 1951, 1957, 1962; Huhner, 1946; Walker and Strauss, 1932).

To be even more specific, Loras (1957) mentions a number of physical infections, inflammations, and injuries which may infest the female genital system, any one of which may lead to painful intercourse and hence sexual disability. His list includes an inflamed bartholin gland, labial tear, infected clitoris, vaginal tear, inflamed urethra, inflamed bladder, genital warts, sore vestiges of a ruptured hymen, vaginal cysts and polyps, inflamed vulva (vulvitis), and a lacerated cervix or cervical cancer.

Kleegman (1959) and Cauldwell (1959) agree that vaginismus (vaginal spasm) and dyspareunia (painful intercourse) can easily be caused by physical lesions or infections or inflammations of the female's vaginal tract. Kleegman, after several decades as a practicing gynecologist, believes that fully eighty-five per cent of women who suffer from dyspareunia have small and undetected vaginal or vulval lesions which may be corrected by proper medical and surgical procedures.

As for the evidence that certain physical diseases and ailments of a general nature may well lead to sexual disability, this is becoming more and more overwhelming as medical findings become more precise.

Thus, A. Rubin (1958) has convincingly shown that in diabetic males from the age of thirty to thirty-four years on, the cumulative incidence of impotence was two to five times as high as in the population of presumably normal males studied by Kinsey and his associates. The incidence of impotence by five-year age groups gradually increased from twenty-five per cent in the thirty to thirty-four years age group to almost seventy-five per cent in those sixty to sixty-four years of age.

Although, therefore, there is every reason to believe that perhaps ninety per cent of male and seventy to eighty per cent of female sexual inadequacy is of psychological origin, it still must not be forgotten that physical factors can play an important part in some cases and that it is rash to assume that the inadequacy is psychologically caused until the possibility of organic involvement is thoroughly investigated.

Sexual inadequacy, contrary to widespread belief, is rarely caused by undersized sex organs. A man who has a small penis can usually satisfy his wife and himself quite well, especially when he and his mate employ certain coital positions (such as rear entry or front entry with the female's legs together, as described in the chapter before this one) where the wife's vagina becomes foreshortened or narrower. A woman who has a small vagina, instead of being sexually inadequate, often gets and gives more pleasure than one with a larger vagina because contact between her organs and the man's penis then tends to be closer and friction is more enjoyable.

When a man has a very large penis or a woman an unusually wide vagina, special adjustments will often have to be made and in extreme cases extragenital techniques will have to be resorted to for full satisfaction. The size of the organs themselves, however, rarely cause sexual inadequacy or incompatibility between mates, except for psychological reasons.

Thus, a man may feel inferior because he has a small penis and may, because of his feelings, talk himself into becoming sexually inadequate. Or a woman may feel that her own vagina is too large or too small or that her husband's penis is over- or under-sized; and because of her childish or irrational attitudes may experience little or no sex fulfillment in her marriage.

Again: many individuals are unduly concerned about their physical characteristics. Females may be disturbed about the size of their breasts or males about their height or their weight. Out of this over-concern for their own (or for their partner's) physique, such individuals may easily create sexual inadequacies in themselves (or help make their mates feel inadequate); but here again we are dealing with psychological rather than true physical or organic causes of sexual disability.

Relationship causes of sexual inadequacy. Sexual anesthesia and disability frequently arise because of sex, love, marital, or other disturbances in the relationship between the disabled person and his or her mate. Relationship inadequacies may include lack of love and affection between the mates; conscious or unconscious hostility or conflict; use of poor sexual techniques; the mate's inhibitions or inadequacies; and the aging of the mate (Lanval, 1950b, 1951; Salzman, 1954; Van Emde Boas, 1950).

Most of the time, lack of love and consideration is the basic issue. In the case of a thirty-two-year-old married woman who recently came to me for marriage counseling and who complained that she had lost virtually all sex desire, even though for the first few years of marriage she had been an ardent sex partner several times each week, it soon became clear that she bitterly resented her husband's lack of love and consideration. Instead of ever doing the things she wanted to do, helping her with the children or the housework, or even talking to her about business and other affairs, he worked, night after night, at his large stamp collection and showed virtually no interest in anything else.

After many months of quiet sulking about his inconsiderate behavior, the wife withdrew sexually, had many fantasies about almost every male (and movie star) whom she saw, and made no effort to obtain or give satisfaction when her husband showed (as, surprisingly, he often did) sex interest.

When I saw the husband in this case and squarely presented to him the point that he could hardly expect his wife to be sexually thrilled with his presence when being in bed was literally the only time she had a chance to speak to him, he was at first shocked and resistant, since he had a picture of himself as a fine husband, who stayed home every night, did not run around with other women, and was a good economic provider.

He was able, at my urging, to see that these husbandly traits might well not be sufficient reason for his wife to be generally or sexually happy and he began to pay considerably more attention to her and her desires for companionship. Almost immediately, their sex life perked up enormously.

In another psychotherapy case, where I was seeing only the husband, in session after session he would complain that his wife was sloppy about everything, including her own appearance, and that he just couldn't maintain any sexual interest in her when she refused to go out of her way to take baths, use perfumes, dress in frilly nightclothes, and do other things to make herself attractive to him.

By further probing, I was able to elicit the facts that this husband wanted his wife to behave exactly as did one of his mistresses whom he had before marriage who (for a tidy sum he was paying for her support) devoted herself exclusively to his sexual purposes.

When his wife, who had three small children and a large home to manage, started falling behind (compared to his ex-mistress) in some of her sexual attentions to him, he had been savagely critical of her and had often berated her for being over-attentive to their children. In this kind of critical atmosphere she had lost most of her incentive to be physically attractive and sexually attentive to him; and things, as they invariably do in these cases, had soon gone from bad to worse, so that she was, probably unconsciously, now leaning over backwards *not* to please him.

My job with this husband was to convince him of the irrationality of his own behavior, which he refused to see because his wife was being equally or more unreasonable.

"How can I be nice to her, as you're urging me to do," he said, "when she is so obviously doing everything she can to neglect herself personally and be unattractive to me? She says that she wants to have sex relations but she won't even take a shower every day, and who wants to sleep with a woman who literally stinks? Why, I don't think she has bathed or showered for a week!"

"That may be," I replied, "but the point is not *that* she doesn't try to please you sexually, but *why*. And, from your own admission, you say you are continually critical and nasty when you are with her."

"But why shouldn't I be? Who *wouldn't* be when his wife acted that way?"

"Most people would be, I grant you; but that's beside the point. They merely would then get in the same sexual difficulties as you are in."

"You think that practically every man who criticizes his wife sooner or later antagonizes her sexually?"

"Not every man, since some wives are so passionate that no matter what their husbands did they would not put up any sexual resistance. But they are rare. Most wives, like your own, will put up either direct or indirect resistance when they are under a constant critical barrage."

"But how can I stop that barrage when she keeps acting the way she does?"

"You might more sanely ask: 'How can I *do* it?' rather than 'How can I *stop* it?' For doing it, as you see, gets you into severe difficulties with your wife; while stopping it would probably alleviate these difficulties rather quickly."

"But it's *easy* to do it."

"Sure: it's always easy to criticize another;—if you *think* that this other deserves to be criticized; if you have a *philosophy* of criticism."

"But I don't have such a philosophy—do I?"

"You darned well do. Every time your wife does something that you think is wrong—and, mind you, this occurred, your criticism, long before she became physically sloppy and unkempt—you immediately say to yourself: 'How *could* she do this wrong thing? She *shouldn't* be doing it! She's got no *right* to do it.' "

"But *should* she be doing it?"

"Why *shouldn't* she? Why shouldn't human beings act, as they always do, in an imperfect and, as Nietzsche said, all too human manner?"

"But you're trying to get *me* to act in a super-human, all-forgiving manner, aren't you?"

"Yes, in a way I am. But not because you *should* be forgiving, understanding, and nice to your wife. For, in an absolute or moralistic sense, there's no reason why you *should*. However, as I am trying to convince you, in a relative or pragmatic sense, for purposes of bettering your own relationship with your wife and increasing your own sex satisfaction, there are several good reasons why it would be *preferable* or *desirable* for you to change your behavior with her, just as it would be desirable for her to change her actions with you."

"You seem to be saying then that, although I and my wife have a moral right to be nasty to each other and that there is no absolute reason why we *should* not be, we would be only harming ourselves by—well, by being the way we have been and continuing to criticize or resist each other. Therefore, you seem to be saying—aren't you?— that I should stop being critical of her and she should stop being sloppy—"

"Not *should* stop being, but it *would be better* if you both stopped being—"

"Oh, yes: I got caught on those *shoulds* again. We should—no, there I go again! *It would be better* if I stopped being critical of her and she stopped being so neglectful of her own personal hygiene and appearance."

"Right. If you stopped telling yourself the silly sentence, 'She *should* be different from the way she is,' and kept telling yourself, instead, 'I would *like her* to be different, now let's see what I can do to help her change,' then the chances are that she would change. But as long as you keep saying to yourself, 'She *should* be different,' (meaning, of course, that 'She is a louse and a bitch if she is not different') she hears only name calling on your part, and she consciously or unconsciously will balk at changing for your *critical* sake and will deliberately lean over backwards to continue being the way she is."

"So the only sane and intelligent thing I can do is to stop telling myself what a louse she is by being the way she is at present and do everything possible to be uncritical of her and help her change?"

"Right. If you will temporarily and uncritically accept her the way she is, with all her sloppiness and unattractiveness, and stop criticizing her for *anything* she does—even though it may hardly be good or best that she does these things right now—then at least she may have some incentive to change. This way, by constantly criticizing her, you are actually giving her an incentive *not* to change."

"How is that?"

"Well, by showing her that you are upset because she is the way she is, you are rewarding her for her behavior.

Because, since you have been so critical of her—even before she began to become sexually sloppy, you will remember—and since she is going to want to revenge herself on you for what she considers your unjustifiable and unfair criticism, why should she not *want* to make you angry?"

"She sees my getting angry, then, as a kind of punishment for my unfairly, in her eyes, criticizing her; and she is glad that I suffer, for this unfair criticism, in this manner. Is that it?"

"Yes, something like that. Everytime she does the wrong thing, in your eyes, you get angry and upset. Therefore your behavior gives her an incentive to keep doing the wrong thing—so that she can keep upsetting you for your unfair criticism."

"Quite a vicious circle, isn't it?"

"Quite. Now when are you going to change your behavior so that you can help cut this vicious circle?"

"You mean by stopping criticizing her?"

"Yes, I mean by stopping criticizing her, no matter what she does, or how 'wrong' you think she is. Not that you may not be right, sometimes, about her so-called wrongness. But what good is your criticism doing to help her overcome her 'wrong' behavior?"

"No good, I guess."

"None at all. It just doesn't serve the purpose that *you* want—to help correct your wife's behavior. And moralizing—or *blaming* another person for her shortcomings—practically never does serve the purpose of helping her overcome her failings. While if you can point out this other person's shortcomings in a non-moralizing, objective manner, and show her that you are completely on her side, then you may help her—help your wife in this case to get over her sexual unattractiveness."

"If I stop criticizing her about sex and cleanliness, she may become better about it?"

"Yes, if you stop criticizing her and act as a good model yourself—by uncomplainingly doing the things in marriage (such as being a good father to your children) that you had better—not *should,* mind you, but *had better*—do, then there is every reason to believe that she will considerably improve in her marital behavior."

With this kind of rational therapeutic procedure, I continued to show this husband how illogical were the thoughts and sentences which he was continually telling himself and acting upon, and how his own super-moralizing and non-forgiving philosophy of life was inevitably sabotaging his marital and sexual relations (A. Ellis, 1958a, 1959c).

Once I induced him to stop blaming his wife and to work at helping her improve instead of critically trying to goad her into doing so, she became much more tidy and clean about her personal hygiene and appearance and their sex relations improved significantly.

Most relationship difficulties between husbands and wives are similarly caused by the fact that one mate has unrealistically high standards of what the other mate should do and feels aggrieved and angry when he or she does not live up to these standards.

Instead of saying, "I would *like* or *prefer* my spouse to do this or that; now let me see how I can help bring about this *desired* result," the first partner says, "It is absolutely *necessary* that my mate act in this or that way; he or she *should* do so." And then the fur starts flying.

Perfectionistic, over-moralizing goals of human behavior, held for oneself and/or others, cause most of the needless emotional insecurity and hostility that exist in this world; and virtually all marital and sex relationship difficulties stem from these kinds of blaming, unforgiving philosophies.

Psychological causes of sexual inadequacy. In addition to relationship problems between mates there are a host of other psychological reasons why individuals become sexually inadequate. Most of these psychological reasons involve irrational or over-exaggerated fears. Thus, a man or woman may become sexually anesthetic or incompetent because of puritanical fears of sex itself, with concomitant severe feelings of shame and guilt; fear of disapproval or rejection by the sex partner; fear of pregnancy or of the responsibilities of fatherhood or motherhood; fear of physical pain; castration and incest fears; fear of failure; and fears of venereal disease (Bergler, 1961; Deutsch, 1944; Katz, 1956; Knight, 1943; Kroger and Freed, 1951).

In addition to these kinds of fear, which may interfere seriously with sexual adequacy, there are possibly many other psychological factors. Thus, an individual may be undesirous or unable to achieve satisfactory orgasm because he or she is fetichistically fixated on some special kind of sex activity (such as relations with young children), is homosexual, is exceptionally narcissistic, is masochistic or sadistic, or has psychotic tendencies. As Rougelot (1958) notes, a mate may be obsessed with, focused upon, or anxious about many practical problems, such as cramped living quarters, lack of sexual privacy, overwork, and financial, social, or child rearing problems.

Caprio (1953) indicates that some individuals, particularly females, may inwardly be protesting their own sex roles and, because they are dissatisfied with this role, may act in a dominating, cynical, and over-aggressive manner to all members of the other sex, including their own mates; and, at the same time, they may unconsciously protest against their own sexuality and help destroy it. Mowrer (1947) agrees and goes even a step further:

"In a personal sense, even more devastating is the confusion many women feel about sexuality itself. I suspect that much of the frigidity and other forms of sexual maladjustment which one sees clinically in modern women stems, not from the puritanical or overly strict training they received as children, but from their current conception of themselves as persons. They commonly have a very depreciating view of femininity and are so imbued with masculine ideals of achievement and competitive success that they are severely unfitted as sex partners.

"For some women whom I have seen clinically, housekeeping, childbearing, and sexuality are all lumped together, consciously or unconsciously, as repulsive and degrading. They want sexuality, but it is a kind of male sexuality to which they aspire, with little or no conception of real womanliness."

The main psychological reason for sexual inadequacy is not, usually, some highly complicated or deeply hidden unconscious cause that has to be uncovered during hundreds of hours of intensive psychoanalysis, but simply the fear of sexual incompetence itself. Because males and females in our society erroneously *believe* that it is most important that they be sexual athletes or achieve many powerful orgasms in the course of an evening, and because they are afraid that they are *not* in this class, they incessantly worry about their sexual prowess—and, in the process, completely defeat it.

Although I have seen hundreds of individuals who were anesthetic or incompetent sexually and have in some instances spent scores of psychotherapeutic sessions seeking the basic reasons for their sexual inadequacy, only in a small percentage of these instances have I not found the main reason to be the individual's fear of sexual failure. He or she fails once or twice, as most of us at times do, then becomes deeply concerned about this failure, and then, precisely because of his or her concern, keeps failing indefinitely (A. Ellis, 1959b, 1961, 1962a, 1963a).

Dr. LeMon Clark (1959b) has excellently stated this problem in relation to male inadequacy: "If a man assumes that he is impotent, if he sets his mind upon the fact, if he goes into any sexual experience with the attitude that he must demonstrate that he is not impotent, he will very possibly fail.

"If, on the other hand, he can approach a sexual experience as a gratifying thing in itself, if he can approach it with the attitude that he is just going to let himself participate with no set goal of any kind that must be accomplished, if he fixes his mind upon the satisfaction of intimate contact with a loved and loving partner, and stops worrying about just what form that expression may take, in many cases he will then go on to normal completion with little or no difficulty."

The main psychological cause of sexual inadequacy, in other words, might well be called distraction or improper focusing. As we indicated in Chapters 2 and 3, sex desire and fulfillment are instigated not merely by physically arousing stimuli but by encouraging and exciting signals from the brain.

If there is any organic interference with these signals (as in cases of paraplegia where the spinal cord is cut) or any psychological interference (as when the individual is distracted by puritanical fears of sex, hostility toward the mate, irrelevant non-sexual thoughts, or anxiety about whether he or she is going to perform adequately) sexual disability will inevitably result.

Unfortunately, our society teaches us in many ways to be sexually distractible. It tells us that sex in its own right is not a good or fine activity and encourages us to hem it in with all kinds of restrictions. It raises us with ultra-moralizing notions of how people *should* behave in their general and marital relations, and thereby predisposes us to become hostile and unforgiving toward our mates. It gives us little instruction in how to focus, specifically, on sexually arousing ideas and objects, and helps us (particularly the females among us) to concentrate on all manners of sexually unexciting things when we are having intimate relations. It gives us enormously perfectionistic ideals of achievement, success, and accomplishment that make us feel like utterly incompetent and thoroughly valueless individuals whenever we fail at any participation, such as coitus.

Under these circumstances it is easy to see how so many individuals, instead of concentrating on their own sexual enjoyment and focusing on how exciting and exhilarating their sex acts with their mates are, are distracted to all kinds of non-sexual and anti-sexual thoughts, with consequent impairment of their sexual abilities.

Then, to make matters much worse, once the status-seeking, success-bound individual of our society notes that he or she is not performing too well sexually, he or she becomes enormously concerned about failure and focuses even more strongly on the pseudo problem of "My God, look how badly I'm doing!" rather than the real problem of "My, sex can be enjoyable! Now let's see what else I can do to add to my own pleasure."

Ineffective, success-oriented cerebral focusing contributes mightily to actual failure in many walks of life. As Dr. George R. Bach (personal communication) observes, it is particularly prevalent among students who go into examinations asking themselves, "Oh, my Lord, will I remember my work well enough to pass?"—and, by virtue of this very over-anxious kind of focusing, they often fail. Similarly, catastrophizing about possible sex failure actually *creates* the terribly-feared incompetency.

Sexual inadequacy, in other words, is largely (though not entirely) caused by the fact that many inadequate individuals (particularly females) are not using proper sexual technique and therefore not obtaining sufficient stimulation of their most sensitive genital areas and, even when they are going through the right physical motions, they are not effectively focusing on the right kind of thoughts, attitudes, and feelings.

In the final analysis, most sexually anesthetic and unsatisfied persons have not learned to think straight. They keep telling themselves (as do all emotionally disturbed persons) illogical and irrational sentences; and it is their own self-verbalizations and self-signallings, rather than other environmental or organic influences, which are mainly responsible for their sexual disabilities and incompetencies.

11.

Overcoming Sexual Inadequacy

Since there are several major types of sexual inadequacy the treatment of this disability will be discussed under three main headings: (a) Arousing desire in difficult instances; (b) achieving orgasm in difficult cases; and (c) retarding orgasm.

Arousing desire in difficult instances. In most instances, sexual desire is easily and spontaneously aroused, in accordance with the principles of stimulation which we previously outlined in Chapters 5 and 6. If your mate is difficult to arouse, you should reread these principles and make every effort systematically and persistently to apply them.

Where difficulties of arousal still remain, it may mean that the individual to be excited is not too well endowed physically (for example, has a sluggish nervous system or endocrine imbalance), is physically tired or debilitated, has been having orgasms too frequently, is not being stimulated properly, or has various psychological blocks against arousal.

If you or your mate are not easily arousable, the following steps may be effective:

1. The relatively unarousable individual should have a complete physical examination to determine whether there are physical causes of his or her condition. In accordance with a physician's instruction, he or she may be placed on a proper regimen of diet, sufficient sleep, adequate exercise, vitamin injections, etc. Sometimes, hormone treat-

ments, such as the use of androgens with a male or a female, may be helpful (Benjamin, 1958; Kupperman, 1959, 1961). Minor operations, prostatic massage, treatment of organic disorders, and other forms of medical intervention can also bring quick relief in about five to ten per cent of the cases where an individual is sexually below par (Mozes, 1959c).

2. The partner who is not easily arousable should engage in sex relations at a time best suited for his or her excitability: for example, when he or she is relaxed, well rested, not pressed for time, away from troubling circumstances, and so forth.

3. The partner who is to do the arousing should make overtures at a time when the mates have been getting along excellently together and when there is a minimum of strain and hostility between them. Occasionally, a not easily excitable mate requires a sado-masochistic tiff with his or her partner in order to stir desire; and if this preference for sado-masochism is mild, it can be catered to. In the majority of instances, however, sex desire is more likely to be aroused by kindness, consideration, and love for one's mate—particularly when this kindness persists in spite of the mate's relative unarousability.

4. Special care should be taken to locate and adequately to stimulate the particular erogenous zones of the individual who is not easily aroused. Sometimes, because of deficient tactile sensitivity or a relatively unresponsive nervous system, such persons need quite prolonged fondling or vigorous pressing, slapping, kneading, squeezing, pinching, or biting of their erogenous zones.

Thus, Lester Dearborn (personal communication) indicates that some females are unusually stimulated by having their buttocks slapped, even though the average female may never desire or require this form of stimulation. Although the more easily aroused partner may not require any kind of persistent or vigorous caressing or kissing, there is no reason why he or she cannot employ it with the less easily excited mate (Mehta, 1938).

5. For many—though by no means all—non-easily arousable individuals, kisses and caresses other than directly genital ones are a waste of time and may even be irritating and anti-exciting. These individuals often need steady, intense, prolonged stimulation of the most sensitive parts of

their genitals; and, if so, that is what they should have. For males who become aroused but easily lose their erections, if the female closes her thighs after penetration, the pressure of her vulva may help the penis, especially if it is a small one, to maintain erection (Lewin and Gilmore, 1951).

6. Non-easily aroused partners frequently require more sexual varietism than more easily excitable mates. They may develop temporary anesthesia for one kind of stimulation and should therefore be offered a variety of other kinds.

7. Where one mate is at first unexcited during sex relations, it may be advisable for the partners to separate for awhile, take a resting period, and then return to sex play after a period of time has elapsed. Sometimes, of course, sex will have to be given up for an entire evening, to be resumed the next day or night. At other times, a half hour or more of rest and relaxation may put one of the mates in a sexual mood even though at first he or she was thoroughly unaroused.

8. In some instances, where there are mild psychological blocks or physical deficiencies, sex arousal may be helped by a physician's prescribing sex hormones, strychnine nitrate, mild intake of alcohol, or other drugs. Kelly (1953, 1961) reports that the application of camphormenthol ointment to the clitoris or liberal rubbing in of hand lotions to the vulva will increase desire in some women.

9. Psychological stimulation is most important in perhaps the majority of cases where the individual is relatively anesthetic. The unaroused partner can help in this connection by deliberately focusing on whatever ideas are sexually exciting to him or her; and the other partner can help by providing verbal and other materials which may arouse the mate—for example, by saying words of endearment, talking about sexually exciting situations, showing distinct interest in the mate, recalling aloud previously stimulating encounters, showing confidence that the partner can be aroused, providing sexually arousing photographic or written materials, etc.

The more creative, experimental, forthright, and courageous the relatively excitable partner can be in these respects, the more may he or she be able to arouse the relatively unexcitable mate. The less arousable partner should also try to have the sexual courage to throw himself or herself fully and wholeheartedly into seeking, striving for excitement and satisfaction.

10. Where the partners are sufficiently sophisticated and well-informed psychologically, they may sometimes tackle any specific sex blocks that exist by frankly considering the possibilities of such blocks and objectively examining them. If for example, one mate feels that the other may be unaroused because of some unexpressed or unconscious antagonism between them, he or she may frankly raise this possibility and explore with the other mate what is the likelihood of its being true.

11. Since most individuals have a longer history of being able to arouse themselves by masturbation than they have of doing so with a sex partner, it may sometimes be appropriate for the unaroused partner to masturbate in the other's presence in order to get his or her excitement under way. Once masturbation has produced sufficient excitability, interpersonal relations between the partners can then take over. It is necessary, of course, that the spouse of the masturbating partner be permissive and objective in this regard and not to feel hurt or degraded because his or her mate cannot more easily and more mutually become aroused.

12. Where none of the aforementioned techniques work and one or both partners still have difficulty in getting sexually aroused, it is usually desirable that either or both mates (preferably both) see a competent marriage counselor, psychologist, psychiatrist, or caseworker. Just a few sessions spent with such a professional expert may well determine if there *is* a special reason for the lack of sexual arousal; and, if so, what can be done about it.

Very often, in my own clinical practice, I have seen individuals who were utterly convinced that they were low-sexed persons who could not get particularly aroused with any partner; and it has sometimes been possible, within from one to five interviews, to show these individuals how to overcome their difficulties or at least to show them that further psychological discussions would probably lead to the resolution of these difficulties.

In the case of a twenty-seven-year-old wife whom I saw for counseling, it would generally take her from forty-five minutes to an hour of active sex play to become ready for intercourse and frequently she got so disgusted and tired in the process that she would give up, satisfy her husband without enjoying coitus herself, and fail to achieve any climax. It was possible to determine, during the very first session spent with this client, that her main problem was her severe fear that she would not become sexually aroused and that consequently she would never become a satisfactory partner for her husband, to whom she was intensely attached and whom she terribly much wanted to please.

When I was able, with highly directive and active methods of rational psychotherapy, to show this woman that she had an overly self-sacrificial philosophy of life, and that she only considered herself worthwhile when she was pleasing someone else, and when I was instrumental in getting her to question and challenge this philosophy, and begin working for her *own* sexual and other satisfactions, she began, for the first time in her life, to focus on her own sex sensations instead of the supposed horror of not being a perfect partner for her husband. Within a month's time, she made great sexual strides and was able to become aroused in a few minutes' time and to achieve orgasm in two out of three acts of coitus.

A male I saw could only obtain a full erection when he had intercourse with prostitutes but was almost completely impotent with his fiancée and kept putting off marrying her because he was afraid that he would never be a satisfactory sex partner.

He had previously gone for a year of psychiatric treatment, in the course of which he had been told that his sex problem was caused by his Oedipal attachment to his mother and his refusal to sully a "nice" girl sexually because of his guilt over his incestuous feelings toward his mother. In spite of this seemingly accurate interpretation, his inability to become aroused with his fiancée continued.

After two sessions with this patient, I took quite another tack and began to show him that his real problem was not any vestiges of his old attachment to his mother but, rather, his dire fear of failing in the present.

Because he paid prostitutes for their sex favors and felt no responsibility to them, he merely focused on his own satisfaction and was easily aroused and satisfied. But with his fiancée, where no payment was involved, he was morbidly afraid that he would not fulfill what he considered to be his sex responsibility with her—namely, bringing her to climax as a result of fairly prolonged intercourse. Because of his fear, he entered every affair with her in a highly distractible mood and naturally was not able to focus on his own sex arousal or satisfaction.

Within nine therapeutic sessions I was able to show this patient that (a) it was not necessary that he be sexually potent in order to bring his fiancée to climax; (b) it was no crime if he failed at sex activity (or anything else); and (c) he was not weak, unmanly, feminine, or worthless, even if he never managed to achieve and sustain a good erection and to bring his fiancée to orgasm through penile-vaginal copulation.

Once he began to see these things, and to define himself as a perfectly good and worthy human being, even if he were not too sexually adept, this individual found little difficulty in focusing on how desirable his fiancée was (instead of how necessary it was to copulate with her satisfactorily); and he soon had no sex problems.

Ironically enough, he discovered that once he began to become fully aroused, it took him from fifteen to thirty minutes of active copulation to have an orgasm. As this often proved unsatisfactory to his fiancée (whom shortly thereafter he married), because she could have several climaxes in a shorter period of time, she sometimes had to satisfy him in non-coital ways. Whereas the problem for which he came for therapy was one of non-arousal he almost ended up with a problem of too adequate arousal and difficulty of achieving orgasm.

In any event, most problems where one member of the pair is not too easily aroused can be solved by the partners practicing and working at the methods outlined in this chapter and in Chapters 5 and 6. In those few cases where none of these methods produces good results, professional aid should be sought.

Achieving orgasm in difficult cases. Exactly as in the case of difficulty of sex arousal, the inability to obtain an orgasm once arousal has been achieved is often the result of (a) failure to obtain proper physical stimulation and (b) failure to think the right thoughts and have rational attitudes toward sex.

Where one or both mates has difficulty in achieving climax, the partners may follow the procedures just outlined for achieving full sex arousal, since they also will frequently be useful for encouraging orgasm.

In addition, here are some specific pointers on facilitating orgasm.

1. In many instances where the individual can theoretically achieve orgasm but actually has great difficulty in doing so, it will be found that he or she has one special locus of sex sensation, such as the underpart of the penis in the male or the clitoris in the female, and that there must be steady, consistent, rhythmic pressure on this spot. Moreover, this pressure must sometimes be light and gentle; and in other individuals it must be heavy and rough.

This kind of stimulation is difficult to perform except with the partner's fingers, as the other parts of his or her body cannot sustain steady, rhythmic pressures. In consequence, the fingers frequently prove to be by far the best organ of sexual approach in these more difficult cases.

2. Steady manipulation of the sensitive spots of a mate who has difficulty achieving orgasm is sometimes onerous for the partner to perform, as it tends to require monotonous, not essentially arousing, and not too physically satisfying activity.

Its monotony can be alleviated, however, if the partner thinks of something stimulating to himself or herself, or imagines some non-sexual event that is interesting and absorbing, or hums tunes or rhythmic patterns to himself or herself, or otherwise uses creative impulses to find satisfactions of some sort while engaged in satisfying his or her mate.

3. With mates who are difficult to satisfy, a build-up technique of manipulation is often desirable or necessary. When the male partner, for example, massages the female's clitoris, he can notice that her sensations increase after a certain period of manipulation, so that her breathing becomes more rapid, her back arches, and her sexual organs begin to press closer against his finger and sometimes to vibrate. He can then interrupt his massaging her clitoris, let her return momentarily to her less aroused position, and then quickly start manipulating her genitals again.

He can bring his partner to a pitch of excitement and

let her sink back again several times. Finally, as the female becomes exceptionally aroused, the male can bring her to orgasm with his finger (or, if she is sufficiently excited, even do so by penile intromission). Females can sometimes use a similar interrupting technique of penile manipulation to bring a male to orgasm.

4. It is supremely important that the partner of a mate who is difficult to satisfy not build up hostility against this mate for being difficult, nor communicate boredom or irritation because of the effort required to give satisfaction.

For one thing, such hostility or irritation will spoil the arousing partner's satisfaction and lead him or her eventually to abhor sex relations.

For another, it will usually interfere considerably with the peace of mind of the less aroused partner and sabotage his or her coming to orgasm (A. Ellis, 1957a).

The best way to avoid the growth of antagonism of this sort is for the more easily aroused partner to realize fully that there is nothing *wrong* with the lower-sexed or blocked mate; that it is perfectly *normal* for many human beings to have difficulty having an orgasm; and that if one's mate happens to be in the difficult class, that is hardly his or her *fault* and in no manner or wise constitutes a *crime*.

It should be especially noted in this connection that there is little evidence that females of other animal species ever receive orgasm and there is some evidence that the female of the human species normally often has difficulty in obtaining an orgasm and frequently does not obtain one at all (Elkan, 1948; Terman, 1951). As Shuttleworth (1959) well puts the case:

"It is inherently easy for all males and inherently difficult for at least a few or some females to reach an orgasm. Orgasm experience is the third step in the development of mature sexuality. An orgasm rewards and reinforces the prior sexual behavior. Males are more often rewarded. Biology and learning give them more sexual drives.

"Two lines of evidence support the above suggestion. The male contribution to the reproductive process requires an orgasm in order that seminal fluid may be ejaculated from the body. There is nothing in the reproductive physiology of females that requires an orgasm. This difference holds for the males and females of all mammals. For a hundred million years the males who could not ejaculate during copulation have left no descendants. It must be clear that it is inherently easy for all males, both preadolescent and adolescent, to reach an orgasm.

"Some significance must be given to the fact that only the human female comes to orgasm with some regularity. There are only scattered, incidental, and uncertain observations suggesting that a few other mammalian females may on rare occasions experience something that looks like orgasm. There is a huge gap between human and other mammalian females at this point. It suggests that the capacity for an orgasm in the human female appeared rather recently in evolutionary history.

"The first human females to be endowed with this capacity probably acquired an evolutionary advantage. Today, a million years later, it is quite possible that a few females are inherently incapable of an orgasm."

Under these circumstances, it may well be that the male who is married to a wife who almost always experiences easy and complete orgasm is just lucky. The average husband may well have some difficulty in bringing his wife to climax; and if he will accept this difficulty with good grace (just as he must accept the fact that females regularly menstruate during much of their married lives), few problems will arise.

Similarly, if a woman will accept the fact that males tend to have greater difficulty in achieving climax as they grow older, and that on occasion she must work fairly hard to bring her husband to orgasm, marital hostility will be minimized and sex and other relations will flow more smoothly.

5. While most individuals who are difficult to help to the point of orgasm need steady, unfrenzied manipulation of some part or parts of their bodies, other individuals need different techniques. Some require intermittent, irregular strokings. Some need very light pressure; others do best with forceful massage. Some need exactly the same technique each time; others require considerable varietism. Some need only physical caresses; others desire considerable accompanying verbalizations. Whatever the unique preferences of your own mate may be in this respect, do

your best (by experimentation and by talking things out) to discover and cater to them in a considerate, loving manner.

6. In some instances, the main technique that will lead to orgasm by either mate is forceful, deep vaginal-penile penetration. In such penetration, the pelvic movements of the spouses are rhythmically synchronized with the penile-vaginal contact and help the individual to focus on orgasm.

Some women need deep penetration for the stimulation of the cervix, near the back of the vagina; or they desire vigorous thrusts so that the pubic region and back of the penis of the male slap against their vulvas with sufficient force. Some males also require deep penetration because the head of the penis needs contact with the end of the vagina or the cervix or because they, too, are stirred by a jarring sensation in their pubic region as the back of the penis and pubic bone crashes against the female genitals.

Where deep or forceful penetration is required by the male but is not possible because of the female's having a short vagina, experiencing pain, or otherwise being inconvenienced, deep thrusts by the male on the outside of the vulva, over the woman's stomach, against her buttocks, between her breasts, under her arms, or between various other parts of her body will often be satisfactory.

Where the woman requires deep or penetrating vaginal thrusts and the male, for one reason or another, cannot oblige with his penis, he can generally do so with his fingers or hand. The fingers can go deep into the vagina and reach and manipulate sensitive spots that the penis often cannot reach. If the woman needs powerful contact with her vulva or clitoris, the male's knee, elbow, fist, palm of his hand, or other parts of his body are often excellent for this purpose.

7. Multiple physical contact is quite desirable in many instances; since there appears to be, often, a summation of sensation when two or more bodily zones are stimulated. A male may need to kiss or caress his wife's breasts or buttocks while she is manipulating or using oral-genital contact on his penis. A female may require that her clitoris be massaged while she is having intercourse or while her husband is simultaneously inserting his fingers in her

anus. All kinds of possibilities are usable and should be tried in cases where bringing one of the partners to orgasm is difficult.

8. It should go without saying, in this modern day and age, that some of the most sexually arousing and orgasm-producing methods are those which for many centuries prior to this have been taboo in our society but are now more widely accepted. Oral-genital contact, anal insertion, mild sado-masochistic forays, and similar so-called perversions are essential for the maximum arousal and satisfaction of literally millions of individuals in today's world.

Consequently, any person whose husband or wife is difficult to arouse or satisfy should be especially unshy about trying all possible techniques, including many of those which were erroneously considered perverted in the past, but which are now commonly accepted as a normal part of human sex behavior.

9. Particularly in instances where one or both mates have difficulty achieving orgasm, any effort to concentrate on their trying to achieve simultaneous climaxes will usually impede rather than help their gratification. For such efforts will normally result in a definite shift of focus which should, on the part of the hard-to-satisfy partner, be clearly concentrated on achieving his or her own climax.

The goal of reaching simultaneous climax, moreover, brings to coitus an additional and non-relevant factor of success-seeking which, especially among worrisome individuals with feelings of insecurity and inadequacy, often is a severe handicap.

The partner who is difficult to gratify has enough problems in attaining climax without adding an additional problem—namely, that of reaching orgasm at exactly the same moment as the other partner. Just as two stout mates cannot expect to use some of the sex positions that two slightly built partners may employ, so couples which include one partner who achieves climax much more slowly than the other cannot expect to try for goals of simultaneity.

10. In some instances, a partner who has difficulty in achieving climax may be helped by his or her mate's resorting to different coital positions from the ones they usually employ. Such different positions may be more exciting; may give more friction on the sensitive parts of the slower

partner; may facilitate direct penile or clitoral stimulation; and may have other advantages. Positions where the female's vaginal canal is shortened or narrowed and where the partner's sex organs may be stimulated during coitus (such as some of the positions described in Chapter 9) may be particularly useful in this respect.

11. Occasionally, it will be desirable or necessary for the mate who has trouble coming to orgasm to manipulate his or her own genitals while having sex relations.

Some individuals need a special kind of touch or rhythm in certain sensitive areas for them to come to climax; and it is almost impossible, in many instances, for anyone else but themselves to employ this kind of contact. If so, they should be allowed to manipulate their own genitals while heterosexual relations are in progress or when they have reached a certain point where such self-stimulation becomes desirable.

Individuals who need this kind of self-help in order to achieve orgasm are not necessarily abnormal or deviated but are usually quite normal.

12. In some instances changing from one position to another while coitus is progressing; or stopping for a while and later resuming sex relations; or otherwise interrupting sex activity may aid a relatively long-timed individual to come to climax when steady coitus does not achieve the desired effect.

13. As noted in Chapter 5 on psychological techniques of sexual arousal, many individuals have difficulty coming to climax because of their failing to focus adequately on sexually exciting images and allowing themselves, instead, to be distracted by unarousing objects or ideas. Such individuals should do their best to discover what is most sexually exciting to themselves and should practice focusing on maximally arousing things when sex relations are in progress.

There is a condition in the male known as anesthetic ejaculation in which the individual obtains orgasm but receives little or no pleasurable sensation along with it (Cauldwell, 1959). There is also a condition, known as ejaculatory impotence, where the male sustains an erection for a considerable length of time but fails to achieve a climax (Kaplan and Abrams, 1958). Both these conditions may result from the male's feelings of hostility toward his mate and his wishing, consciously or unconsciously, to hold out on her.

Various other emotional factors may be involved, and intensive psychotherapy may be necessary to get at the root of such a problem. Simple distraction may also be involved in some instances, with the male's focusing inadequately on stimulating objects or ideas.

In females, a somewhat frequent cause of retarded orgasm or complete lack of climax may be the individual's failing to define orgasm properly, believing that it is something extraspecial (with bells ringing and lights flashing!), and therefore failing to pay sufficient heed to her own orgasmic sensations and to enjoy them. A most revealing letter in this connection was written to the magazine, *Sex and Censorship,* after it had reprinted my article, "Is the Vaginal Orgasm a Myth?" (A. Ellis, 1953a). This letter, from a woman in Texas, reads as follows:

"Dear Editor: I have just finished reading your last issue of *Sex and Censorship.* And although I was very pleased with the issue in its entirety, I was especially impressed by the article "Is the Vaginal Orgasm a Myth?"— by Albert Ellis, Ph.D.

"In my opinion every serious-minded female seeking sexual satisfaction in any manner whatever should read this article. It is enlightening; it is educational; it is instructive.

"During three years of married life, I was unable to reach what *I* thought an orgasm to be. Actually, I didn't know what an orgasm was. To my mind an orgasm was a composite of something mysterious, something other women enjoyed all the time unless they were frigid. Never having experienced what I thought to be an orgasm, I quite naturally assumed I was frigid.

"Sex I enjoyed, and as much as I could get!—BUT, I felt cheated. I felt as though Nature had played a mean trick on me. This is what ignorance does to people, causes them to make false, premature conclusions. This kind of thing can destroy a personality, as it almost did mine.

"But I found out from this wonderful article that all women don't experience orgasm in the same way, or with the same overt manifestations exhibited by other women. Somewhat enlightened now, (I've read the article over and over!), I have come to know what orgasm is to *me,* and to know *when* I experience it. The enjoyment I get out of sex just happens to involve several orgasms, instead of the NONE I had considered myself capable of experiencing. And I was going to see a psychiatrist!

"Thank you, Dr. Ellis. Thank you, Mr. Editor of *Sex and Censorship*. And my husband thanks you!"

Evidence such as that shown in this letter indicates that retarded or non-existent orgasm may really be a matter of definition: that if a woman unrealistically expects her climax to be one kind of thing and it is something quite different, she may feel that she doesn't receive it at all. Intensive and extensive sex education, in instances such as these, may prove to be quite helpful.

14. If your partner is difficult to bring to orgasm you should particularly try to show that you do not need or require him or her to have a climax on every single occasion. The less you exaggerate the importance of your partner's always coming to climax, the more comfortable he or she will tend to feel with you and the more likely he or she may be to achieve orgasm.

15. When the usual physical and psychological techniques of aiding a partner to achieve orgasm do not work, it is sometimes advisable to resort to mechanical apparatus to achieve this effect. Thus, when a woman is difficult to satisfy because she requires prolonged or forceful pressure on some sensitive region, such as her clitoris, the male can sometimes effectively employ mechanical devices, such as a rubber eraser or an electric vibrator, to help him apply the kind and degree of pressure she needs.

It has been reported by Dr. LeMon Clark (1949) that the use of such mechanical contrivances as the electric vibrator, particularly in the case of a female who has never had an orgasm, may help create a channel or pathway of nervous excitation which, once it is opened, may thereafter be instrumental in facilitating further orgasms. Even though producing initial orgasms in this manner may be rather difficult, once the first climax is obtained others may follow more easily.

In the case of a woman who can achieve climax through intercourse but who has some difficulty in doing so, it is sometimes desirable for the male partner to wear a condom to which are attached feathers or other objects, or to place a washer of sponge or foam rubber around his penis, thus making for closer and stronger contact between his organ and his partner's vaginal walls. Condoms specially prepared for this purpose (French ticklers) cannot usually be purchased in this country but it is not too hard to manufacture suitable similar devices if one finds them desirable.

It is not so easy to think of and employ devices which the woman can use in order to help her husband come to climax when he has trouble doing so. There is no reason, however, why she, too, at times cannot use electric vibrators, clamps, sponges with holes in the center, and other materials which may be helpful in certain special cases. There seems to be no sense to humans' being squeamish in relation to their sex desires when, to facilitate eating and drinking needs, they do not hesitate to use spoons, knives, forks, chopsticks, drinking straws, etc.

16. As noted previously in this chapter and also in Chapter 6, some partners require sexual intercourse itself, with or without extended preliminaries, to reach a full state of arousal.

Kegel (1952, 1956) has particularly emphasized the role of the vaginal muscles (the pubococcygeus muscle in particular) in exciting a woman and helping her achieve orgasm. He insists that in many instances where the female is unable to reach climax, her vaginal muscles are slack and need strengthening by specific exercises; and he has invented a special device, the perineometer, to aid vaginal exercising (Riedman, 1957).

Dr. LeMon Clark (1958b) has also discovered, in his gynecological and sexological practice, that "when I could get women to develop control of the sphincter muscle of the vagina so that they could voluntarily contract it during intercourse, they reported that intercourse was much more satisfactory."

It has also been found, and noted in the sexological literature for many years (Bloch, 1908; H. Ellis, 1936; Forel, 1922), that when the female learns to use her vaginal muscles adequately and to contract and control them during coitus, she may exert unusually satisfying pressures on the male's penis, add considerably to his excitement, and induce him to have an orgasm easier and more quickly than he might otherwise be wont to have it.

Even, therefore, though some of the enthusiasts about exercise of the vaginal muscles may be somewhat overstating the case—since most women still have the main seat of their sensation and orgasm-producing capacity in their clitoral rather than vaginal areas—there is little to be lost and sometimes something to be gained by a woman's controlling and strengthening her pubococcygeus muscle.

The actual control of vaginal muscles can be done through exercises with Dr. Kegel's perineometer, which can easily be carried on by the woman at home; or by the woman's focusing on stopping her flow of urine or pretending to check the act of defecation. During intercourse, the female can likewise use her sphincter muscles to bear down on the male's inserted penis, and thereby learn to contract the vaginal walls around the shaft of the penis.

As usual, it must be noted that if all the foregoing methods of bringing a partner to orgasm are tried and none of them is effective, so that your mate continues to be non-orgasmic fairly frequently or at all times, it may well be that he or she (or perhaps you) have a severe physical or psychological problem; and professional aid should be sought. That even the most difficult cases can often be cured by medical or psychological treatments is well attested by a number of published case histories.

In one of my own cases, for example, I saw a thirty-four-year-old wife and mother who had never been able to have an orgasm with her husband, although she had on many occasions become quite aroused and almost reached the point of climax. Thinking that perhaps her husband's poor sex technique might be an issue, she had tried several extramarital affairs. But even though she selected quite experienced lovers, she still remained far short of orgasm with them.

It was easy to ascertain that this patient considered her own mother to be a whore, since she had frequently caught her with lovers when the patient was a child; and that the patient was therefore determined not to enjoy sex in the same kind of illegitimate and presumably "wicked" manner in which her mother had previously enjoyed it. But giving the patient insight into this origin of her frigidity served not a bit to enable her to overcome it. She still, with her husband, got close to the point of orgasm but, even after an hour of various kinds of genital massage, failed to reach any peak.

What proved to be much more effective was my showing the patient that she not only hated her mother but, more importantly, hated herself because (a) she came from such a supposedly "bad" family; (b) thought that she was wicked for being hostile to her mother; (c) had always refused to buckle down to difficult responsibilities in life, such as taking care of her children and her household; and (d) had always been convinced that she was "a moron."

When this patient was shown that her entire philosophy of life or basic set of assumptions consisted of thinking herself worthless, and when she was induced and persuaded to question, challenge, and tackle that silly and irrational set of assumptions, she started, for the first time in her life, to enjoy herself in many ways, including sexual participation.

She had to be trained—as most of my sexually inadequate patients have to be trained—to focus adequately on arousing stimuli when having sex relations; but it was not difficult to get her to do this kind of focusing once she accepted the basic assumption that she *was* worthwhile and that she *did* have a right, as a human being, to enjoy herself.

As the patient said in the course of one of our final sessions: "It's all so different now from the way it used to be with me! I go to bed with my husband and he's just the same as ever before. Sometimes he's in the right mood and wants to help me sexually in every way and at other times he's as gruff as a bear and only wants to satisfy himself, if he thinks of sex at all. But no matter how he is, I keep myself from getting upset, and focus, just as you taught me to do, on my own excitement and my own feeling.

"Occasionally, I have to keep working at the focusing before it has any real effect. But most of the time I use the sex images that I have found worked before. And where these images used to be the picture of how kind and loving my husband was at times and how his love made me worthy, the images now tend to be of the times I received satisfaction even when he was not so kind and loving—the times I really worked on my own excitement and sort of gave myself most of the pleasure. And whenever I get the thought, which I only get once in a great while now, that maybe I'm just sexually incompetent and maybe I just don't deserve to have anyone work so hard to give me a climax, I quickly put that thought behind me, and say to myself: 'Why am I so lowly and undeserving? Why *don't* I deserve all the enjoyment I can get out of life, including all the sex enjoyment?'

"I immediately see that I do deserve this enjoyment and that I deserve it even if my husband isn't kind and loving —and, in fact, even if no one in the whole world ever cared for me. And that's the greatest feeling of all, I think: the thought that I am deserving and worthy no matter *who* cares or does not care for me. Why, that thought alone can almost bring on an orgasm these days!"

Even the most stubborn and deep-seated cases of difficulty or inability to achieve an orgasm can often be psychotherapeutically attacked and successfully treated when the patient and therapist are both persistent (Pillay, 1948, 1950). For the most part, however, such problems can be solved by the application of the kinds of methods we have just been outlining—methods that psychologically and physically get at the root of this fairly common sexual handicap.

Techniques of retarding orgasm. It is sometimes desirable, though not often absolutely necessary, that a husband or wife learn to retard orgasm. Thus, a husband may ejaculate so quickly once he has been aroused that he virtually never can have intercourse with his wife and he may also preclude considerable pleasure of his own because of such quick ejaculation. Or a wife may achieve an orgasm so quickly that there is virtually never sufficient time for her husband to ejaculate in the course of coitus. In some instances, she may be able to continue coitus and have a second orgasm; but in other cases she may not be in any suitable mood for continued relations once her first (and sometimes final) climax has occurred.

This does not mean that rapid orgasm on the part of husband or wife is necessarily pathological. Frequently it is not: since many young men and women are so well endowed biologically and have sex relations so infrequently in our society that it is normal and natural for them to become exceptionally excited during sex preliminaries and to have quick orgasms. As Kinsey and his associates (1948, 1953) have implied, these individuals may merely be highly-sexed persons.

It is also to be noted that, especially for the male of the

human species, novelty has a considerable influence on quick ejaculation. Once a male becomes accustomed to having coitus with a sweetheart or wife, he may be able to have intercourse with her for a long period of time without coming to climax; sometimes, he may even find difficulty attaining an orgasm. But this same male, when having relations for the first time or the first few times with a new partner, may ejaculate very quickly after entry, or even before his penis has entered his partner's vagina.

Similarly, I have spoken to females who attained climax out of unusual excitement and novelty, on their first sexual encounter with a male but who rarely or never were able easily to do so again, even with the same partner, for the rest of their lives.

Quick orgasm is generally not of great significance unless two sex partners *make* it so. If either or both mates *believe* that a man or a woman is sexually deficient if he or she comes to climax rapidly, the one who achieves quick orgasm will *consequently* tend to become disturbed; and, because of this disturbance, this individual may tend to keep having quick orgasms.

In intercourse, just as in the case of masturbation, the reaching of climax quickly is, in itself, a harmless and often non-pathological aspect of sexuality. But if you erroneously *think* masturbation is harmful, you will usually become nervous, guilty, and upset about it; and if you *think* rapid orgasm harmful or unmanly or unwomanly, you will become disturbed about your rapidity.

As has been emphasized throughout this book, quick climax is not necessarily injurious to satisfactory sex relations because coitus is only *one* form of sex fulfillment and even if a husband and wife were never able to have climactic intercourse they could still, all their married lives, have mutually pleasing sex relations and climaxes. It is therefore rarely absolutely necessary for one mate to overcome his or her tendency to have quick orgasm in order to satisfy the other partner.

On the contrary, it is occasionally desirable for a husband or a wife, for his or her own sake, to *have* a rapid climax. Thus, some females find that coitus becomes painful and irritating unless it is brief; and some males can enjoy coitus only for a short period of time, but become annoyed or irritated if it continues for several minutes or more. Such individuals should, for their own maximum satisfaction, have quick climaxes; and, often, they deliberately learn to do so. For these individuals determinedly to prolong their sex relations, assuming that they would be able to do so, might well prove to be harmful rather than beneficial.

Granting, then, that quickly achieved climax is not always unsatisfactory and that in some cases it may even be preferred, the fact remains that in other instances it is desirable for the husband or wife to learn to delay his or her orgasm. Under these circumstances, some of the techniques that can profitably be employed are the following:

1. One of the best retardants of rapid climax is an increased amount of sex relations. Particularly in the case of the male, the individual who comes quickly the first time may come much less rapidly the second or third time during the same evening. Both males and females, on the other hand, who have orgasms only once a week or less may find themselves becoming most excited and having their climaxes very quickly on the occasions when they do engage in sex relations.

Individuals, moreover, who have never or rarely had heterosexual relations tend to exaggerate their value and to become over-excited when they do have coitus. Familiarity in this area tends to breed the same kind of relative indifference that it does in many others. The more often one has intercourse and the more routine it becomes the more difficult it may be for one to have an orgasm—especially if one continues to have relations with the same partner. Rapidly climaxing individuals, therefore, often become much slower-timed when they have more frequent sex engagements.

2. Premature orgasm in the male or female tends to become aggravated when the individual worries over his or her ability to prolong coitus. This is what happens in connection with most motor acts of human beings: the more one worries about them, the less successful one tends to be at accomplishing them.

As I have shown in several publications on rational psychotherapy (A. Ellis, 1957a, 1962a, 1963a, 1963d; Ellis and Harper, 1961a, 1961b), human beings cause virtually all their own emotional upsets by consciously or unconsciously telling themselves certain illogical thoughts or sentences.

In the case of premature orgasm, the individual is usually telling himself, "Maybe I won't be able to succeed at lasting long in intercourse and if I don't that would be awful!" Then, after he has had a few initial experiences of what he considers to be failure, he says to himself: "Oh, how dreadful it is for me to fail like this! What will my partner think of me? What an incompetent fool I am! I'm sure that she's not satisfied this way and that she'll despise and hate me. Oh, how terrible!"

Repeating sentences like this to himself over and over again will cause this individual, in most instances, to continue his pattern of prematurity. For he is so concerned about his present and past performances that he has no time and energy to concentrate on the real question: "How can I focus on sex enjoyment and thereby better my performance in the future?"

Instead, the individual who has too-rapid orgasm should stop telling himself self-defeating sentences and should say to himself sentences like this: "All right, so I have a tendency to come quickly. So what? If my partner really loves and understands me and has some knowledge of sex, she will realize that this is common and will think nothing of it. Besides, I can always satisfy her in other ways, so what great difference does it make if I do come quickly?

"Granting that it may be desirable to learn to come more slowly, I am sure that I can do this if I will stop beating myself over the head and will start doing the things that are necessary to overcome this tendency. The worst that can happen is that I will fail; and if so, as I just said, I can still satisfy my mate in other ways. So let me relax and enjoy sex as best I may and gradually work on this prematurity problem."

If he takes an attitude like this, the rapidly ejaculating individual will most likely, after he has learned something about himself and sex, overcome his problem.

If, however, he continues to tell himself how awful, how frightful, how terrible his premature ejaculation is, and what a worthless individual he is for having this handicap, he will almost certainly make himself—yes, *make* himself —worse and worse.

3. Because the individual who ejaculates prematurely often focuses on and catastrophizes about his own quick performance, he will usually help himself considerably if he learns to concentrate on something outside himself. The human brain works something like a high speed computing machine, which essentially focuses either on one of two settings, but not both, at a single instant; and, as Berg and Street (1953) point out, "No one can fully concentrate upon two things at the same time."

If, therefore, the male who tends to ejaculate quickly will force himself to focus on his wife's reactions, on how to please her, how to rouse her to a pitch of sexual excitement, he will tend to kill two birds with one stone: first, he will help her have orgasm more quickly; and, second, he will divert his attention from himself and give his penis a chance to function at a normal level of arousability without his worrisomely triggering it off with self-catastrophizing thoughts.

The more, then, that a male becomes absorbed in his mate's sex reactions, the more he concentrates on doing everything possible to please her and give her satisfaction, the less he is likely to be over-concerned about his own rapid ejaculatory tendencies. As noted previously, if he will focus, while he is having intercourse, on caressing his wife and trying to stir her to greater heights of performance, he will sometimes find that his caresses, instead of exciting him further, may be somewhat distracting and enable him to last longer in coitus.

The main thing, however, is not the diverting acts that he performs but his aim and his thoughts while performing them. Exactly the same motor act, such as a man's caressing his wife's breasts, can be employed (a) to stimulate himself further and help bring on an orgasm or (b) to divide his own sexual attention and thereby help retard his orgasm.

The psychological technique of diversion or anti-focusing does not have to be limited to an individual's concentrating on his or her mate in order to retard orgasm; any other counter-thought will tend to work just as well. Because, as we have shown, human beings achieve orgasm largely by concentrating on sexually exciting images and thoughts, they can to a large extent reverse this process by focusing on non-sexually exciting ideas and fantasies.

Thus, if a male is having intercourse and wants to delay his orgasm, instead of thinking of sexual topics, of how beautiful his wife is, or what a pleasure it is to be engaging in coitus, he can literally force himself to think of non-sexual subjects—such as his problems at work, whether or not he should buy a new car, how the children are getting along, what the solution is to a certain mathematical problem, etc.

Or he can think of some distinctly non-sexual image, such as a house, a painting of a landscape, an old man, or anything else he considers non-arousing. In this way, husbands or wives may retard their climaxes for considerable periods of time while engaging in active sex relations.

In a few instances, it may be advisable for the individual to engage in some distracting motor activity while he or she is having intercourse. Thus, a man or woman can smoke, play with a pencil, doodle, or manipulate a rubber band when engaged in coitus—particularly if he or she is in a supine position—while his or her partner is doing the active surmounting. Many partners, it is to be expected, would object strenuously to this kind of motor distraction, as they would feel that it makes sex relations too impersonal and unromantic. Where both partners are ultra-realistic, however, it may have some advantages for orgasm retardation.

4. Once a human being gets to a certain point in sex arousal, it is almost impossible for him or her voluntarily to control orgasmic contractions. Nonetheless, just before this point of uncontrollability is reached there are some measures of self-control that can often be effectively employed. The same muscles which are employed to control defecation and urination (the anal sphincter and the perineal muscles) have some connection with the muscles that importantly influence orgasm and ejaculation. If, therefore, the individual will practice tightening or relaxing his or her anal or pelvic muscles when orgasm seems to be approaching, it will often be found that it is possible to head off climax. The more one practices conscious relaxation or tightening of the muscles in the anal and perineal areas, the more likely is one to achieve a certain amount, and sometimes an excellent amount, of control over having an orgasm.

Similarly, by gaining control over one's breathing one

may also be able to hold back one's climax for awhile. Most useful in this respect appear to be (a) inhaling deeply at the point one thinks that orgasm is approaching; or (b) taking a deep breath and, after holding it for a moment or two, slowly and calmly exhaling. Not only will this kind of breathing have a soothing, anti-exciting effect on the body as a whole but it will also serve to distract one from intense sexual stimuli and thereby help to retard orgasm.

5. By having coitus slowly, with short strokes and a good many pauses in between thrusts, one can often ward off climax, sometimes almost indefinitely. Whenever one feels that one is about to have an orgasm, one slows down coital movements or stops entirely for awhile; then, when things have quieted down, one becomes more active again.

In cases where husband and wife wish to have simultaneous or near-simultaneous climax, the husband can leave his penis almost motionless inside the vagina while he keeps pressing its base, with a side to side, up and down, or circular motion, against his wife's vulva and, especially, against her clitoral region, while she remains fairly still. He thus can wait until she approaches climax before he lets himself go and produces his own orgasm by active coital movements.

If the male moves his penis in a circle instead of a straight in and out way, he also may be able to vary his sensation so that it does not become too overwhelming and lead to climax. Also: by pressing against the vaginal wall with the *upper* side of his penis, instead of using the more usual pressure of its lower side against the lower vaginal wall, the male may be able to reduce his sensation and last longer in coitus.

Not only, of course, must the male remain at times motionless if he is to interrupt his own state of arousal, but the female must, at the same time, be relatively inactive in her movements—else she will communicate sensation to him and he may have a rapid ejaculation. In some cases, it will be desirable for the male to withdraw his penis entirely from the vagina and resume clitoral or other foreplay with his mouth or fingers, thereby helping the female to reach such a high state of excitement that she can quickly and easily have orgasm once he reinserts his penis. Or both partners can merely hold each other and rest for awhile, until their excitement has sufficiently cooled so that they can resume coitus or other sex relations again without immediately achieving climax.

6. In certain coital positions there is either less physical contact between the sex organs or it is more possible for the individual to control his movements. Thus, as we have indicated in the chapter before this, when the male is on his back with the female mounting him in a face to face position, he may find that he is able to last considerably longer than when he is surmounting the female.

Any positions that enable the slower-reacting partner to do most of the active pelvic thrusting while the faster-reacting one is relatively passive will tend to retard the latter's orgasm.

7. In some instances it is advisable for the individual who comes to orgasm too quickly to employ a nerve-deadening ointment, such as Nupercainal ointment or creme, applying it to the penis, clitoris, or other sensitive regions that are likely to trigger off orgasm.

Dr. G. Lombard Kelly (1953, 1957, 1961) has done much experimentation in this respect and has excellent results. He finds that a small quantity of nerve-deadening salve, applied to the genitals fifteen to thirty minutes (and sometimes an hour) before intercourse may retard orgasm considerably and lead to greater sex satisfaction. Sometimes, in cases of extreme sensitivity, nerve deadening creme can be applied to the genitals thirty minutes before intercourse and applied again ten minutes before. Where difficulties of erection are involved, such analgesic ointments should not be used and may even cause additional difficulties; but where erection is good but lasting power is low they may prove quite helpful.

Lubricants also tend to make the penis less sensitive and may enable the male to prolong coitus if they are liberally employed. Condoms, occasionally even two or three of them used simultaneously, can also serve as nerve deadeners, since they usually reduce male (and sometimes female) sensation and thus help to retard orgasm.

8. If an individual is too aroused by his or her mate's sexual odors, which is admittedly a rare possibility, he or she may encourage the partner to minimize the effect of these odors by bathing just before intercourse; or may

chew a strongly odored gum or other substance to block his or her own sensitivity.

What is perhaps more likely is that one partner, especially the male, may become too aroused by either the sight of his mate's nudity or her becoming nightdresses. In these instances, the wife can be induced to wear less attractive attire or the couple can have sex relations largely in the dark, where the exciting effects of visual stimuli will be minimized. Whenever one of the mates is particularly aroused by any of the partner's attributes, special care can often be taken to reduce the influence of these attractive (and sometimes fetichistic) attributes.

9. In some instances, it is possible for one to retard one's orgasm by engaging in extended preliminaries before coitus, as some persons reach a point of semi-exhaustion in the course of such extended foreplay and therefore are less easily aroused. This is a dangerous technique, however, since it may easily boomerang and lead to high-pitched excitement and hence the attainment of climax almost immediately after copulation begins.

It would probably be wiser for the rapidly climaxing partner to try to have sex relations with his or her mate when he or she is physically tired or not feeling quite up to par. Going to such extremes, however, also defeats its own end, since the object of retarding orgasm is not to destroy sexual pleasure but, if possible, to enhance it, and if people have relations when they are not greatly desirous or are fatigued, they may be slower-timed in their reactions but may also suffer lack of enjoyment.

10. Hirsch (1951, 1957, 1962) recommends, for males who are prone to reach quick orgasm, daily massaging of the penis for ten to fifteen minutes a day, with or without desensitizing creme, including the massaging of the area under the scrotum to make it less sensitive to stimulation. Occasional momentary squeezing of the penis with the hand, he says, will also help toughen and desensitize it. As yet there is no amount of evidence to indicate that this kind of desensitizing techniques will work well with very many individuals.

11. Kelly (1957) points out that "external pressure on the veins that drain the blood from the erectile tissues of the penis will naturally keep the organ distended. Even an

erect penis can be made a little stiffer and larger, especially the head of it, by deep pressure on the dorsal veins of the penis. This pressure may be applied by a rubber band or by the thumb or the tip of the forefinger." He has found that another site where deep and continued pressure will change a partial into a complete erection is on the central point of the perineum. He therefore advocates, for those males who tend to lose their erections easily that they have intercourse in a sitting position, with the partner sitting astride on the lap, while they press on their own perineal areas. He recommends that this be done with the aid of a special perineal support or brace and is still experimenting with the manufacture of a suitable device for this purpose.

Kelly is also a somewhat enthusiastic proponent of the coitus training apparatus of Loewenstein (1947). This is a device that the male can attach to his penis when he has difficulty in sustaining an erection for any length of time; and with its use he can have intercourse whether or not his penis is flaccid. Many such devices have been invented; but most of them are useless and even harmful. Loewenstein's is one of the best made and it does serve the purpose for which it was designed. Perhaps the greatest advantage of this type of apparatus is psychological rather than physical—since some males, once they find that it is possible for them to have intercourse with the apparatus, thereby gain confidence in themselves and later on are able to sustain their erection without using the device. In this country the coitus training apparatus is prescribed and distributed by Dr. G. Lombard Kelly, 842 Greene Street, Augusta, Georgia.

12. Kelly (1957) and Mozes (1959c) also point out that a number of medical, surgical, and physical remedies are sometimes helpful in cases of premature ejaculation. Thus, circumcision may help the quick ejaculator if his foreskin is too long and the glans of the penis is too sensitive. Alcohol taken in moderate amounts may have a calming effect on nervous individuals and assist as a muscle relaxant. Changes in diet and hormonal therapy may have value for some individuals; as may bed rest and sedation in the case of persons who are overly fatigued, tense, or physically below par.

Temporarily, the use of quick acting barbiturates (such

as nembutal and seconal) may be useful as sedatives if taken a half hour before coitus. These medical and physical measures, however, are only to be employed in instances of severe premature ejaculation where the individual needs special care.

13. It is sometimes possible for the male to use a nonsexual erection for purposes of coitus and with this kind of erection to maintain active copulation longer than he ordinarily would be able to do. Thus, most males get morning erections and may not be particularly sexually desirous when they obtain them. If, however, these males copulate at this time, they may be able to do so for a longer period than usual.

It is also possible for some males to continue intercourse after they have had orgasm and their erections have begun to subside. In so doing, they may be able to bring the female to climax. They may also, in the process, acquire more confidence in their sex abilities and therefore be able to maintain their regular erections for longer periods.

14. As usual, we must close this section by adding that whenever all possible measures have been taken to retard the orgasm of one or both mates and thereby to increase their sex satisfaction and none of these measures seems to be effective, medical and psychological help should be sought, to determine why the individual comes to climax too quickly and what steps may possibly be taken to remedy this state of affairs.

On the medical side, it is sometimes possible for a physician to prescribe diet, vitamins, hormones, rest, sedation, surgery, and other measures which may be helpful. In the great majority of instances, however, it will be found that premature ejaculation by males or unusually rapid climaxing by females is a psychological problem and can be solved by effective counseling or psychotherapy.

The same thing is true, though to a lesser degree, of cases where the male is able to achieve an erection and orgasm but not to sustain his erection sufficiently long to have satisfactory intercourse. This disability is often something of a combination of lack of sufficiently focused sex desire (since, once he becomes desirous enough to achieve erection the male is not able to maintain that desire and sustain adequate tumescence) and premature ejaculation (since many males with this dysfunction ejaculate when the penis is soft and often do so before or quickly after entry into the vagina is effected).

Males who cannot adequately sustain their erections sometimes, particularly when they are getting on in years, have hormonal deficiencies; but most young males who are in this category have psychological problems and have to learn how to focus sufficiently well on sexually exciting stimuli to achieve and maintain an erection. At the same time they must learn how not to over-focus so that they obtain an orgasm before they are adequately tumescent.

In the treatment of individuals suffering from premature ejaculation or inability to sustain an erection, I have found that classical methods of psychoanalysis, which I practised for several years, rarely are too effective and that the technique of rational psychotherapy, which I have been applying for the last five years, is unusually efficacious. Merely showing an individual, as is done in psychoanalysis, that his or her sexual inadequacy stems from childhood complexes, such as a male's guilt over his incestuous attachment to his mother or a female's penis envy, seldom enables him to overcome this inadequacy—even when such interpretations are true (Cleckley, 1957).

The reason for this is that, in our present society, as distinct from the Vienna of Freud's day, people tend to have sex problems largely as a result of what Piers and Singer (1953) have called shame as distinguished from guilt. Whereas the guilty individual feels that he is wicked or sinful for engaging in some sex thought or act (such as an incest fantasy) and that God may punish him for his iniquity, the shameful person feels that he is wrong in the sense of being inadequate or incompetent for thinking or doing something (such as failing at coitus) and that people won't love him or will criticize him for being inadequate.

Just because Sigmund Freud (along with Havelock Ellis, Iwan Bloch, Magnus Hirschfeld, Norman Haire and other sex pioneers of the early part of the twentieth century) existed and fought against the concept of sexual sin, people today are more likely to feel ashamed (inadequate) rather than guilty (sinful) about their sex conduct.

Classical psychoanalysis, moreover, like most other traditional forms of psychotherapy—such as Rank's relationship therapy (F. Karpf, 1953; Rank, 1950), Jung's individuation technique (Jung, 1954), Horney's analytic method (Horney, 1937), Sullivan's analysis of interpersonal relations (Sullivan, 1947, 1954), and Rogers' nondirective or client-centered method (Rogers, 1951)—focuses mainly on getting the disturbed individual to see how he originally acquired irrational, self-defeating attitudes and then helping him, through a permissive and accepting relationship with the therapist, to acquire less self-sabotaging views (Fenichel, 1945; Freud, 1925-50; Glover, 1955; Jones, 1955-57; Munroe, 1955).

Unlike the more directive psychotherapeutic methods—such as those of Adler (1927; Ansbacher and Ansbacher, 1956); Phillips (1956), and Thorne (1950)—the methods of historical interpretation, analysis of transference relations, and non-directive and non-critical reflection of the patient's feelings do not forthrightly attack the individual's deep-seated philosophies of either guilt or shame; and they are therefore often ineffective in the treatment of patients with serious sex or other problems (Eysenck, 1953).

The system of psychotherapy which I call rational psychotherapy (A. Ellis, 1957a, 1962a, 1963a, 1963d, 1965b) is especially designed not only to show individuals how they originally became disturbed but to demonstrate how they are *sustaining* their disturbances by still believing the nonsense, or illogical ideas, which first led them to feel and act in an aberrated fashion.

Rational therapy differs from most other forms of therapy in that (a) not merely the facts and psychodynamics of the patient's behavior are revealed but, more to the point, his underlying philosophies or ideas which lead to and flow from these historical facts; (b) a concerted *attack* is made on the irrational beliefs that are disclosed in the course of the therapeutic process; (c) emphasis is placed far less on the disclosure of the individual's unconscious drives or feelings than on revealing his unconscious and irrational *attitudes* which underlie these drives or feelings; (d) the therapist literally *teaches* the patient how to observe his (unconscious) illogical thinking and how, instead, to change his internalized sentences and to think straight; and (e) the patient is usually encouraged, urged, or helped to take emotionally reeducating *activity*.

By way of illustrating how rational therapy is employed in helping individuals to overcome their sex problems, we may take the case of a twenty-five-year-old male whom I saw because he kept either losing his erection as soon as he started to have intercourse with his wife or ejaculating within a few seconds after penetration.

It was quickly apparent in his case that he did have a somewhat classical Oedipus complex—which I do not often see among my patients today, but which from time to time does turn up—and that he always had been guilty about having sex relations with any female partner because his mother, who was still young and attractive, had literally taught him that sex was for procreative purposes and that "more worthwhile" people enjoyed themselves with "higher" and "better" pursuits.

Consequently, this patient had had only two or three abortive attempts at intercourse before marriage and had married a rather unattractive physician, a few years older than himself, who was a highly intellectual and (according to his mother's and his own standards) "more worthwhile" sort of person. He had been potent with his wife until she became pregnant with their first and so far only child; and since that time, though the child was now two years of age, he had never been completely sexually adequate.

It was easy to see why this patient was afraid to be potent—or, to risk a pun, was scared unstiff—and it was not difficult to get him to accept the interpretation that his impotency originally stemmed from his mother and his conscious belief that sex for the sake of fun was improper. Unfortunately, however, his acceptance of these interpretations had no particular effect on his sexual competence.

The patient was then shown that, while his *primary* disturbance may well have been connected with his relations with his mother and his antisexual beliefs thus engendered, his *secondary* (and for the moment *more* important) disturbance was connected with his feelings of shame, of incompetency, of failure. That is to say, his society (and, in his particular case, his father more than his mother) had raised him to believe wholeheartedly that the worst possible thing in the world, and in many ways even worse than enjoying himself sexually, was being a weakling, a nincompoop, a failure.

Consequently, when he first started to become incapable of sustaining an adequate erection, instead of asking himself the simple questions: "*Why* am I failing sexually?" and "What can I do *not* to keep failing?" he kept telling himself, over and over, "See what a failure I am! This proves what I've always suspected: that I'm weak and no good! Oh, my God: how awful it is for me to be this incompetent and unmanly!" By repeating these kinds of catastrophizing sentences the patient (of course!) kept focusing and refocusing on sexual failure rather than success and he could not possibly overcome his disability.

It must be remembered, in this connection, that (as we stressed in Chapters 2 and 3) both male and female sexual arousal and incitation to orgasm are mainly mediated through impulses from the cerebral cortex of the brain and are basically cognitive in origin. And when we focus upon non-sexual notions—such as the idea that it is awful or catastrophic when we are not becoming sufficiently erect or are prematurely achieving a climax—it is literally impossible for us to focus, simultaneously, on sexual ideas. The result, in the male, is inability to obtain or maintain erection.

I have not found a single case, recently, of male inadequacy where, no matter what the *original* cause of the problem, the afflicted individual was not *secondarily* telling himself how horrible it was to be impotent, convincing himself that he was a terrible failure and that, as such, he would doubtless continue to be inadequate.

So with this patient. He kept, once his first symptoms arose, ceaselessly watching himself, expecting himself to be sexually weak, worrying about his weakness, and continually giving himself a difficult time. Once he was shown exactly what he was doing and what nonsensical catastrophizing sentences he was telling himself to sustain his erectile and ejaculatory difficulties, and once he started *contradicting* this nonsense that he kept telling himself, he quickly began to improve.

Thus, this patient began to see that it was *not* terrible—but only expectable—for him to be sexually inadequate, considering his upbringing. I induced him to admit to himself that he was *not* an incompetent or a failure just because he had sex problems. I forced him, generally, to question his entire concept of masculinity and failure and to see that *doing, trying, working at* things are more important than necessarily *succeeding at* or doing them *perfectly*.

Once he began to surrender his philosophy of the necessity of achieving absolute success and perfectionism, he was able to watch his sexual behavior more objectively and to focus on sexually exciting stimuli.

At the same time (though this seemed less necessary with this patient since he had already, by himself, worked through some of his originally mother-inculcated puritanism) I also tackled his basic beliefs that sex was wicked outside of procreation and that incestuous desires toward one's own mother were horrible to contemplate. On two levels, then, by attacking (a) his original antisexual philosophy that first led to his sex problem and (b) his secondary philosophy of success and perfectionism that encouraged him to retain, sustain, and aggravate his original symptoms, I directed this patient to more rational modes of thinking about himself and his sexuality.

Whereas, when I used to do classic psychoanalysis, I mainly would have concentrated on the first of these points, I now, with the use of rational therapy, mainly concentrate on the second point and find this kind of focusing to be much more effective. Almost invariably, with few exceptions, I find this to be true in cases of male and female psychosexual disability.

I also find that, although I see many people every year who specifically come to me with severe sexual problems, I rarely see one who has what I would call a real sexual disturbance. Invariably, my patients have *general* emotional difficulties, which stem from their poor, illogical, and self-defeating *general* philosophies of life.

Their sex symptoms almost always are derivatives of these idiotic general creeds or assumptions; and when their basic beliefs, of which they are unconscious in the sense of not knowing how important they are to their lives, are forthrightly brought to their attention, ruthlessly revealed and analyzed to show how ridiculous they are, and consistently attacked, discouraged, and rooted up, their sex problems do not automatically vanish but are at least much more susceptible to specific re-educating instructions.

To the usual psychotherapeutic techniques of exploration, ventilation, excavation, and interpretation, the rational therapist adds the more direct methods of confrontation, confutation, depropagandization, and re-education. He thereby frankly faces and resolutely tackles the deepest seated and most recalcitrant patterns of sexual and general disturbance.

12.

Having Sex Relations
Under Special Conditions

There are several special conditions under which it may be advisable to modify the usual kind of sex relations which a couple may have. Some of these special conditions and the desirable modifications to be taken when they exist will now be discussed.

Sex relations during menstruation. Many peoples of this earth rigidly refrain from intercourse during menstruation, largely because of irrational taboos. Until recently, there has also been a distinct taboo against menstrual coitus in our own country (Kelly, 1959). Although many of the reasons for this taboo are as senseless as those of the primitives who think menstrual blood is poisonous and who therefore interdict copulation when a woman is having her period, there may be some realistic disadvantages to having intercourse at this time.

1. Many couples find coitus during menstruation rather uncomfortable because of the presence of menstrual blood and the sensitivity of the vaginal area at this time, especially during the first day or two of a heavy flow.

2. Having intercourse at the end of a woman's period may in some cases lead to a stirring up of her flow, which has previously become lighter; and she may consequently be somewhat inconvenienced.

3. The female may experience irritation of her vaginal tract because of the sensitive condition of her organs dur-

ing menstruation; and the male, unless he uses a condom, may contract urethritis or penile irritation. Actually, however, few cases of male and female difficulties in this connection seem to exist even with those who fairly regularly have coitus during the woman's period.

On the other hand, refraining from intercourse during menstruation deprives many couples of considerable satisfaction especially when the wife's period is a six- to seven-day affair or where she is notably aroused during this time. Consequently, many couples do have intercourse during menstruation and, as just noted, few of them report serious consequences.

To make menstrual coitus more satisfactory, a woman can douche just before having it and then use her diaphragm, if she has one, as a temporary plug to stop her menstrual flow during copulation. She should, however, remove her diaphragm shortly after intercourse has ended (taking the precaution of douching again if no other contraceptive is employed and she wishes to avoid becoming pregnant). The male, as indicated above, may wear a condom during intercourse, even though he may usually not wear one at other times.

For individuals who do not want to have intercourse during the wife's period but who are nonetheless highly aroused at this time, other forms of stimulation, especially manual manipulation of the genitals, should be quite acceptable and should lead to orgasm. If the wife prefers to have no satisfaction herself, there is still no reason why she cannot satisfy her husband with extragenital techniques.

Sex relations during illness. Fairly frequently in almost any marriage one of the mates will be ill while the other will be well. At such times, the ill mate often should not be having intercourse or other forms of sex relations—especially if these have been banned by his or her physician. Nor can the other mate, at such times, expect the ill partner to be too interested in satisfying him or her sexually.

At the same time, there are many forms of illness in which sex relations of a not too strenuous nature are encouraged—just as mild exercise is advocated for individuals recuperating from certain operations and illnesses.

Even when an individual has a serious ailment, such as a heart disease, it may often be more beneficial for him or

her to have occasional, not too strenuous, sex participations than to refrain entirely from sex engagements.

In such instances as these, care usually should be taken
to employ coital positions which are most satisfactory to
the ailing mate. Positions where this mate is relatively passive are often to be preferred. Thus, if the ailing partner
is lying on his or her side or back, rather than surmounting the other partner, over-strenuous intercourse is less
likely to occur than if he or she takes a more active position. Or forms of relations in which the ailing partner does
not have actual coitus but is still brought to orgasm are
often to be preferred to copulation.

Where one of the partners is ill or convalescent, the
circumstances under which sex relations are had are likely
to be important. Usually, the ill or convalescent partner
should engage in sex play when he or she is well rested, is
relaxed, is in a good mood, has not had relations too recently, and is not going to do any arduous exercise after
having sex activity. Again: individuals with serious diseases or ailments who have intercourse usually should not
go in for extended precoital play but should skip some of
the preliminaries and begin coitus relatively quickly.

When an ill individual cannot have intercourse or other
forms of sex relations, there is often no reason why he or
she cannot in some manner satisfy his or her partner. Particularly where one mate has a long but not too debilitat-
ing ailment or injury, he or she should make some effort
to see that the other mate is sexually satisfied—otherwise,
underlying or open resentment is likely to develop (Ellis,
1963a).

In any major illness, the physician's word should be
law: since he alone can usually tell whether a particular
patient, with a certain kind of ailment, is capable of having this or that kind of sex relations (Klumbies and Kleinsorge, 1950). But assuming that the physician presents no
objections, the couple involved should not use a disease or
injury as an absolute sign that sex activity must cease.
Common sense and love are most essential in sex (as in
all other) husband-wife relations.

Sex relations during pregnancy. The kind and frequency
of sexual activities during a wife's pregnancy vary enormously with her general health and her capacity to carry a
child successfully. In most instances where the pregnancy

is going normally and there is no reason to believe that there will be any unusual difficulty, coital and non-coital relations can be continued up to four to six weeks (and sometimes even up to two weeks) before birth. In many normal cases, Masters and Johnson (lecture at American Association of Marriage Counselors, 1961) insist, no harm is done if intercourse continues up to the very day of childbirth. But, in other instances, intercourse or other modes of sex activity may have to cease almost immediately after the onset of pregnancy, because the over-stimulation of the wife may lead to a miscarriage.

When sex relations are had during pregnancy, the following precautions should be maintained:

1. Coitus itself should be had in some position where there is no undue pressure on the wife's abdominal region. Side entry and rear entry positions are usually preferable (as indicated in more detail in Chapter 9).

2. Deep penetration of the male's penis into the vagina should be avoided and should decrease with advancing pregnancy. Extreme caution, as Cauldwell (1958) notes, should be taken after the sixth month. "Even though there are those who believe that full intromission of the organ is necessary," he states, "a surprisingly large number of women will reach a climax with slight penetration where they have failed with ordinary deep penetration."

3. Husband and wife should see that their genitals are scrupulously clean when having coitus.

4. There should be no coitus, normally, during the last two to four weeks of pregnancy. Actually, there seems to be little evidence that having coitus right up to the day before labor is injurious (since some primitive peoples, such as the Chukchee, seem to do so with no harmful results); but it is probably best to stay on the safe side in this respect and to refrain during the last weeks.

For non-coital relations, particularly in regard to the wife's satisfying her husband extracoitally, these rules can be somewhat relaxed. Manual and oral stimulation are especially to be resorted to in place of coitus when it is desired but inadvisable.

Sex relations during the menopause or change of life. Women normally have their menopause or change of life between their fortieth and fiftieth years and at this time experience some profound hormonal and physical changes. There is less definite evidence that men have a change of life at this time; but, after they reach the age of sixty, both males and females often suffer serious losses of the sex steroids which help regulate a good many of their bodily functions and they may both need sex hormone replacement (Masters, 1955, 1957b, 1958; Masters and Ballew, 1955). Otherwise, they both tend to join what Masters calls the "neutral gender."

In addition, some men and women, because they have failed to do what they really wanted to do or thought they should do up to their middle age become depressed and discouraged when they see their declining years approach; consequently, they have a rough time of it, mentally and physically. If these individuals had been less emotionally disturbed and more rationally goal-directed during their lives, it is possible that they would suffer less serious "change of life" symptoms (Lazarsfeld and Kadis, 1958).

A prevalent myth is that a woman, because she loses her reproductive power at the time of her menopause (because her ovaries no longer function as they previously did) also loses her sex drive. This is not necessarily true; although temporarily, while she is undergoing change of life, a female may have little sex desire. In many instances, however, the reverse is true: a woman may have distinctly increased sex urges during menopause.

Once a woman's menopause has been completed, there is no reason why she should not have a reasonably active sex life. In many instances, she is freed of the fear of pregnancy and since the time is far past for puritanical coyness, she may have considerably augmented desire once she is past the change of life. It is more likely to be her husband, in many instances, whose sex needs significantly decrease—not because of any dramatic "change," but because males generally decline sexually, slowly but surely, from the age of twenty onward.

But sex activity in the declining years of life is the rule rather than the exception. A report in the journal *Surgery, Gynecology and Obstetrics* indicated that only a small percentage of young women (under thirty years of age) who had had hysterectomies, or removal of their uterus and ovaries, had slightly less satisfactory sex relations; the remainder experienced no change or else had more satisfactory sex acts than they previously had. Similarly, older women whose ovaries no longer function after the menopause may be little affected sexually, even though their sex organs may change, with the lips of the vagina becoming smaller and thinner and the uterus becoming progressively smaller (Herrick, 1957; Mills and Cameron, 1959).

The *British Medical Journal* notes that painful coitus may sometimes occur in women who have passed the menopause, as a result of their lubrication glands becoming somewhat atrophied. This condition may be remedied by the use of a suitable lubricating jelly during intercourse. Sometimes it may be desirable to administer local or general female hormone (estrogen) therapy. But if a couple is in good health and there are no pathological conditions, the *Journal* concludes that "regular coitus can then often be satisfactorily maintained into old age with benefit and comfort to both partners."

LeMon Clark (1959a) also notes that "far from being detrimental to health in middle and later life, the nervous, emotional relaxation incident to a full and complete sexual experience may be definitely beneficial. Even in cases of vascular hypertension, high blood pressure, attempts to get along without intercourse, thereby creating emotional tension within the individual, may be far more detrimental than any strain incident to moderate, reasonable sexual intercourse promoting the release from tension brought about by orgasm."

Sex adjustment during advancing years will be aided if the husband and wife, once they are in their fifties or sixties, realistically accept their sex urges *as they are* and do not artificially try to over-activate or under-activate these urges. If they are still quite vigorous sexually, fine! Let them be as active as they wish, assuming that they do not have any organic ailments that could make coitus dangerous.

If a husband and wife are not as sexually aroused during or after the woman's change of life as they previously were, let them graciously accept this fact and not begin to think that they are no longer "masculine" or "feminine" or no longer worthwhile. Sex is but one, albeit a major, part of life; certainly it is not all of life (Daniels, 1953).

Probably the main hazard of late middle and old age from the sexual standpoint is that one of the mates may become much less sexually interested than the other, even though previously they were fairly equally paired in this respect. In some instances, the husband will have less sexual interest than the wife; while in other instances the male will remain sexually hale and hearty until his seventies, while the female loses all or most of her desire years earlier.

In either of these eventualities, extracoital stimulation becomes of real importance if the mates are to continue to have good sex-love relations. The mate who has little or no desire can still, in nearly all instances, satisfy the mate who has more desire; and should, out of love, friendly feeling, and the wish to continue a good relationship, *want* to do so. Unless the demands of one of the mates is onerous—which is not very likely in the case of most individuals over the age of fifty—there should be little difficulty achieving a continuing fine sexual adjustment if the little-desiring mate uses good sense and affectionate helpfulness.

13.

Sexual Deviations

It is surprisingly difficult to define exactly what is a sexual deviation. Sex books and discussions often devote large amounts of space and time to the so-called deviations, perversions, or abnormalities; and yet there is little agreement among the writers and discussants as to what, essentially, constitutes deviated behavior.

As I have shown in previously published papers and books (A. Ellis, 1952b, 1963a, 1963e, 1965a), various authorities have insisted that a sexually deviated or perverted act is one that is (a) statistically abnormal or infrequently resorted to by members of the general populace; (b) biologically or procreatively inappropriate; (c) psychologically unhealthy or immature; or (d) ethically or morally "bad" or "wrong." None of these criteria, I contend, are satisfactory because, in the last analysis, each depends largely on social norms or on culturally approved standards; and these norms and standards differ enormously from one community to another.

Thus, from a statistical standpoint, masturbation and petting are widely prevalent in our country; while, instead, homosexuality seems more frequent among young Arabian males. Who, then, are we to call deviated or sexually abnormal—ourselves or the Arabs?

From the standpoint of mental health or emotional "maturity," it may be healthful and mature for a Scandinavian girl to have an "illegitimate" child but unhealthful and "immature" for a modern American girl to do likewise.

And where it was relatively "healthy" for an ancient Greek male to be largely homosexual in his interests and acts, it is (as we shall show below) distinctly "unhealthy" or "neurotic" for a modern American male to be predominantly homosexual.

From a so-called biological or procreative standpoint, all acts which do not lead to childbearing, such as masturbation and petting, would have to be called perverse; while forcible rape or an adult male's being attracted exclusively to thirteen-year-old girls would have to be deemed perfectly "normal." A married couple's having intercourse with the use of contraceptives would also have to be viewed as abnormal or deviated behavior.

From a moral or theoretical point of view, a woman's having an orgasm in marital intercourse may be looked upon as wicked (as it actually is viewed in some communities, including some fanatical religious groups in our own country); while a woman's remaining with her husband when she does not have sex satisfaction may be seen as a virtual crime in other communities (as it seems to be viewed among some fanatical romantic groups among our avant garde liberals). Which of these women, the one who does or the one who does not have a climax in marital relations, are we to consider a pervert?

Although the usual definitions of sexual deviation would seem to be prejudiced and parochial, and none of them can be *absolutely* upheld, there does seem to be one that holds up fairly well for people living in our own society as well as for most individuals in most societies: namely, a psychosocial approach to deviation.

This definition starts with the assumption, which I first stated in *The American Sexual Tragedy* (1963e), that an individual who has no sexual defects (such as an injured penis or neuromuscular deficiencies) may be considered to be sexually deviated if he can *only,* under *all* circumstances, enjoy one special form of sexual activity: or if he is obsessively-compulsively fixated on a given mode of sex behavior; or if he is fearfully and rigidly bound to one or two forms of sexual participation.

This definition of sexual deviation—or sexual neurosis—is the only one that seems to be consistent with that which is usually given of a non-sexual deviation or neurosis. A non-sexual neurotic is an individual who, out of some kind of illogical fear, favors one kind of behavior (such as staying alone in his room) and disfavors another kind (such as going to social functions or riding on trains). A sexual neurotic or deviant, similarly, may be said to be an individual who, out of irrational anxiety, rigidly refrains from one kind of behavior (such as heterosexuality) and adheres exclusively to another kind (such as homosexuality or masturbation).

By the same token, a non-sexual neurotic often becomes obsessively-compulsively attached to a given form of conduct—such as touching picket fences, keeping his room inordinately clean and tidy, or remaining thoroughly attached to his mother. And a sexual neurotic or deviant becomes obsessively-compulsively attached to a given form of sex conduct—such as copulating with women who have small feet, or who wear bloomers, or who whip him.

This does not mean that individuals cannot *logically* favor or prefer one kind of sexual (or non-sexual conduct to another. They can (Kepner, 1959). Thus, it is possible for a woman to prefer staying by herself to attending social functions or prefer being a Lesbian to being heterosexual—provided that she has, for a reasonable length of time, unprejudicedly *tried* both alternatives (that is, tried sociality *and* asociality or heterosexuality *and* Lesbianism) and then merely decided that she likes one mode better than the other.

If, however, this same woman rarely or never tries, say, social functions or heterosexuality and still insists that they are worthless, pleasureless activities, we can only surmise that she has some irrational fear of these kinds of acts and that she is compulsively attached to other activities because of her fear. Under these circumstances, we would have to think of her as being neurotic.

Moreover: even if this woman tries social functions and heterosexuality and finds them relatively unsatisfactory as compared to staying at home and being homosexual, it would be suspicious if she *always,* under *all* circumstances, rigidly sticks to her preferences. Granted that she usually may dislike social affairs, why should she always find them distasteful—especially, say, when something is to be gained, such as a job promotion, by attending one? And granted that she prefers Lesbians, why should she, in the face of suffering possible grave penalties for being homosexual, always engage in Lesbian acts and refuse more safely available, albeit somewhat less satisfactory, heterosexual affairs?

If we forget about sex for a moment and transpose the problem of deviance and neurosis into, say, the analogous problem of eating, the core attitudes behind deviation will probably become much clearer.

Suppose, for instance, that an individual who is in good physical health and has no special allergic reactions tries all kinds of foods, eats at different hours, and uses several types of crockery. He finally decides that he prefers meat and potatoes to all other foods, that he likes to eat one large meal a day, at three in the morning, and that blue plates are best for him. Under these circumstances, many of us might think this individual peculiar; but we would have no scientific grounds for calling him neurotic or deviated.

Suppose, however, this same individual insists, after little or no experimentation, that he will eat *nothing* but meat and potatoes; or that he *only* will eat at three in the morning, even if he is starving; or that he must eat *exclusively* on blue plates and cannot eat on dishes of any other color. Or suppose, if meat and potatoes are arbitrarily banned in his community and a stiff jail sentence is given to anyone discovered eating them, he *still* insists on ingesting only this kind of food and refuses to touch any other kind of easily available victuals. Or suppose that he is utterly revolted by every other kind of food except meat and potatoes and winces with disgust every time he sees others eating these other foods.

Such an individual, obviously, has a distinct, illogical *fear* of most foods, or of different eating times, or of non-blue plates. From a psychological standpoint, he is clearly abnormal, fixated, compulsive, or neurotic.

Suppose—to use an opposite example—that a person enjoys many kinds of foods but that, without really ever having tried meat and potatoes, or after trying them once or twice and finding them mildly unsatisfying, or after trying them only *after* he has convinced himself that they cannot be appetizing, he insists that these foods *must be* utterly revolting and he either never tries them again or occasionally tries them with great prejudice and keeps insisting that they are tasteless or disgusting. From a psychological standpoint, again, this person would have to be classed as distinctly phobic or neurotic.

So, too, are sexually fixated or compulsively driven people neurotic. Irrationally ignoring the *many* possible kinds of sex participation, they rigidly adhere to a single mode or two. Or, in some instances, they try a variety of sex acts (such as masturbation, homosexuality, exhibitionism, and peeping) but fearfully refrain from other common modes (such as heterosexuality).

If these people, without fear and after a fair trial, simply *preferred* one kind of sex behavior and *preferred* to eliminate another kind, that would be one thing. But when they are thoroughly *fixated* on one mode and *phobic* toward another, they are clearly afflicted with sexual deviation or neurosis.

I am reminded, in this connection, of a story told to me by Donald Webster Cory, author of the excellent book, *The Homosexual in America* (1963), and himself one of America's outstanding bisexuals, about the time when he was among a group of fixed homosexuals, one of whom was describing to the other members of the group an experiment that had been done to test the odor of used menstrual pads.

According to Cory, almost all the other members of the group turned visibly pale and showed extreme discomfiture; and several of them insisted that unless the speaker stopped his description, they would begin to retch. This is an excellent illustration, I feel, of the extreme ideological prejudice which a neurotic or a deviate can acquire against even the thought of an irrationally feared object or event (in this case, the homosexual's fear of female genitalia).

It is important, for the sake of scientific clarity, that we be utterly consistent in our definition of sexual deviation and that we eschew existing superstitions which are based on an erroneous view of animal sexuality. Thus, it is often held that, since lower animals only have heterosexual intercourse and rarely or never resort to such acts as masturbation or homosexuality, it is "unnatural" and "perverted" for man to do so. This is sheer nonsense: animals frequently masturbate and often resort to homosexuality.

Besides, the argument, that, because man is an animal, he should necessarily do what other animals do is hardly a legitimate one.

The other end of this argument is equally fallacious; that because man has a mammalian heritage (as the Kinsey researchers accurately keep pointing out) and mammals engage in all kinds of sex acts, including homosexual behavior, when humans engage in these same acts they are only "normal" and are never "abnormal" or "perverted."

This argument is partially correct in that homosexual activity *in itself* is not abnormal or deviated, since its roots are well established in man's biological plurisexual heritage. But when an individual's homosexual acts become fixated, fear-impelled, or obsessive-compulsive then, we must again insist, they are just as deviant as would be his frantically or compulsively eating, running, or making noises—all of which are also part of our mammalian heritage.

At the same time, we must not fall into the unscientific trap of viewing as "perverted"—as the writers of the Old Testament did—any sex act which is non-procreative.

We know today, as the ancient Hebrews did not, that human sexuality is designed for fun and frolic, as well as for procreative ends. If non-procreative acts actually were deviated we would have to call millions of married individuals who use contraceptives, as we noted above, sex perverts.

Even so liberal a sexologist as Van de Velde (1926) makes the mistake of defining "normal" sex behavior as follows: "That intercourse which takes place between two sexually mature individuals of opposite sexes; which excludes cruelty and the use of artificial means for producing voluptuous sensations; which aims directly or indirectly at the consummation of sexual satisfaction, and which, having achieved a certain degree of stimulation, concludes with the ejaculation—or emission—of the semen into the vagina, at the nearly simultaneous culmination of sensation—or orgasm—of both partners."

In this definition, he labels as "abnormal" any sex act which makes use of artificial means (such as a massaging device), which is even slightly sadistic, which is not always intended to end in orgasm, which is ever anything but heterosexual, which results in extragenital orgasm for either partner, and which ends in penile-vaginal copulation but not in almost simultaneous orgasm.

On every one of these counts Van de Velde is wrong. Perfectly normal and non-perverted sex behavior may *at times* be homosexual, somewhat sadomasochistic, artificially aided, undirected toward orgasm, extragenital, and non-productive of simultaneous climax. It is only when the sex participant invariantly resorts to some of the acts Van de Velde describes, and does so out of compulsive fear or hostility rather than out of moderate preference, that he can accurately be called abnormal or perverted.

If we eliminate unscientific and vague definitions of deviation, it should be clear that a human being's engaging in many acts which have frequently been labeled as "unnatural" or "perverse" may or may not constitute his being deviated.

Thus, if a male engages in homosexual activity during his teens, becomes heterosexually oriented by the time he is an adult, but occasionally (especially when he is isolated from females) re-engages in homosexual acts, we cannot justifiably call him a homosexual or a deviant.

A fixed homosexual is one who, after reaching adulthood, *exclusively* or *mainly* lusts after members of his own sex and has little or no desire for members of the other sex.

A fixed homosexual is a deviant not because he engages in inverted acts but because, out of an irrational fear of heterosexuality, he does not desire heterosexual activities. If he were truly bisexual or ambisexual and had spontaneous, non-compulsive desires for members of both sexes he would not necessarily be sexually deviant or neurotic. He might, on other counts, however, be emotionally disturbed not for having but for giving in to his bisexual desires, just as a person might be neurotic not merely for having but chronically giving in to the desire to steal when he lived in a community which severely punished thieves.

Our typical Greenwich Village type homosexuals are deviant or neurotic because they not only engage in inverted sex acts, but usually are (a) compulsively homosexual; (b) irrationally afraid of or disgusted by members of the other sex; (c) rebelliously insistent on flouting their homosexuality, in spite of the legal penalties and other difficulties which are attendant upon such flouting; and (d) exceptionally defensive about their homosexuality, usually will not admit that it is limited or neurotic, and often contend that they are better off than or superior to heterosexuals. The deviation of these homosexuals consists not in the kind of sex act they perform but the fearful and hostile *manner* in which they perform it.

As Alfred Adler pointed out many years ago (Ansbacher, 1958), the fixed homosexual who typically inhabits our metropolitan areas generally, by his entire way of living (rather than just by his sex acts), is expressing (a) an exaggerated psychological difference which he thinks exists between man and woman; (b) a more or less deep-seated revolt against adjustment to the normal sex role; (c) a tendency to depreciate females; (d) compensatory tendencies to alleviate the feeling of inferiority he feels in the face of the overrated power of woman; and (e) a display of increased oversensitivity, ambition, defiance, distrust of others, and the desire to dominate. McReynolds (1959), Cory (1958, 1963, 1964), and R. Harper (1959b), although apparently unaware of Adler's position heartily concur about the defensiveness, self-destructiveness and pseudo-creativeness of the vast majority of fixed homosexuals.

Once we define sexual deviation in the psychological manner in which we are now doing, we must be consistent and objective about whom we label as deviant. Just as we may call a person deviant because he is a fixed homosexual, so we may also, at times, have to term him deviant because he is a fixed and invariant heterosexual.

Thus, we have the cases of many heterosexuals who under *no* circumstances would consider foregoing their usual heterosexual activities for masturbatory or homosexual acts—even, for example, if they were imprisoned only with members of their own sex for thirty years. And we have many other heterosexuals who, in their marital relations, will adhere *only* to one form of activity, such as coitus with the male surmounting the female, and will under no conditions resort to petting, kissing, or other coital positions.

Such individuals, obviously, have some arbitrary or irrational *fear* of non-heterosexual or non-coital relations. Therefore, even though the form of their sex activity is perfectly "normal," their general sex outlook is deviated or abnormal.

Are we to conclude, then, that the only individual in our society who is perfectly normal sexually is one who engages in *all* kinds of activity, including heterosexual, homosexual, and animal relations?

Naturally not: any more than we would contend that anyone who did not thoroughly enjoy *all* kinds of food would be abnormal.

A *reasonable* restriction or constriction of one's sex desires and acts, in accordance with personal individualization, is only to be expected; and a reasonable channelization is also to be expected—especially in a country, such as our own, where the laws and mores actively propagandize the citizens against certain sex practices, such as homosexual activities, and in favor of other practices, such as heterosexual participations.

The fact remains, however, that when an individual in our society *completely,* under *all possible* circumstances restricts himself to one, and only one, quite specialized form of sex behavior, and when he does so not out of mere preference, after first engaging in considerable experimentation, and not because of some unusual physical anomaly but out of an arbitrary, illogical, or fear-induced notion, then he is sexually deviated or neurotic.

By the same token, an individual who utilizes several kinds of sexual outlets but who will under no circumstances even try another common kind of outlet (such as masturbation, coitus, petting, or genital kissing), is to some extent deviated, though perhaps to a lesser degree than the person who rigidly adheres to a single outlet.

If the mode of sex behavior to which a deviant rigidly is attached is a broad one, as well as one which is socially approved in the community in which he resides, then he may be relatively little deviated or neurotic.

Thus, an individual in our society who only engages in heterosexual relations, including kissing, petting, and several different coital positions but who under no conditions will ever consider masturbating or having homosexual relations, may be considered a minor deviant.

By the same token, a person who masturbates, pets, and has several kinds of heterosexual coitus but who will under no circumstances try oral-genital relations (which today are becoming acceptable among educated persons) with his or her mate is also deviated; but probably to a minor degree.

On the other hand, an individual in our society who, under normal conditions, refuses to try sex relations with members of his own sex or with animals can hardly be called deviated: since these are still highly frowned upon and legally penalized activities. At the same time, if this individual refuses, under quite *abnormal* conditions (say, on a desert island, where there is no sexual alternative) to consider having homosexual or animal relations, then we may justifiably call him a deviate—though a minor one.

We are including in our concept of sex deviation, in other words, the concepts of both *fetichism* and *anti-fetichism*. If a person is irrationally driven or inordinately compelled to do a certain limited (and sometimes bizarre) kind of sex act in order to achieve satisfaction, he is a fetichist and hence deviated. If he is fearfully or arbitrarily biased against and repelled by any kind of sex activity, particularly one that is widely accepted in his community, then he is an anti-fetichist and also deviated.

We are also differentiating, in our concept of sex deviation, between (a) sexual deviants and non-deviants and (b) major and minor deviants. All sexual deviants, we are saying, irrationally and arbitrarily narrow down their potential sex activities and either fearfully under-perform or compulsively over-perform in certain sexual areas.

Minor deviants narrow down their potentially pleasurable experiences less than do major deviants. Thus, a minor deviant may practice several modes of sex conduct (including masturbation, homosexuality, and petting with females) but may fearfully refrain from one other mode (such as heterosexual coitus).

A major deviant will tend to limit himself to one particular act (such as exhibitionism, masturbation, or homosexual relations with young boys) and to refrain from all or most other acts.

We may also distinguish between sex deviants who commit statutory offenses and those who do not. Thus, an individual who only enjoys masturbation or who only becomes sexually excited when his heterosexual partners wear pink bloomers will not normally commit any offense if he follows his deviant proclivities; while an individual who exclusively engages in homosexuality or sex relations with animals will be a sex offender if he resides in the United States or most other civilized nations. Deviants who commit actual statutory offenses will tend to be more emotionally disturbed than those who commit no such offenses—since, by resorting to illegal acts, they are putting themselves in jeopardy and therefore acting in a self-defeating manner. Many exceptionally disturbed deviants, however, never commit any statutory offense.

One other kind of possible sex deviation should be considered and that is what might be called *disordered sexuality* or *general compulsive sexuality*.

Some authorities, such as Allen (1949), Kahn (1937), Karpman (1955), and Pollens (1938), have pointed out that sex deviates, particularly those who get arrested for committing sex offenses, frequently engage in several kinds of activities. Thus, on different occasions a man may be arrested for exhibitionism, peeping, and homosexuality; and this same individual may be married and have a record of many successful heterosexual participations. Obviously, he is not fetichistic or anti-fetichistic; but just as obviously, since he keeps getting into difficulties and is often driven to commit new sex offenses, he is hardly sexually normal.

In my own experience with these kinds of deviates, both in my work as Chief Psychologist of the New Jersey State Diagnostic Center (a special psychiatric facility for examining sex offenders) and in my private practice as a psychotherapist, I have found that this generalized type of sex deviate is quite disordered or compulsive and that his disorder stems from intellectual subnormality and/or extreme emotional disturbance.

Usually, these individuals are more or less psychotic; and, just as they are driven to perform all kinds of bizarre non-sexual acts (such as senseless thefts, arson, assault and battery, and even murder) they are also compelled by their thoroughly disordered thinking to commit several different kinds of sex acts which, in themselves, may be fairly harmless but which are banned by their communities.

This type of individual with generally disordered or compulsive sexuality is significantly different from the usual fetichistic or anti-fetichistic deviant in many respects. The common ground on which they meet is that of emotional disturbance; but the usual kind of deviate may be (though not necessarily is) considerably less disturbed than the general sex deviate.

Sexual deviation, then, stems from an individual's having some illogical, irrational, childish, fixated fetichistic (or anti-fetichistic), inflexible *ideas* about what he may or may not do sexually. As such, it does not necessarily refer to his *practicing* a given form of sex behavior but to his *wanting* to adhere to a deviant mode even when alternative modes are freely available.

A person who is exclusively homosexual because there are no women available is not necessarily a deviant; but one who exclusively desires sex relations with members of his own sex, even though he actually has no homosexual activity because he fears arrest or hasn't the courage to risk rebuff by other males is, actually, deviated. An overt deviant is one who puts his fear-impelled ideas into practice; a latent deviant is one who would like to do so but for one reason or another does not.

Many psychologists and psychiatrists, particularly those of Freudian orientation, talk of "latent homosexuality" in connection with individuals who consciously believe that they are heterosexual but who unconsciously are attracted to members of their own sex. This definition of latent homosexuality is exceptionally vague and loose: since virtually all so-called normal human beings have *some* unconscious homosexual urges. The mere fact that we are all biologically bisexual or plurisexual means that, in most instances, we will *sometimes* be sexually attracted to members of the same sex; and, even, as the Kinsey figures show, that we will tend to have a few homosexual episodes during our lives.

Real latent homosexuality occurs, however, when an individual consciously feels that he is entirely or almost entirely heterosexual but when, unconsciously and actually, he has *considerable* or *almost exclusive* homosexual leanings. That such latent homosexuality exists in some individuals is certain, judging from clinical evidence; but that latent homosexuals, in the true sense of the term, frequently exist in our society is dubious.

Another classical psychoanalytical concept which unfortunately has taken wide root since Freud first expounded it (Freud, 1938) is the idea that human beings are "naturally" polymorphous perverse—meaning, that they are biologically plurisexual—and that they "normally" go through, first, the stage of masturbation, then homosexuality, and finally heterosexuality.

This theory contends that when individuals do not finally attain heterosexual orientation, but remain "fixated" on the polymorphous perverse or homosexual levels, they are deviates. It also holds that individuals have pregenital or partial sex instincts—such as those of desiring caressing, fondling, kissing, and anal contacts—and that when they remain fixated on the pre-genital levels they again become deviates—such as homosexuals, sadomasochists, exhibitionists, etc.

Although this Freudian theory has some degree of validity—since human beings are biologically plurisexual and can become fixated on some aspect of their potential sexual range and thereby become deviated—it includes a whopping untruth: namely, that there are almost invariant "normal" stages of human sexual development and that the average person goes neatly through these stages.

Actually, as I have found with many individuals seen for intensive psychotherapy and as Pomeroy (1958) has observed, some people never experience certain stages (thus, never contemplate or engage in homosexual relations); others go through certain stages in reverse (for example, first have a homosexual and *then* a masturbatory phase); still others easily flip back and forth, from one so-called stage to another (for instance, first become heterosexual, then homosexual, then heterosexual again); and some follow different patterns.

Sexual deviation, therefore, does not consist of a regression to or fixation upon an early "normal" stage of sexual development; but rather a fixation upon a distinctly limited or disordered form of sexuality at *any* stage in the individual's life. It implies (a) biological plurisexualism or the *capacity* to experience sex satisfaction in several different ways at all ages in an individual's existence; and (b) psychological fetishism, anti-fetishism, or compulsivity.

In the last analysis deviation is an arbitrary, childish, fear-inspired renunciation of some of one's innate capacities for sexual enjoyment or an equally childish rebellion-impelled refusal to exert a reasonable degree of social control over one's sex drives. Sex deviation is thus a special kind of neurosis or psychosis.

Causes of sexual deviation. Although sex deviants have been clinically and experimentally studied for the last century and there is considerable agreement among authorities as to what the basic causes of deviation are, there is also considerable remaining disagreement, particularly in relation to the causes of homosexuality.

The older authorities, such as Krafft-Ebing (1922), H. Ellis (1935), Hirschfeld (1920, 1936, 1948), Bloch (1908), Carpenter (1911, 1914), Forel (1922), Moll (1912, 1931), and W. Robinson (1912, 1929), almost universally held that homosexuality is constitutionally rooted, that homosexuals are born and not conditioned, and that hormonal and/or genic imbalances cause sexual deviation. This view, with some modification, has also more recently been expressed by Gide (1952), Baker (1959), Bauer (1934), Benjamin (1959), Brunori (1958), Curran (1938), Glass and McKennon (1937), Kallman (1952), Lang (1940), Mercer (1959), Neustadt and Myerson (1940), Newman (1936), Rosanoff (1938), Sanders (1936), Simpson (British Medical Assn., 1955), Steinach (1940), Witschi (1932, 1937, 1942), and Wright (1935, 1938, 1941).

On the other hand, the vast majority of modern psychologists, psychiatrists, psychiatric social workers, sociologists, and other professional workers are quite convinced that homosexuality and other sex deviations are not caused by hormonal, constitutional, or genetic factors but that they are the result of psychological or environmental influences. To list some of the outstanding proponents of this view would take many pages. A few of those who have espoused this psychogenic theory of the causation of homosexuality are: Adler (1917, 1939a, 1939b), Allen (1949), Allen and Broster (1938), Barahal (1940), Bergler (1956), Bieber et al, (1962), Caprio (1952), Cory (1959), Davis (1929), Dean (1936), Devereux (1937), Ferenczi (1950, 1955), Fielding (1932), Freud (1924-50, 1938), Glueck (1956), Hammer (1957), Henry (1934, 1941, 1955), Henry and Gross (1941), Hamilton (1925, 1929, 1936), Kahn (1937), Kelly (Terman and Miles, 1936), Kinsey (1941), London (1933, 1937), London and Caprio (1950), Money-Kyrle (1932), Pollens (1938),

Pomeroy (1958), Schilder (1942), Stekel (1922, 1933), Swyer (1957), West (1955), Westwood (1953, 1960); Wittels (1929).

My own clinical and scientific studies of sex deviants over the last twenty years have convinced me that fixed homosexuality is distinctly not an inborn or innate pattern of sexual behavior and that it is psychosocially acquired or learned. My main reasons for believing this are as follows:

1. *No* mode of sexuality, including heterosexuality, seems to be instinctive or innate. We are all born as plurisexual beings, who must learn to channelize our hormone-impelled sex drives into certain specific pathways; and there seem to exist no specific psychological mechanisms for insuring that they must go in one direction or another. Although the power of our sex urges is, to some extent, inherited, the direction depends on our thinking, emoting, and attitudinalizing—all of which are largely learned (Wardell Pomeroy, in Lyon, 1959).

2. Although many attempts have been made to prove that homosexuals have different kinds of hormones, enzymes, anatomical structure, or other physiological makeup than heterosexuals, all such studies, to date, have turned up absolutely no convincing evidence (Swyer, 1957).

3. Studies of human hermaphrodites have conclusively shown that no matter how physically mixed-up these individuals may be they are, in the great majority of instances, heterosexual in relation to the sex-role with which they are raised (A. Ellis, 1945; Money, 1961). If homosexuality were innate, this would not be true.

4. It is quite possible (as will be shown later) to treat fixed homosexuals with psychotherapy so that they become thoroughly interested in heterosexual activities and, in some instances, become one hundred per cent heterosexual in their orientation and sex participations. If homosexuality were inborn it would be treatable by physical medicine (which it has never proven to be); but it would be highly unlikely that a completely homosexual outlook would be changed by psychotherapy.

5. There is an enormous amount of evidence to show that homosexuality, throughout all ages and all lands, as well as among subhuman animals, significantly increases whenever (a) heterosexual relations are unavailable or

difficult to achieve and (b) homosexual relations are not condemned or punished (Bohm, 1949; Edwardes, 1959, Edwardes and Masters, 1962; Licht, 1932; Wood, 1940b). If homosexuality were truly inborn, this wide fluctuation with environmental circumstances would not exist.

6. A certain percentage of homosexuals, as Brown (1961) has shown, are not merely sexually oriented toward members of the same sex but are sex-role inverts—that is, they adopt the entire role of the other sex. Thus, we have the so-called "fairies" among male and the "butches" among female homosexuals, who often dress and act in an other-sex manner.

The feminine ways of the "fairies," moreover, and the masculine ways of the "butch" Lesbians are *more* extreme than the femininity of normal females and the masculinity of normal males. Quite obviously, sex-role inversion is not inborn but is learned, usually at a very early age.

7. Almost forty per cent of normal heterosexual males, as Kinsey and his associates (1948) have shown, at some time during their lives engage in homosexual acts. But a very high percentage of fixed homosexuals never, under any circumstances, try heterosexual acts—even though they have no real way of knowing how "disgusting" such activities would be.

Clearly, the mechanism involved in this compulsive withdrawal from heterosexuality on the part of so many homosexuals is born of strong attitudinal prejudice and is not innate.

8. As previously shown in this chapter, sex deviation, almost by definition, is a concomitant of neurosis or psychosis. And although there may be some kind of predisposing constitutional factor in emotional disturbance, there is virtually no authority today who does not believe that neurosis is largely caused by environmental or psychological factors in the early and later life of an individual. There are a few psychologists and psychiatrists such as Hooker (1957), Baker (1959), and Bell (1959), who believe that it is possible for someone to be a fixed homosexual and not to be emotionally disturbed; but virtually all professional workers who are not themselves homosexual or do not have some personal tie to homosexu-

als believe that exclusive or fixed homosexuality and some degree of emotional disturbance are synonymous.

Is there, then, no truth whatever in the theory, which has been especially propounded by Magnus Hirschfeld (1920) and recently revived by J. D. Mercer (1959) that homosexuals are constitutionally predisposed to their behavior and that, presumably because of genetic influences, they are immaturely developed in comparison to heterosexuals?

Yes, there probably is *some* truth in this theory as it applies to *some* homosexuals. In the Mercer version, this theory states that "it is a logical conclusion that the homosexual complex is only one of the deficiencies which, in sum, are characteristic of racial or individual infantilism, not atavistic—a turning backward—but a failure to develop the most advanced adult traits.

"Here we may note a very close association of traits that are characteristically infantile wherever found with traits that are characteristically homosexual: some degree of emotional instability, for instance; failure of a developed ability to fix attention. The list might be long and most illuminating."

The grain of truth in this theory probably is that many seriously disturbed individuals, especially those who are borderline and outrightly psychotic, have a biological, genetic predisposition to being infantile or disturbed; and that many (though by no means all) such exceptionally disturbed persons easily tend to acquire (especially in our antisexual society) disordered sexuality, including homosexualism.

Even if this were true, this would hardly prove, as Hirschfeld and Mercer are too eager to conclude and as Kallmann (1952) at times seems to imply, that homosexuality is *directly* congenital or inherited. Psychotics frequently take off their clothes and, if not restrained, saunter out in public in the nude. But this does not prove that they are congenital nudists.

The chances are that human sex drives are quite nondirectional in character from a biological standpoint (that is, they are bisexual or plurisexual); that normal individuals in our civilization learn, for social reasons, to channelize their non-directional drives into more or less exclusively heterosexual pathways; and that severely disturbed individuals (whether or not their disturbance is congenitally predisposed or is fully learned and acquired) frequently are not able to take the rather difficult, competitive, highly responsible heterosexual pathways but more easily fall into irregular, irresponsible, obsessive-compulsive homosexual or other deviant patterns of behavior.

Assuming that fixed homosexuality and other forms of deviation do have important psychological causes, one of the most important of these is the fact that the individual who becomes deviated, as a result of sex teachings which usually derive from his childhood and adolescence, learns to be fearful of or guilty about certain sex-love acts. And, because he has biological sex drives which usually urge him to seek *some* kind of outlet, he becomes fixated, instead, on substitute acts.

So it is that a male who learns that heterosexual coitus is dangerous or wicked may easily become fixated on masturbation or homosexuality. Or, to punish himself for having intercourse, he may only engage in it in masochistic or other limiting ways.

Even more important in many instances is the fact that the individual may be raised to be terribly afraid of being inadequate or incompetent at sex-love relations of one kind and may therefore retreat to a different kind of relations. A male may fear that he is too impotent, too ugly, too stupid, or too worthless to have satisfactory sex-love or marital relationships with females and he may therefore withdraw from the field of heterosexuality and concentrate on other sex-love modes at which he feels more competent —for example, may try being a passive partner in homosexual relations.

Again: an individual may originally have such pleasant experiences with one form of sex act (such as relations with young children) that he becomes convinced or afraid that he will not be able to duplicate these experiences with other forms of sex behavior (such as having sex relations with adults). Consequently, he becomes fixated on the early kind of conduct.

Once the individual, because of feelings of fear, shame or inadequacy, does become sexually deviated, he usually berates himself for having acquired deviant tendencies; and this additional shame and self-disparagement help him to become obsessively-compulsively fixated—just as his guilt about lying or stealing and his fear that he will not be able to stop this kind of behavior may help him become a compulsive liar or thief. Sexual neurosis, like general neurosis, thus tends to become self-perpetuating and often to become more deeply ingrained as the years pass. Finally, the individual becomes utterly convinced that he *cannot* behave other than in a deviant fashion and he discontinues all attempts to try to overcome his deviation.

The sex deviant, moreover, often unconsciously rationalizes his disturbance (as do many non-sexual neurotics) and concludes that he is as well as or even better adjusted than the non-deviated individual. If he lives in a large metropolitan area, he frequently joins a group of other "gay" individuals, conforms to the special way of life of this group, and feels socially "accepted" and even "superior" to members of the heterosexual community. Yet, underneath, because of the danger of ostracism by heterosexuals and of actual socio-economic sanctions being leveled against him, he also tends to feel unaccepted and "inferior." In consequence, he becomes woefully confused and even more disturbed than he originally was.

Because of society's persecution of homosexuals and the pernicious effects which such persecution has on many individuals, a great many homophiles keep contending (especially in such publications as the *Mattachine Review* and *One,* which are devoted to combating anti-homosexual prejudice) that social disapproval of homosexuality is the basic cause of emotional disturbance among deviants. This would appear to be rationalization and wishful-thinking. Although it is probably true that, in a perfectly permissive and non-persecuting society, individuals who engaged in homosexual acts would not feel worthless and harried, it is also true that in such a society there would be few *fixed* or *exclusive* homosexuals.

First, our society drives many human beings into sexually deviant or neurotic patterns of living. Then, to compound the felony, it persecutes them after they have become deviant and helps make them more disturbed.

There is no reason to believe, however, that any fixed homosexuals become neurotic or psychotic *only* because, once they turn deviant, society harasses them. There is more reason to believe that in some instances individuals participate in mild homosexual behavior, then feel worth-less because society excoriates this behavior, then out of their feelings of worthlessness become fixed deviants, and finally wind up by feeling even more worthless.

Although sexual deviance, as we shall show in the next section of this chapter, is by no means synonymous with homosexuality, homophilism is doubtlessly the most im-portant form of deviance in our country; since we have probably well over a million males and scores of thou-sands of females who, for most or all their lives, are exclu-sively or largely homosexual in their interests and acts.

These homosexuals, as we have been indicating, may be indirectly influenced in some instances to take up a devi-ant way of life because of their physical abnormalities (such as a male's having a feminine build) which help make them fearful of heterosexual relations and hence prejudiced in favor of homosexual activities. But, at most, this kind of physical influence is an indirect rather than a direct cause of homosexuality; and there is much reason to believe that the great majority of homosexuals cannot be distinguished physically from the majority of heterosexu-als.

Some psychological writers attribute the cause of homo-sexuality to one or two major reasons—particularly the supposed Oedipus complex reason. That is, they assume that some boys become so guilty over lusting after their mothers and afraid of being castrated by their jealous fa-thers that they thereafter cannot face any other woman sexually and consequently turn to and become fixated upon men.

There is good reason to believe, from clinical evidence, that occasionally this is true today and that fixed homosex-uals sometimes have unresolved Oedipal feelings which significantly influence their feelings of self-worthlessness and their assumption of homosexual roles.

There are, however, many other major reasons why indi-viduals become fixed homophiles. Some of these reasons include: (a) the individual's being deliberately raised by his parents to assume the role of the other sex; (b) his failure, for a number of reasons, to succeed in his own-sex role; (c) his identification with a strong parent of the other sex, particularly when his own sex parent is weak;

(d) his hostility toward or fear of members of the other sex; (e) the many difficulties he may encounter in achieving satisfactory heterosexual relations in this society; (f) his being able more easily to find love and approval from members of his own than members of the other sex; (g) his experiencing early homosexual satisfactions and his tendency to become neurotically or fearfully fixated on these immature levels of behavior; and (h) his specific or general psychological problems and disturbances, of which his homosexuality may be a mere symptom (Ellis, 1965b).

Other sex deviations, which we are about to describe in the next section, also generally have multiple rather than single causation. Usually, the deviant has severe feelings of personal inadequacy and worthlessness; feels that he cannot be successful in socially approved forms of sex activity; childishly gives in to some substitutive form of sex behavior; severely blames himself for being a deviant and becomes obsessively-compulsively attracted to repeating his perverted acts. The deviant often winds up by being thoroughly hostile and rebellious against society and its limitations and sometimes therefore becomes sadistic and antisocial in his sex outlets. Serious sex deviants, we must again insist, are hardly to be distinguished from general neurotics and psychotics except in their somewhat different symptomatology. Emotional disturbance is still at the core of their deviant way of life.

Types of sexual deviation. There are many different modes of deviation, some of which will now be briefly outlined and discussed.

Homosexuality. We shall say little here about homosexuality since we have devoted much of the previous two sections of this chapter to it. Homosexual behavior, as we have noted, is not in itself abnormal; because all of us have some homosexual tendencies and it is not unusual if we occasionally put our homophilic desires into practice. When, however, a man or a woman who theoretically has several other forms of sex activities available passes these up and largely or exclusively adheres to homosexual contacts, we may call such an individual a fixed homosexual and say that he or she is deviated.

Transvestism. Transvestism (also called transvestitism,

cross dressing, or eonism) arises when an individual, almost always a male, delights in wearing and is sexually
stimulated by clothing usually worn by the other sex.

Some authorities, such as Stekel (1922, 1933) and
Allen (1949), believe that homosexuality is the main or
primary root of transvestism and that even when transvestites do not overtly engage in homosexual activities they
unconsciously would like to do so. They point to the fact
that many transvestites are homosexuals as well—such as
the Greenwich Village type "fairies" who enjoy going to
dances in "drag" costumes.

Most modern authorities, such as Brown (1961), Kinsey, Pomeroy, Martin and Gebhard (1953), Overzier
(1958), Storr (1957), and Thoma (1957), insist that
most transvestites, including drag queens, are quite heterosexual in their inclinations but still receive a thrill when
dressing in the clothing of the other sex. Men who occasionally like to wear women's dressing robes or women
who wear men's pants for convenience rather than for sexual excitement can not legitimately be called transvestites.

As Overzier and Thoma have shown, transvestism is
not organically caused but is a psychological condition
that can be treated and cured.

Transsexualism. Harry Benjamin (1954) has coined
the term transsexualism to describe the inclination of individuals, of whom relatively much has been heard in recent
years, who not only want to dress in clothing of the other
sex but also wish to have their bodies, and particularly
their sex organs, surgically changed so that they can actually look like members of the other sex when they are
nude. Assuming that these individuals are not hermaphrodites (discussed in the next chapter) who have physical
abnormalities which can and should be surgically corrected, transsexualists are exceptionally deviated persons
who cannot stand any aspects of their own-sex role and
who fearfully and compulsively insist that they should be
surgically changed.

Actually, since there is no known method, as yet, of
truly changing the inborn sex of an individual, these
transsexualists are reaching for the moon. But still they
insist on trying to obtain surgical intervention to "change"
their sex. I have interviewed a half dozen transsexualists,
all of whom came to try to enlist my aid in finding a

surgeon who would operate on them, and have found all of them to be borderline or outrightly psychotic. This would be expected of any individual in our society who is so determined to change his sex role as to insist on artificial castration or other mutilation of his sex organs.

Exhibitionism. Normal human beings derive distinct satisfaction from exhibiting their nude bodies and genitals to others—especially to persons with whom they would like to have sex relations. When, however, an individual exclusively or mainly obtains satisfaction from exhibiting himself to others; when he does so compulsively, in spite of his own conscious wishes to refrain; or when he does so in a flagrant, illegal fashion that will almost certainly get him into difficulties as a sex offender;—he is then practicing exhibitionism in a neurotic, deviated manner. (Rickles, 1950.)

Sadism. The urge to be somewhat sexually aggressive or sadistic to one's partner, especially at those times when one is having difficulty getting fully aroused or coming to orgasm, is within the normal range of sex behavior (Dearborn, 1946). But when one *always* requires intense sadistic behavior for arousal or satisfaction or one is *intensively* and *extremely* sadistic (particularly with unwilling sex partners) one is acting in a neurotic, hostility-driven, or deviated fashion.

Sexual sadism, like most sex neuroses, often has little to do with the sex urge itself but springs from other underlying disturbances, such as a general hatred of the other sex, a need to prove that one is strong or "masculine," a desire to protect oneself against imaginary onslaughts from one's sex partners, and other aberrated ideas and attitudes.

Masochism. The desire to have some degree of physical pain inflicted upon oneself in order to aid sex gratification is another aspect of sexual normality when it is kept within reasonable limits. As soon, however, as one is unable to achieve arousal or orgasm without having fairly intense physical pain or mental humiliation inflicted on oneself, one begins to lap over into sexual deviation.

It is commonly noted in psychiatric texts that masochism and sadism tend to go together, with the sadistic individual also being masochistic and vice versa. This is sometimes true—since both sadists and masochists tend to be severely disturbed individuals who may easily have more than one symptom of their disturbance—but it is also often not true. Many sadists have little or no masochistic urges—except in the sense that, if one looks closely and psychiatrically enough at anyone—one can easily "discover" traits opposite to those which they have on the surface.

Necrophilia. A necrophiliac is an individual, usually a male, who is sexually aroused by the sight of a human corpse and sometimes tries to have sex relations with a cadaver. As in the case of necrosadists and sex murderers, necrophiliacs almost always are mentally deficient or psychotic.

Necrosadism. Nerosadism consists of sadism that is vented on corpses. Necrosadists enjoy mutilating corpses in order to excite themselves sexually or bring themselves to orgasm. Technically, if an individual only occasionally practiced necrosadism during his lifetime, he would not necessarily be a sex deviant. Actually, however, even when once performed, this act is so bizarre and would be so pleasureless to the average individual that anyone performing it should be suspected of being mentally deficient or psychotic. Statistically speaking, it appears to be an unusually rare form of sex behavior.

Sex murder. A sex murderer is an individual who finds sex arousal and satisfaction in the course of killing another individual, usually of the other sex. Like necrosadists, sex murderers are invariably in a state of extreme amentia or psychosis when they commit their acts. Although much newspaper and magazine publicity is given to sex murderers, they actually seem to be quite rare.

Many murders are committed by sex attackers or rapists, who fear detection or want to keep their victims quiet. But these individuals should not be confused with real sex murderers who kill solely in order to enhance their own arousal or satisfaction.

Fetishism. Niemoeller, in his *American Encyclopedia of Sex* (1935), gives an excellent definition of fetishism: "A condition of, or manifestation of, sexual aberration or perversion in which the patient's libido has become so fixed upon and associated with some quality, part, feature, etc., of another person, or of persons in general, or upon an article of clothing or a stuff or material, that the sexual impulses can be aroused, and often gratified, only by or in connection with the particular object or fetish in question. The fetish may be a woman's breasts, hair, feet, her odor, or any odor, a shoe, underwear, a kid glove, velvet, crystalware, etc."

Non-deviated individuals frequently resort to mild forms of fetichism in that they are notably attracted to their partner's (or anyone's) breasts, feet, biceps, underwear, etc. But an individual who is exceptionally or exclusively fetichistic is definitely deviated.

Narcissism. Narcissism exists when an individual becomes sexually excited and fulfilled mainly or exclusively from contemplating, admiring, and caressing his own body rather than that of another; or when he is continually obsessed with mirror-images or photographic reproductions of himself. Masturbation may appear to be narcissistic but it is well within the normal range of sex behavior and is definitely not a sexual deviation when practiced under usual circumstances.

Real narcissism exists when the individual prefers self-stimulation to other kinds of sex activity and thinks of himself, rather than outside persons or things, while he is masturbating (or while he is engaging in other sex outlets). Extreme narcissists seem to be rare and often are mentally deficient or psychotic.

Pedophilia. Pedophilia, originally called pederasty, exists when an adult is sexually attracted to and engages in activities largely or exclusively with young boys. Today, the term pederasty is loosely used to include anal-genital relations between grown males as well as boys and is therefore a homosexual act. Pedophilia, however, is now a more accurate term to describe a male's being obsessively-compulsively attracted to boys and is a distinct form of deviation. Most normal males probably have slight inclinations to be excited by boys; but those who have extreme, possessive-compulsive, or exclusive inclinations in this direction are sexually neurotic or deviated.

Sexual attachment to children. Sexual attachment to children is broader than pedophilia, in that it includes heterosexual and lesbian attachments as well as interests of men in boys. Some males are largely or exclusively attracted to small girls, even to infants; and some females are sexually obsessed with small boys.

Although a small element of such attraction to children

is normal, when an individual becomes unusually or mainly attracted to infants or children, he or she is definitely deviated and will prove to be neurotic or psychotic.

Gerontophilia. Just as some individuals are extremely attracted to young children, others are obsessed with older persons. Young girls, particularly, may become wildly infatuated with aged men rather than with younger boys or men. Such inclinations, when extreme or consistent, constitute sex-love deviation.

Peeping, mixoscopia, or voyeurism. Although virtually all normal humans derive some sexual excitement from viewing members of the other sex, especially when these others are in the nude, anyone who mainly or exclusively derives satisfaction from this procedure and who obsessively-compulsively engages in peeping activities, is a mixoscope or voyeur and as such is a sex deviant. Like exhibitionists, voyeurs are often individuals who are quite inhibited and who feel sexually inadequate and therefore resort to toned-down modes of sex participation instead of risking more forceful and direct modes. The Peeping Tom is usually a harmless individual but can also be a nuisance and is frequently arrested as a sex offender.

Pygmalionism. Individuals addicted to pygmalionism are largely or exclusively attracted to and aroused by statues, especially statues of nude women, and may masturbate before or defile such statues. Like many other types of deviates, they are rare.

Bestiality. Bestiality exists when an individual of either sex becomes sexually aroused or satisfied through any kind of contact with an animal. Sometimes bestiality consists of actual coitus or anal-genital relations between man and beast; but in other instances it arises when males or females take interest and pleasure in sexually stimulating animals.

A mild degree of bestiality, or even exclusive bestiality when no other sex outlets are available, is not necessarily abnormal or perverted; but when men or women become exceptionally or consistently or exclusively attracted to animals they may be called sex deviants.

Addiction to pornography. Pornography originally referred to the literature on prostitutes or prostitution but has recently come to mean the deliberate employment of sexually arousing pictorial or reading matter. An individual's becoming aroused by perusing or reading pornographic sex material is certainly one of the most common of all sex acts; and, in our puritanical society, which places a premium on open displays of sexuality precisely by banning them, any person who shows a reasonable degree of interest in pornographic representations is certainly normal and non-deviated.

When, however, a man or woman cannot become sexually excited except through viewing pornographic representations or when he or she is obsessively-compulsively addicted to viewing pornography, such a person is definitely deviated. In one post office case in which I testified in regard to alleged obscene matter it was shown that one man purchased, in a short period of time, several thousand dollars worth of photographs and drawings of nude and semi-nude women. Such an individual, though perhaps harmless, is distinctly a sex deviate (Cross, 1959).

Other sex deviations. Although most acknowledged sex deviations are rather uncommonly employed by the general populace, there are many other frequently utilized sex acts which, while *in themselves* non-deviated, may be practiced in a perverted *manner.* Indeed, *any* sex mode may under *some* circumstances be considered a deviation.

Thus, heterosexual coitus, anal-genital, oral-genital, and hand-genital relations are all perfectly healthy, non-fixated forms of sex behavior in most instances. When, however, these acts are exclusively, fetishistically, fearfully, or obsessively-compulsively performed, they may easily turn into deviations. A man who feels so guilty about having intercourse with any woman that he is afraid to look her in the eye while having it, and consequently always enters her vagina from the rear, is a distinct sex neurotic or deviate —even though he is engaging in a sex act that under *most* circumstances would not in the least be aberrated or perverted.

We repeat, then, what we previously noted in this chapter; that it is often not the *kind* of sex act that makes an individual a deviate but the *manner* in which and the *attitude* with which he performs it.

The treatment of sex deviants. Can sex deviants, including homosexuals, be successfully treated so that they overcome their aberration? Most certainly they can. Just as non-sexual neurotics can be helped to overcome their illogical fears and to think straight, so can sexual neurotics.

If sex deviants are willing to undergo and work at a psychotherapeutic process, there is no doubt that they can be helped to understand exactly why they originally became deviated, how they are irrationally maintaining their deviated tendencies, and what they can do to become non-deviated.

Many students of homosexuality have taken an extremely pessimistic view of the possibility of curing fixed homosexuals. Thus, Bredtschneider (1959), a committee of the British Medical Association (1955), Curran and Parr (1957), Freud (1924-50), Hirschfeld (1920), Mercer (1959), Vincent (1961), and the Wolfenden Report (1957) have been quite sceptical of any cures and have categorically stated that they are almost impossible.

On the other hand, an increasing number of psychotherapists have in recent years been publishing reports of successful treatments of homosexuals and some of them have presented extended case presentations to support their claims (Allen, 1949, 1952; Beiber et al, 1962; Caprio, 1952; Creadick, 1953; Fink, 1954; A. Freud, 1951; Henry, 1941, 1955; Hadfield, 1958; Harper, 1959b; Laidlaw, 1952; Lewinsky 1952; London and Caprio 1950; Maclay, 1960; Nedoma, 1951; Poe, 1952; Robertiello, 1959; Rubinstein, 1958; Shentoub, 1957; and Westwood, 1953). Other clinicians, such as Gurvitz (1957), have also presented reports of successful treatment of exhibitionists and other kinds of deviates.

As I have shown in several papers and books dealing with the treatment of homosexuals (A. Ellis, 1952b, 1956b, 1959a, 1959b, 1962a, 1963a, 1965b), the cure of deviants must be seen realistically if treatment is to be effective. From a realistic standpoint, cure does *not* consist of inducing a deviant individual to forego *all* his unusual sex interests; rather, it consists of getting him to eliminate the exclusiveness, the fear, the fetishistic fixation, or the obsessive-compulsive elements which accompany these interests.

Take, for example, someone whose exclusive or main sexual activity is voyeurism or peeping. In attempting to cure this individual, it would be silly to try to induce him to be totally uninterested in looking at unclothed members of the other sex—since the normal male in our culture has distinct voyeuristic tendencies. The therapeutic goal should be, instead, to induce the voyeur to tone down his peeping; to limit it to legally permissible situations (for example, witnessing burlesque shows); and, especially, to add to his peeping *other* sex interests, such as having heterosexual affairs.

Similarly with homosexuals. The object of the therapist should not be that of trying to induce a homosexual to forego all interests in his or her own sex; but, instead, that of helping him or her to eliminate fears of the other sex, to enjoy and eagerly anticipate heterosexual affairs, to be an effective partner in heterosexual relations, and to eliminate obsessive thoughts about or compulsive actions concerning homosexuality. In the process, some homosexuals, as I have found, actually do turn from one hundred per cent homoerotically inclined to one hundred per cent heterosexually inclined individuals; but this is not necessarily the goal of treatment.

If the treatment of deviants is looked upon from this realistic standpoint, there is no doubt that much can be done to treat deviants who wish to overcome their sexual disturbances. In many instances, moreover, individuals who are not greatly desirous of losing their deviant tendencies, but who come to psychotherapy for other reasons, can be helped to improve significantly.

In a study of forty homosexuals whom I treated with rational therapy (A. Ellis, 1956b), it was shown that sixty-four per cent of the male and all the female patients were distinctly or considerably improved; and that of the twenty patients who came to therapy with little or moderate desire to overcome their homosexual problems, fifty per cent nonetheless achieved distinct improvement in their heterosexual relations.

In a later study (A. Ellis, 1959b) of sixty-six homosexuals treated with rational psychotherapy, it was found that one hundred per cent of the bisexuals, fifty-four per cent of the fixed homosexuals, and twenty-eight per cent of the homosexual inverts (that is, "fairy" type males and "butch" type females who practiced complete sex-role inversion) were considerably or distinctly improved in their orientation toward heterosexuality as a result of therapy.

The notion, therefore, that it is impossible to cure sex deviants in general and homosexuals in particular is a myth that has largely been spread by orthodox Freudians, who follow Freud's mistaken notions in this connection, and by deviants themselves, who often *want* to believe that they were born the way they are and that there is no possibility of their being cured.

Laws against sexual deviation. Many forms of deviation, such as homosexuality, pedophilia, and bestiality, are legally banned in most modern nations and are stiffly penalized. Thus, an individual who commits, according to several of our state laws, "unnatural" sex acts or "crimes against nature" may be imprisoned for as much as twenty years (Bowman, 1958; Sherwin, 1949).

The question is: Should sex deviates be persecuted and penalized in this manner?

In the debate over the now famous British Wolfenden Report (1957), which recommended that English law be changed so that homosexuality among consenting adults not be considered a crime unless there existed other extenuating circumstances, Lord Denning asked: "First, is it wrongful? No one can doubt that, I hope. The Bible calls it 'an abomination'; the Statute Book describes it as an 'abominable crime'; and the old lawyers, when they framed their indictments, thought it was a disgrace even to name it; and it was an offence not to be named amongst Christians. So it is wrongful."

The Lord Bishop of Rochester concurred: "My Lords, may I therefore conclude by expressing the belief that the emotion and moral indignation and horror which are aroused in the human heart by the thought and contemplation of unnatural vice, and which find expression in the Holy Scriptures, both in the Old and in the New Testaments, are probably more right in teaching us our attitude towards unnatural vice than academic discussion divorced from reality."

As a result of this kind of anti-homosexual attitude, the British Parliament has as yet done nothing about implementing the Wolfenden Report, even though such a respectable body as the Assembly of the Church of England endorsed the Report (Report of Church Assembly, 1958)

and many staid British citizens highly favored its substance (Bailey, 1956). The Wolfenden committee's recommendations in regard to prostitution have been partly
acted upon by the English parliament but its recommendations regarding homosexuality have been completely
ignored.

In spite of this refusal to change laws against homosexuality, which has also been mirrored in the United States,
where the American Bar Association's recommendations
for liberalization of our anti-homosexual statutes have also
gone unheeded for the last several years, the psychological
and psychiatric answer to the question of whether sex deviates should be persecuted and penalized must be a re-
sounding: No, they should not.

In the first place, laws which punish sex deviants are
usually badly written and fail to distinguish real from
pseudo deviates. Thus, they often include as "deviation"
oral-genital or anal-genital relations between husbands and
wives. Except in unusual instances, such sex acts are not
in the least abnormal or deviated and certainly should not
be legally proscribed.

On the other hand, laws against deviation take no cogni-
zance of many clearcut deviations—such as violently sado-
masochistic relations between husbands and wives—and
are therefore woefully inconsistent. As Dr. Ralph Brancale
and I pointed out in our book, *The Psychology of Sex
Offenders* (1956), sex statutes are frequently vaguely and
poorly written; so that they fail to delineate or adequately
distinguish among deviations and offenses as seen by psychologists, sexologists, and other authorities.

Secondly, even when sex statutes properly define deviates they unjustly and unrealistically penalize these individuals. For deviates, as we have been insisting in this
chapter, are illogically fearful, neurotic (or psychotic) persons who are emotionally aberrated.

There is no question that in some instances (for example, where the deviate has forced his attentions on children
or committed a sex murder) sexually disturbed individuals
should sometimes be placed in protective custody and not
be permitted to roam around in the community. But, even
in these instances, deviates should be *treated* rather than
punished for their aberrations. If they were so treated,

many or most of them would eventually be cured of their deviational tendencies; while if they are merely jailed there is little chance of their improving.

Deviants who are arrested and convicted for their sexual behavior should be penalized, if at all, in direct relation to their offense and not in a highly emotionalized, exaggerated manner. An individual, for instance, who assaults a girl sexually should receive the same kind of sentencing as one who assaults girls non-sexually.

As Maxey (1959) has stated, "There is no more moral justification, ecclesiastic nor legal, for the punishment of homosexual acts by consenting adults, than there is for penalizing the performance of sexual acts by heterosexuals, who are not married. The only exceptions in both cases are when blackmail and fraud are involved, or acts are performed in public places offensive to decency and good behavior. If offenses involve minors (heterosexual or homosexual), men and women should be dealt with on exactly the same basis."

The main point of any sane mode of dealing with deviates is their being helped rather than punished, cured rather than ostracized (Chesser, 1949; I. Rubin, 1959c).

The fact that homosexuals and other deviants ought not be persecuted by their communities should not be confused with the false supposition that they are perfectly healthy, normal individuals who should happily keep going their deviant ways.

As Donald Webster Cory (1958), one of America's leading self-declared homosexuals, has stated, it "would be a fallacy to believe that although homosexuality is psychogenic in origin, the homosexuals are not more maladjusted, neurotic, etc., than the population at large and that where they are more disturbed it is caused by the social pressures. This is untrue and is an evaluation motivated by the fact that such a picture will presumably make the homosexual life more palatable to the public. There are great anxieties and disturbances among large masses of homosexuals—there have to be. Some people feel that giving this true picture of the situation hinders understanding between homosexuals and heterosexuals. I don't know why."

It is up to us, the public, to recognize that homosexuals

and other deviants are emotionally disturbed individuals and, precisely for that reason, as well as for general principles of justice, accord them the right to be unmolestedly sick and to be restrained only when their behavior clearly impinges on the rights of others.

Although sex deviation certainly constitutes a serious problem in our society and one that should enlist much thought and effort toward its solution, there is no point in our condemning or looking down upon deviates any more than there would be in our excoriating and penalizing non-sexual neurotics.

Deviates are usually fearful, inadequate, self-hating, unhappy individuals. Why should we make their lot harder than it already is?

Laws against other sex offenses. Not all sex offenses which are legally penalized in most civilized countries are sex deviations. Such acts as sexual assault, rape, intercourse with an underage partner (statutory rape), incest, sex relations with a minor, fornication, adultery, and prostitution are also banned and punished in various jurisdictions (Kling, 1965; Pilpel and Zavin, 1952; Ploscowe, 1951; Sherwin, 1949, 1951a, 1951b; 1952). Some sex offenders, such as homosexuals or exhibitionists, are sexually deviated, as we have indicated in this chapter; and others, such as those who commit incest, may not be deviates in the usual sense but may be psychiatrically deviated nonetheless—that is, may fearfully or rebelliously feel driven to defy a public ordinance.

Sex offenders may be divided into four main categories (Ellis and Brancale, 1956): (a) Normal offenders who are not sex deviates (for example, some individuals who commit adultery or have sex relations with slightly underage partners of the other sex). (b) Sexually deviated but psychiatrically non-deviated offenders (for example, exclusive homosexuals who remain sufficiently well integrated to pursue their sex behavior without getting into serious social difficulties). (c) Sexually *and* psychiatrically deviated offenders (for example, compulsive exhibitionists who are so disturbed that they keep getting officially apprehended). (d) Sexually non-deviated but psychiatrically deviated offenders (for example, psychotic persons who masturbate in public or walk naked in the street).

Technically, as Kinsey and his associates (1948) validly point out, so many sex acts are legally banned in our society that some ninety-five per cent of the male population at some time or other during their lives commit a sex crime. Most of these individuals are sane enough never to get into serious trouble; but if one studies convicted sex offenders one will find that they usually are quite disturbed individuals—and that their disturbance is instrumental in their being caught and convicted in many instances.

Like sex deviants, most convicted sex offenders, particularly the young ones, are definitely treatable with intensive psychotherapy (Buckle, 1949; Foster, 1947; Neal, 1959) and many of them would not have to be institutionalized if they received proper treatment in their communities. Instead of being oversexed, many of them, such as the exhibitionists and peepers, are often terribly inhibited, underlyingly puritanical individuals who have to be released from their deep-seated feelings of worthlessness and guilt (Karpman, 1954; Tappan, 1960).

The treatment of sex offenders would be immeasurably improved if our sex statutes were sensibly overhauled so that they only proscribed those acts which involve (a) the use of force or duress; (b) an adult's taking advantage of a minor; or (c) public sex acts which are distasteful to the majority of those in whose presence they are committed. Sex acts other than these, which are engaged in private between two competent adults, should not be subject to legal processes or penalties (Bowman, 1958; Ellis and Brancale, 1956).

A special kind of sex offense in many communities is prostitution, for which the procurer and prostitute, but not the patron, are usually penalized. Although prostitution in most civilized areas is significantly decreasing, because of the increase in non-prostitutional premarital sex relations, about two-thirds of white males in the United States have some experience with prostitutes (Kinsey and associates, 1948; I. Rubin, 1959).

Prostitutes, accurately defined, are not merely promiscuous or loose women but those who copulate for reasons other than sex and love satisfaction—namely, for cash (Benjamin, 1939a; Benjamin and Ellis, 1954; Benjamin and Masters, 1944; K. Davis, 1937).

Prostitution has been legally banned or regulated for several centuries; and it must be admitted that it has several distinct disadvantages (Karpf, 1953). Males who patronize prostitutes may be robbed, arrested, blackmailed, and infected. Females who serve as ladies of joy may easily fall into the pitfalls of dope, liquor, pimps, prisons, illness, and hospitalization.

Nevertheless, prostitution marches on. Some of the main reasons why males keep patronizing prostitutes include the following: (a) When premartial relations are discouraged, as they frequently are in our society, imperious male sex drives seek prostitutional outlets. (b) Many males, for various reasons, do not wish to become emotionally involved with their female partners. (c) Some males are acutely varietist in their desires. (d) Many males are too shy, inadequate, or handicapped to obtain sex partners on non-prostitutional bases. (e) Some males are semi-impotent or require sex deviations that normal girls, including their own wives, will not easily tolerate.

On the female side, girls continue to resort to a life of prostitution for gain, adventure, romantic attraction, temporary or part-time occupational reasons, and the satisfaction of various neurotic needs (Ellis and Benjamin, 1954; Greenwald, 1957). Even though it has its unsavory aspects, it is questionable whether prostitution should be totally banned. A distinction may be made in this connection between vice and crime (Benjamin, 1931; Vollmer, 1936; Harding, 1938).

Vice consists of activities which may be harmful—such as gluttony, smoking, and alcoholism—but which, nonetheless, humans have a right to engage in to their own destruction. Crime consists of activities which harm *other* human beings and which therefore should be legally restrained.

It is legitimate to combat vice with education, advertising, propaganda, publicity, etc. It is questionable whether it is legitimate to try to legislate it out of existence.

The one effective way to minimize prostitution is to minimize unnecessary sex restrictions. Contemporary sex laws and customs, by discouraging and penalizing masturbation, petting, premarital sex relations, and various other sex practices, make some amount of prostitution virtually mandatory. The more liberal these sex mores become, the less prostitution there will tend to be.

Prevention of sex deviation. The question often arises and is particularly raised by parents with teenage children: How can we prevent a boy or a girl from becoming a sex deviate? Fortunately, there are some very specific and practical answers that can be given to this question—even though, in our present society, it would be somewhat difficult to carry out these answers. Some of the prophylactic measures that can be taken in this connection are as follows:

1. Children should be raised with a healthy, thoroughly non-guilty attitude toward human sexuality. They should be taught, from an early age, that sex in all its aspects is a good and beneficial activity, as long as it does not result in one individual's specifically, needlessly, gratuitously, or forcibly harming another person or taking advantage of a minor (A. Ellis, 1963e, 1965a; R. Harper, 1959a; Harper and Harper, 1961).

2. They should be taught that some laws are necessary for the governing of sex, love, and marital relationships and that, for their own good as well as the good of others, they simply must follow these laws and rulings, no matter what their biological impulses may be. But they should also be taught that when they do not conform to certain necessary social-sexual laws, they are mistaken and self-defeating but are not blackguards or villains who should ceaselessly blame themselves for their misdeeds.

3. They should be strongly encouraged to have wide-ranging heterosexual experiences, particularly including petting to orgasm, from an early adolescent age and to be thoroughly unguilty about their heterosexual participations.

4. They should be given extensive and intensive sex education, in an objective and impersonal manner, and should be specifically instructed about sex deviations. They should be shown that, rather than being wicked and horrible, deviational conduct is childish and disturbed and that it is to be dispassionately observed and combatted rather than looked upon with horror and self-blame.

5. Above all, children and adolescents should be raised so that they like themselves, do not care overly much what others think of them, are willing to take risks of sex-love

rejection, and do not believe that they must always get exactly what they want at the moment they want it. In a word: they should be reared so that they are generally as well as sexually mature.

If this kind of sex and personality education is given to our youngsters, there will be very little danger that many of them will turn out to be serious sex deviates. And those who do become deviated can then, with relatively little difficulty, be effectively treated and cured.

14.

Sexual Anomalies and Ailments

A great many sexual anomalies and ailments exist, some of them rare and some fairly common. A number of the most important and interesting of these conditions will now be discussed.

Dyspareunia. Dyspareunia or painful intercourse is normal in some females when they are first getting used to coitus but is unusual if prolonged for more than a few weeks. In the female, it may result from various physical causes, such as a small vaginal entrance, inflammation of the sex organs, a thick or inelastic hymen, an infected ovary or tube, shrinkage of the vagina (in older females), sagging of the pelvic structure, lack of lubrication, or poor sexual technique.

As mentioned previously, Dr. Sophia Kleegman (1959) believes that about eighty-five per cent of the women who are afflicted with persistent dyspareunia have small and undetected lesions of the genital tract which are usually correctable by minor surgery or other medical measures.

Some women who are afflicted with dyspareunia make their own conditions worse by consciously or unconsciously closing their thighs tightly just prior to sexual contact because they fear having painful intercourse. They may even thereby bring on spasms of vaginismus (see below) and increase their own difficulties immensely.

Dyspareunia occasionally exists in the male and may arise from an inflamed urinary opening, a too tight or irritated foreskin, other sensitivities of the penis, or psychological causes. In both males and females, psychological origins of dyspareunia may include fear of intercourse, general tenseness, fear of pregnancy, hostility toward the spouse, and a host of similar reasons.

Any male or female who experiences pain in intercourse should first consult a medical specialist (especially a gynecologist or urologist). If physical examination discloses no reason for the pain and an attempt to employ better sex technique and lubrication does not ameliorate it, psychological consultation should be sought. The longer the condition continues, the harder it often becomes to cure it.

Vaginismus. Vaginismus consists of strong spasmodic contractions of the muscles at the entrance of the vagina and resultant blocking of penile-vaginal intromission. Like dyspareunia in females, it is not an unusual occurrence, provided that it persists only a short time after initial intercourse. If it lasts for some period of time, it is pathological and tends to have very similar causes to feminine dyspareunia. In most instances, it results from extreme fears of having intercourse and/or poor personal relations between mates. Before any self-cure is attempted, medical and psychological examination should be sought.

Priapism. Priapism, or prolonged erection of the penis or clitoris that is not accompanied by sexual desire and cannot be relieved by orgasm, is a rare anomaly. It is usually caused by neurological disease or genito-urinary irritation and may accompany such afflictions as leukemia, tularemia, sickle-cell anemia, syphilis, and multiple sclerosis. It may be mildly or intermittently experienced and in the latter case is sometimes troublesome but not too serious. In its more severe manifestations it is a serious ailment and requires specialized medical attention.

Nymphomania. Nymphomania exists when a woman has intense desire which is not relieved by intercourse or orgasm and which may drive her to near-madness. In its true form it is exceptionally rare and, like most anomalies of this type, seems to be caused by unusual conditions of neuromuscular disease.

The vast majority of women who are described in the literature as "nymphomaniacs" are nothing but highly sexed females who are quite promiscuous and whose behavior would hardly be noticed if they were males. True nymphomaniacs are seldom found outside the disturbed wards of mental hospitals.

A good number of women who are compulsively driven by their own psychological disturbances to have promiscuous sex relations exist; and many of these can be cured of their compulsive promiscuity by rational-emotive psychotherapy, as I and Edward Sagatin show in our book on *Nymphomania* (1964).

Satyriasis. The masculine form of nymphomania is called satyriasis and consists of intense, uncontrollable, and insatiable desire on the part of a male. Like nymphomania, it generally results from severe neuro-psychiatric disease or disorder. It is quite rare and requires medical treatment. What often passes for "nymphomania" and "satyriasis" (or Don Juanism) is a psychological rather than a physical disorder, where the individual keeps restlessly seeking for heterosexual acceptance and love, mainly to relieve his or her own severe feelings of inadequacy, lack of masculinity or femininity, or general feelings of emotional disturbance.

The classic Freudian position is that a Don Juan is actually a latently homosexual individual who is merely trying to reassure himself of his own masculinity. A more sensible position would be that he is an emotionally weak, though not necessarily homosexual, individual who is trying to reassure himself of how "strong" or "masculine" he is.

Dysmenorrhea. It is normal for many women to experience some amount of pain during their menstrual periods; but when this becomes quite intense or disabling it is no longer in the normal range. Dysemnorrhea, or painful menstruation, may be caused by an incomplete development of the uterus, hormonal imbalance, ovarian tumors, endometriosis, and various other pathological conditions. It calls for prompt medical diagnosis and treatment and, in some instances, for psychological consultation.

Leucorrhea. Normal females may have a small amount of discharge from their vaginas, as they secrete mucous from the walls of the vaginal tract. When this discharge becomes copious and appears as a whitish or yellowish discharge, it is called leucorrhea and is usually a symptom of some physical or emotional upset. Leucorrhea may result from a variety of causes, including infection of the reproductive tract, displacement of the uterus, erosion of the cervix, over-vigorous use of douching, venereal infection, etc. It requires prompt medical and sometimes psychological attention.

Trichomoniasis. Trichomoniasis is a common disease of the female vaginal tract and, less commonly, an affliction of the male's urethra. It is caused by an organism called trichomonas and seems to exist independently of penile-vaginal relations but may be spread by such relations. In the female it causes burning, itching, odorous discharge, and other local sensations; and in the male may cause urethritis, prostatitis, or vesiculitis. It can be cured, though sometimes with difficulty in the female, by proper medical treatment (Williamson, 1958).

Urethritis. Non-specific urethritis, or inflammation of the urethral tract which is not related to gonorrhea or other infections, is a fairly common ailment that is not necessarily sexual in origin but may be related to sex activities. Males, in particular, may develop or aggravate it by having sex relations in a violent, frequent, or under-lubricated manner. It is usually symptomatized by a light colored, moderate discharge from the meatus and by itching, burning, or mild pain at urination. Under proper medical treatment, it usually clears up within a short time.

Anyone who has a tendency toward urethritis should give some thought to adapting his or her coital or extracoital relations so that minimum irritation to the meatus and urethra is caused.

Cystitis. Cystitis, or inflammation of the bladder, sometimes occurs in females (and occasionally in males) as a result of irritation of the genitals from too violent intercourse or of the transmission of an infectious organism from one partner to another. "Honeymoon cystitis" sometimes occurs after somewhat violent defloration of the bride by the groom. It is usually not a very serious ailment and can easily be treated by a competent physician.

Cryptorchidism. Cryptorchidism or cryptorchism occurs when a male has one or two undescended testicles. If both testicles are undescended, atrophy, and lose their sperm producing and hormone producing functions, the male may develop eunuchoidism, or absence of the major masculine physical characteristics. Where only one testicle is undescended, no important consequences may result and the male may be quite potent and fertile.

Cryptorchidism may often be successfully treated by waiting for the male's testicles to descend (if he is quite young when the condition is discovered), by hormonal treatments, or by surgery.

Prostate gland trouble. Prostate gland trouble, especially enlargement of the prostate, is common in men who are past the age of sixty and much less common in younger men. It is usually benign but may in some instances be the result of cancer and should consequently receive prompt medical attention.

The main signs of prostate trouble are urgency, frequency, and smarting in connection with urination. There may be partial urinary obstruction, incomplete emptying of the bladder, and bleeding (Hirsch, 1952). Other effects, such as uremia and high blood pressure, may also set in.

Recent findings (Kaufman and Goodwin, 1958) indicate that prostate gland enlargement may possibly be the result of too much female sex hormone (estrogen) and insufficient male hormone (androgen) being produced by afflicted males. Treatment by androgen-estrogen therapy and other measures is often effective; and in some instances surgery is indicated.

Eunuchoidism. A eunuch is an individual who once possessed regular descended testicles but who has had them surgically or accidentally removed (or who, occasionally, is the victim of congenital atrophy). If castration occurs before he has reached puberty, he usually fails to develop some masculine characteristics and remains sexually neuter. He is also sterile. If his castration occurs after puberty, he will become sterile but may retain most of his masculine characteristics and may remain sexually potent for some time.

A eunuchoid is an individual who is almost a eunuch. He has testicles, which may or may not be descended, which are immature, atrophied, diseased, or otherwise decidedly under-functioning. Such individuals usually have sex and other hormonal imbalances, particularly deficiencies of the gonadotropic function of the pituitary gland. They can often be helped to function more adequately and to develop masculine characteristics by hormone injections or implantation.

Hermaphroditism. Normally, when a human being is still in its early developmental stages in its mother's uterus, it has an undifferentiated set of sex organs. After it is six weeks in the embryo stage, hormonal changes take place which cause the male's organs to develop into a penis, testicles, scrotum, etc., and the female's to develop into a vagina, clitoris, vulva, etc.

Occasionally, however, something goes wrong with the embryonic development so that a child that should have developed into a "pure" male or female actually takes on characteristics of both sexes. Thus, it may grow into an adult who, internally, has ovaries and a uterus but, externally, has a penis. Or it may become a person who has a penis-like organ as well as a vagina.

Individuals who have some of the major characteristics of both sexes are called hermaphrodites. In the older methods of classification, individuals who have both ovarian and testicular tissue were called true hermaphrodites and those who have only ovaries or testes but have peculiarities in regard to their genitals or reproductive organs were called pseudohermaphrodities.

Recently, it has been found that there are many factors other than the structure of the gonads that influence the sexual conditions of hermaphrodites (and non-hermaphrodites); and consequently there are many new classifications of hermaphrodites (Jones and Scott, 1958; Money, 1961; Moore, 1959) and still more are likely to be added as new data accumulates.

The latest findings indicate that the sex of an individual depends on at least seven basic factors: (a) the arrangement of the chromosomes; (b) the structure of the gonads; (c) the form and structure of the external sex organs; (d) the form and structure of the internal sex and reproductive organs; (e) the functioning of the sex hormones; (f) the sex in which the individual has been reared; and (g) the sex which the individual adopts and applies to himself. If there is agreement or consistency among the first five of these factors, the individual is a normal male or female; if there is disagreement or internal inconsistency among them, he is an hermaphrodite. If the first five of these characteristics agree but the last two differ from these five, the individual is physiologically a male or a female but, for psychological reasons, he will be a homosexual, a transvestite, or some other kind of sex deviant.

Instead of being homosexual or bisexual, as one would expect if homosexuality were physically caused, the great majority of hermaphrodites are actually heterosexual in relation to the way they were originally raised (A. Ellis, 1945; Money, 1961). That is to say, if an hermaphrodite is raised as a girl, even though he only has testicular tissue and has genitals that are largely masculine, he will very likely be attracted only to males; and, if an hermaphrodite is raised as a boy, even though only ovarian tissue is present, he will very likely be attracted only to females. This is one of the best existing proofs that only the power and not the direction of the sex drive is innate or inherited.

Hermaphrodites normally are created during the first six weeks of their lives, when they are still in utero. In some instances, however, after a child is born it may suffer from a tumor of the outer layer (cortex) of the adrenal gland, which results in a large amount of male sex hormone being thrown into the blood stream. This may cause precocious sexual development in boys, so that a child of four or five years acquires adult-size sex organs and desires; or, in females, it may cause virilism—the development of male body hair, voice, an enlarged clitoris and other male characteristics (Allen and Broster, 1938; Jones and Scott, 1958).

Hermaphrodites can often be surgically and medically helped to become more like one sex than the other. Thus, an individual who has both a penis and a vagina, and who would rather be female than male, can have the penis removed and be given female hormones to aid in her feminine development. Or, if this individual would rather be male than female, he can have his vagina sewn up and can be given male hormones.

Some well publicized cases of individuals who are "changed" from men to women, or vice versa, are really cases of transsexualists (see Chapter 14) who are genitally and reproductively normal but who, because of serious personality disturbances, feel an overwhelming desire to belong to the other sex and to dress and act like members of this other sex. These are not hermaphrodites but psychologically aberrated persons who cannot bear to live in accordance with their genetic sex role.

Genital injuries. All kinds of injuries can occur to the male or female genitalia as a result of accident, criminal abortion, childbirth, disease, etc. Occasionally, such injuries may be caused by sex relations, as by very forceful coitus.

Usually, the vagina is such a distensible organ and the penis so well constructed that the most vigorous kind of intercourse will not lead to genital injury. Even when the male has a large penis and the female a relatively small vagina, injury through regular copulation will rarely occur.

At the same time, there are a few individuals whose genitals are relatively fragile or who are built so that they can be harmed by vigorous sex relations. There are also other persons who, when they are savagely and sadistically attacked in the course of coitus, may be genitally injured. A reasonable amount of care in this connection, especially by those who are predisposed to physical injury, will assure that difficulties of this sort will rarely occur.

Crab-lice. Crab-lice are insects related to head lice, which sometimes fasten on the genital parts, particularly the pubic hair, and are acquired from coitus with an infected person. They lead to severe itching and scratching, but may usually be eliminated by using benzyl benzoate preparations mixed with a little DDT or other medication applied under medical supervision.

Infantilism. A certain number of males and females are psychosexually immature because of improper functioning of their hormones. The hypogonadal individual may be normal in structure or may be dwarfed or physically disporportioned. Such an individual often has some degree of under-development of his or her genitals and/or reproductive system.

In mild cases, infantile individuals are fairly normal sexually, even though they may sometimes be infertile. In more severe cases, they have little or no libido. If discovered sufficiently early, some of these persons can be treated with hormone injections and many overcome their infantilism to some extent.

Penis captivus. Penis captivus, or the capture of the penis by the vagina so that the male cannot release himself, is supposed to occur from time to time but is so rare that few authentic cases can be found in the sexological literature. Although it is theoretically possible for a woman to have a vaginal spasm that will catch her partner's penis at its base and, by thus constricting it, prevent this partner from losing his erection, this is not likely to happen because virtually every male so caught would lose his erection out of fear or annoyance and would easily be able to withdraw. A number of males, nearly all of whom are severely emotionally disturbed, *fear* penis captivus; but virtually none actually experience it. In many years as a sexologist and psychologist, I have never come across a single authentic case.

Venereal diseases. The main veneral diseases that afflict human beings are gonorrhea and syphilis; although several relatively less prevalent ailments, such as chancroid, yaws, granuloma inguinale, and lymph-granduloma venerum, exist and are at times troublesome.

Both gonorrhea and syphilis are almost always spread by direct sexual contact; as the organisms that cause these diseases are quickly killed when exposed to air or water. Gonorrhea may be non-sexually transmitted to young females, whose vaginal mucous membrane is thin; and, more frequently, syphilis is transmitted by non-genital contact, such as kissing or touching an individual who has the disease and who has an open sore from which syphilitic infection may be transmitted.

The first signs of gonorrhea are usually evidenced about two to five days after exposure. The male tends to feel pain upon urinating and to have a discharge, sometimes blood-tinged, from the penis. The female sometimes is completely asymptomatic at first; but may have painful and frequent urination, itching and burning of the vulva, and discharge from the vagina and urethral opening. Medical diagnosis is made from a microscopic examination of smears and cultures taken from the urinal canals, which reveal that the cause is the gonococcus.

Early syphilis, in its primary phase, usually starts with a painless sore, called chancre, which develops at the spot where the individual becomes inoculated and which generally appears from twelve to forty days after infection. The chancre tends to heal slowly, in three to eight weeks. Secondary syphilis, when the spirochetes which cause the disease have been disseminated through all the tissues of the body and start producing lesions, may lead to many ailments, including malaise, persistent headache, nausea, vomiting, deafness, hoarseness, and several types of skin lesions.

Late or tertiary syphilis usually occurs years after the original infection and may result in the involvement or destruction of many different parts of the body, such as the skin, the cardiovascular system, the skeletal system, and the central nervous system (Blau, 1961).

The best way to avoid becoming infected with syphilis or gonorrhea is to avoid sexual contact with individuals of the other (or same) sex who are likely to have these ailments. Today, these types of venereal disease are rare among non-promiscuous individuals from middle class and professional backgrounds. They are more common among promiscuous persons from lower class backgrounds—especially, among common prostitutes or men who frequent these types of prostitutes. If, therefore, one restricts one's sex activities to fairly well educated persons who are known to restrict their sex participations to relatively few partners, one has little chance of contracting any venereal disease.

The second best way to avoid venereal infection is to employ a condom with all partners one has reason to suspect might be infected. The male should insist on using a condom when having sex relations with any girl he does not know very well; and the female should insist on the man's using one when she has any reason to suspect that he might have syphilis or gonorrhea. Venereal disease can still be caught even though one uses a condom but the risk is considerably reduced.

The third way to avoid venereal infection is, under medical supervision, to take a penicillin tablet or other suitable drug prior to sexual contact and to wash the genitals thoroughly with soap and water after contact (Blau, 1961).

Treatment of syphilis or gonorrhea is a medical problem, which usually involves the administration of penicillin or other antibiotics. Anyone who thinks that he or she may be infected should immediately receive medical therapy.

15.

Fertility and Sterility

Conception occurs in women when the male ejaculates semen into the vagina and when some of the sperm contained in this succeed in swimming upward into the womb and passing through the womb into the woman's fallopian tubes. Impregnation can also occur when semen is deposited at the vulva, outside of the vagina, and sperm make their way into the vaginal canal and into the womb; but this is uncommon.

Before she can be impregnated, a woman must go through the process of ovulation: which means that from one of her two ovaries, which lie on each side of the womb and next to her fallopian tubes, she must release an ovum or egg, generally once every menstrual cycle, usually around the middle of the cycle (or between the twelfth to sixteenth day in a twenty-eight day cycle).

The sperm cells from the male's semen tend to concentrate in the upper part of each of the female's fallopian tubes after these sperm have passed through her womb; and when the egg or ovum enters one of these tubes it is met by one of the sperms, which then adheres to and penetrates and thus fertilizes it.

The fertilized ovum then passes into the uterus and attaches itself to the special lining which has been prepared for it during each period by the female's hormonal cycle. There it begins to subdivide and resubdivide into many more cells, which keep growing and dividing to form the embryo which is later to be born as a child.

Toward the end of carrying the embryo for nine months and feeding it through a membrane called the placenta with nutrients from her own body, the female usually begins to experience labor pains, or contractions, which are set in motion by one of her reproductive hormones. As these continue for a while, her uterus or womb keeps contracting and finally expels the foetus, or unborn child, through the cervical opening (which widens considerably for this purpose) and through the vagina into the outside world. This is the process of childbirth.

In order for conception to take place, therefore, and to lead to childbirth, several events must occur: (a) The male must produce healthy spermatozoa and ejaculate these in sufficient quantities into the vagina of the female. (b) These sperm cells must be sufficiently motile to wend their way to the fallopian tubes of the female. (c) The vaginal tissues and mucous secretions of the vagina and cervix must be prepared to help the survival and movements of the sperm. (d) The female must produce a healthy egg or ovum and this must be ejected into her fallopian tube. (e) While in the tube (where it stays only for a day or two) the egg must meet and be penetrated by a vigorous sperm cell. (f) The impregnated egg must move into the uterus and attach itself to its wall or lining. (g) It must receive sufficient nourishment while so attached to be able to keep dividing and growing. (h) It must remain attached to the wall of the uterus for approximately nine months and continue to receive adequate nourishment through the placenta attached to the mother's uterus. (i) It must finally be expelled safely through the cervical opening into the vagina and then through the vaginal opening into the world.

There are many processes, then, which have to take place before proper fertilization and full-term pregnancy can occur; and each of these processes tends to have many biochemical details as requisites for its proper completion.

In consequence, if any of these basic processes or any of their major details are seriously interfered with, fertilization will not take place; or the foetus will be destroyed before it reaches full growth; or it will finally be born but in a deformed or monstrous way (Masters, 1957a).

There is a common misconception that a woman cannot

conceive if she does not have an orgasm. This is not true. Orgasm capacity and fertility may have something in common—since women who are exceptionally tense because they do not obtain orgasm or do not come to climax because they are tense may also be so neuromuscularly taut as to produce spasms of the fallopian tubes or other parts of their reproductive apparatus and therefore may remain infertile. But there are many frigid women who become pregnant, so that there is no clearcut relationship between frigidity and infertility (Cesar and Dubcovsky, 1957).

Because of all the complications involved in the process of conception and birth, the fertility of different women varies enormously. It sometimes requires many acts of coitus, without the use of any birth control measure, for an egg cell to be properly inseminated; and in about ten per cent of the times when ova are fertilized they do not, for one reason or another, achieve maturity but produce foetuses which are spontaneously aborted before childbirth occurs.

When a couple tries to have children but does not succeed, we say that this couple is infertile. Infertility may arise because either the male or female has some incapacity or difficulty. The main causes of infertility in the male are diseases (such as mumps or gonorrhea), penile defects, undescended testicles, and hormone deficiencies.

The main causes of female infertility are diseases, tumors, hormone deficiencies, injuries, vaginal anomalies, infantile organs of generation, disease or atrophy of the ovaries, closure or obstruction of the fallopian tubes, impenetrable hymen, vaginismus, overacid condition of the vagina, and partial closure of the cervical opening.

In some instances, neither of the mates is absolutely infertile but both are relatively so: which means that they are not able to have children with each other but may possibly conceive with other partners. In the majority of instances, it is probably the wife rather than the husband who tends to be absolutely infertile; but in perhaps forty per cent of the cases it is the husband.

Infertility should not be confused with sexual inadequacy. A sexually inadequate male may have difficulty impregnating his wife because he is not able to ejaculate semen into her vagina; but if his semen were otherwise conveyed to her uterus (for example, by placing it on a vaginal tampon and inserting the tampon at the entrace of her cervix), he might prove to be perfectly fertile. On the other hand, many men who are entirely adequate sexually are unable to impregnate their wives because their sperm cells are absent, deficient, or dead.

It is also possible—though difficult to prove with certainty—for a man or woman to be infertile, not for any physical reason but because of psychological disturbance. Thus, as noted before, a woman, because of emotional upset, may have spasms of her fallopian tubes which produce temporary infertility.

Husbands and wives who desire children and who have proved to be infertile for two years should go for medical examination to determine what the cause of their infertility is. A microscopic examination of the male's sperm can determine whether he is producing a sufficient number of seed cells and what is the condition of these cells. If he shows deficiencies in this respect, he can sometimes be successfully treated with hormone injections or other medical measures.

It was once thought that too frequent intercourse was a cause of a male's producing few or poor sperm cells; but it has been found (Lampe and Masters, 1956) that frequent coitus is only likely to affect the sperm production of the infertile rather than the relatively fertile male.

Examination for female infertility is usually more complicated than examination of the male, as women may have a number of conditions which interfere with their ability to conceive or carry a pregnancy to completion. Their hormones (which include several sex and reproductive hormones) may not be secreted or functioning properly; their tubes may be blocked; their wombs may be too severely tipped, etc. Consequently, fertility examination and treatment of women may include hormone assays; taking their temperature regularly to see if and when ovulation is taking place; blowing out their tubes; lifting their wombs back into place; hormone injections; dilation of the cervix, etc. (Hotchkiss, 1952; J. Rosen, 1952).

Facilitating fertility. Assuming that a husband and wife have been thoroughly examined and found not to be absolutely infertile but that the wife is still having trouble conceiving, the couple may try the following procedures to increase their chances of conception:

1. Husband and wife should keep in as good physical condition as possible, obtaining sufficient rest, proper diet, exercise, fresh air, etc.

2. In some cases coital relations should not be had too frequently but should be spaced every few days.

3. Coitus should be engaged in mainly around the middle of the woman's cycle or around the time of ovulation, after a short period of abstinence. This time can be calculated by keeping track of several cycles and seeing when the midpoint is likely to occur. Some women notice their own ovulation by experiencing a slight twinge of pain (mittelschmerz or middle-pain) at this time at the right or left side of their lower abdomen.

In almost all cases a woman's temperature drops slightly the day before ovulation and rises somewhat radically, sometimes two degrees or more, on the day of ovulation. If, under medical supervision and with the use of a special thermometer designed for this purpose, a woman keeps exact records of her temperature she can often determine just when ovulation occurs.

4. Coital positions may be used which favor fertilization. The face to face position with the woman lying on her back and her hips elevated slightly may be the best position for most couples. After intercourse, the wife should hold this position for several minutes, sometimes with a pillow under her buttocks, so that the semen will not flow out of the pool near the cervix (Dickinson, 1950).

5. In cases where both mates are fertile but there is some condition preventing the male's sperm from entering the cervix, artificial insemination may be resorted to. Artificial insemination using the husband's sperm (A.I.H., as it is called) is done by a physician by collecting sperm from the husband and injecting it at the mouth of the wife's womb (Lehfeldt, 1961a).

6. In cases where the female is fertile but the male infertile, artificial insemination using an outside donor (A.I.D., as it is called) may be done. In this event, a suitable donor is selected by the physician and his sperm cells are injected at the mouth of the womb. Artificial insemination

using a donor may lead to some legal difficulties in certain countries or various states of our own country; but it is nonetheless used in thousands of cases every year.

7. Since sterility in some instances may be the result of psychological factors, psychotherapy may be indicated for husband and wife, particularly the latter, and may prove to be effective in a number of instances (Bos and Cleghorn, 1958).

16.

Pregnancy

As we previously noted, pregnancy occurs when one of the many millions of sperm cells which are contained in a normal male's ejaculate reaches the female's fallopian tubes and penetrates the egg. The fertilized egg then begins to divide and grow until the foetus that it produces is sufficiently developed to come to birth.

Signs of pregnancy. There are several signs of pregnancy, none of which is entirely infallible but some of which are quite reliable:

1. Usually, a woman stops menstruating when she becomes pregnant. Occasionally, however, women keep menstruating during their pregnancies. And quite often women stop menstruating temporarily for a variety of reasons other than pregnancy—such as illness, anxiety, hormonal imbalance, or living under conditions of stress. Many women who stop menstruating for these reasons are not pregnant; and some, in fact, are sterile.

2. Often, women become nauseous, ill, and irritable during the first few months of pregnancy and develop so-called "morning sickness." Many women, however, feel wonderfully healthy all during pregnancy; while other women develop "morning sickness" for psychological reasons even when they are not pregnant.

3. As pregnancy develops, a woman's abdomen, which is distended by the growing foetus, normally begins to swell. On the other hand, some women (especially tall ones) swell very little during the first five or six months of

pregnancy; while many non-pregnant women swell considerably, because of increased weight, abdominal tumors, or other conditions. It is even possible for a woman to have pseudocyesis, or false pregnancy, in the course of which she swells enormously and seems certainly to be carrying a child but actually is not pregnant.

4. Several tests, such as the Ascheim-Zondek and Friedman tests, are usually diagnostic of pregnancy. In these tests, urine from a woman is injected into a mouse, rabbit, rat, or frog; and the animal is observed to see if significant changes, caused by hormone substances excreted in the urine of pregnant females, take place. Blood serum may be similarly employed. Urine and blood tests can show diagnostic results in a few hours or a few days, depending on which type of test is employed. The tests give accurate results about two weeks after conception has occurred or ten days after a missed period.

Urine specimens should be taken before breakfast and consist of at least four ounces of urine. The specimen should be delivered to the laboratory or physician's office in a well washed bottle or other container, be kept cool, and have about three drops of Tricresol, lysol, or creolin added as a preservative if it is to be sent some distance or tested some length of time after being taken.

Pregnancy tests today are quite reliable, as they show pregnancy in about 98 per cent of the cases if they are positive. If they are negative, however, there is still a slight possibility that the woman may be pregnant.

5. Examination by a gynecologist can often reveal whether a woman is pregnant three weeks or more after conception has occurred. This kind of examination, however, is also not infallible; as various conditions (such as obesity, retroverted uterus, or a tumor of the uterus or ovary) may make diagnosis difficult. A combination of a gynecological examination and a properly evaluated test is the most reliable means of early diagnosis.

6. About four to five months after she has conceived, a woman may feel the foetus moving around inside her. A physician can then use a stethoscope to listen to the heart beats of her unborn child; and at this time an absolutely certain diagnosis of pregnancy is warranted. Prior to this time, diagnosis may be reasonably certain but not absolutely sure. (Guttmacher, 1955).

Because of the possibility of misdiagnosis, it is most important that any woman who thinks that she is pregnant undergo a thorough medical examination, often including pregnancy tests, before she assumes that she actually is. Particularly in cases where, for one reason or another, it is necessary to bring the pregnancy to a halt (as in cases where the woman is not able to bear a child because of some severe physical or emotional disturbance), it is absolutely necessary that a correct diagnosis be made.

For lack of such a diagnosis, hundreds and perhaps thousands of unnecessary "abortions" occur each year because it was assumed that a woman was pregnant when actually she was not.

Interruption of pregnancy. Normally, a pregnancy will continue for about nine months, when a full-term child is born. Sometimes, however, a woman is not able to carry her child to full-term and the foetus is prematurely ejected from the womb, resulting in what is called a miscarriage. Women who have tendencies toward this kind of spontaneous miscarriage should be under strict medical attention. If, on their physician's advice, they avoid strenous activity and take prescribed hormones or other medication during the first months of pregnancy they usually can be helped to carry their children to normal labor (Javert, 1959; Masters, Maze and Gilpatrick, 1957).

From time to time, women will carry their embryos almost to full term but then have a premature labor and delivery, six, seven, or eight months after conception. Such premature births were previously quite hazardous to the child. Today, however, with modern incubation methods, it is usually possible to keep a premature infant alive with little or no ill effects.

When a pregnancy is artifically interrupted, an abortion results. Most civilized nations of the world, for various reasons, have strictly forbidden such artificial interruption of pregnancy except under unusual conditions, as where the life of the mother would be endangered if pregnancy were not interrupted.

At times, the Soviet Union has been liberal about legalizing abortions and at other times strict. The Scandinavian countries tend to be most consistently liberal in this respect but even they do not cavalierly accept abortions (Tietze, 1959b). At present, legal abortions are quite inexpensive and easy to obtain in Japan and over a million officially reported abortions may be done in a single year.

In spite of the legal restrictions that are usually placed on abortion, several million abortions appear to occur throughout the world every year because women, often for economic reasons or because they are not married to the fathers of their unborn children, prefer not to complete their pregnancies (Devereux, 1955; Van Emde Boas, 1952).

In the United States, one highly-qualified and professionally-minded physician, G. Loutrell Timanus told a conference on abortion that he had, in a period of thirty years' practice, performed 5,210 abortions himself. He also estimated that another physician whom he personally knew performed about 40,000 abortions over a period of fifty years of practice (I. Rubin, 1959a). For the United States as a whole, it is impossible to estimate the exact number of abortions that take place but the figures range from 200,000 to 1,200,000 a year, with many authorities inclined to accept the larger figure (Calderone, 1958; H. Rosen, 1954; Rongy, 1933).

Many women, before resorting to criminal abortion, try to use mechanical methods of self-abortion, such as hot baths, strenuous exercise, horse back riding, and violent coitus. Others resort to hormone injections. Still others employ drugs, such as laxatives, massive doses of quinine, or ergot derivatives, which are not too effective and which, whether or not they work, are often dangerous.

A few women, out of sheer desperation, resort to self-induced abortions, which they perform with long needles, skewers, hatpins, and other instruments, often with tragic consequences to themselves and their embryos (Mozes, 1959d). Most women who wish to end their pregnancies artificially resort to illegal abortions by mid-wives or physicians.

Under these conditions, where non-medical or illegal medical aid is sought to induce abortion, serious damage may be done to mothers and their unborn children. Consequently, there have been many attempts to legalize abortion or at least to minimize present-day restrictions on it; since an abortion done under hospital conditions by a competent physician will not normally result in infection, sterility, or any of the other undesirable results of criminal abortion.

Recently, the American Law Institute approved a proposal to permit legal therapeutic abortion, under controlled conditions, for the sake of the mother or the unborn child. All such attempts to liberalize abortion codes have failed and will probably continue to fail in the near future, largely because of highly emotionalized attitudes on the part of the opponents of legalized abortion. Under the circumstances, where a couple heartily desires to avoid bearing children, a rigid adherence to proper birth control technique (which is discussed in the next chapter) is most advisable.

In the United States, therapeutic abortion may be legally performed if a woman's life is seriously endangered by her having a full-term pregnancy. Although medical opinion in this respect is more liberal than it was in past years, legal and religious opposition is still considerable, so that therapeutic abortions are actually relatively rare (Lehfeldt and Ellis, 1959).

Sex determination. For many centuries, men have been trying to discover how to determine the sex of a child before it is born and how to influence what its sex shall be before it is conceived. The first of these questions appears to be virtually solved today, as independent researchers abroad and at home have recently discovered almost foolproof tests of the sex of an unborn child.

The second of these questions—how to determine the sex of a child before conception—probably will also be solved eventually. Whether such knowledge, when it exists, will be put to good use is more questionable.

For many prejudiced reasons, parents often want a boy or girl; and, when their prejudices are intense and profound they are usually emotionally disturbed and would hardly make the best parents for either a male or a female child. Under such circumstances, it would be best for them to seek psychological aid rather than chemical means of determining the sex of their children.

Influence of mother's experience on the child. It was once thought that whatever the mother might do when she was bearing a child would seriously affect her offspring. Then medical opinion swung to the other extreme and held that nothing a mother might do, except injure herself severely or partake of a poor diet, would affect the foetus.

Today, opinion has swung back somewhat to the earlier position: for we believe that severe emotional upsets on the part of the mother may have some effect on her health and her autonomic nervous system and hormonal secretions. Since products from the mother's body may reach the foetus through the placenta, it is possible for her severe emotional upsets to affect her child. Belafsky (1958) has indicated that fear and guilt during her pregnancy may cause many of the physical ills and complaints that occur at this time. And Peer (1958) has shown that maternal stress during pregnancy appears to be a more important factor than heredity in the cause of birth defects in the infant.

In consequence, it is wise for the mother to see that she keeps in the best possible physical and emotional condition while she is pregnant. If there are any unusual influences in her life at this time, she should try to eliminate them. If she cannot manage to remain relatively free from severe emotional disturbances, she should seek psychological aid.

Genetic and eugenic influences. A child is not only influenced by his prenatal and post-birth environment but is also importantly affected by the genes that he inherits from both his parents. In certain instances, if serious inheritable diseases exist in the family background of the wife or husband, there is a high probability that the child will be predisposed toward such diseases.

Some child fatalities may be secondary to inheritance. Thus, every person is born with an RH-positive or RH-negative type of blood. If the mother is RH-negative and her child is RH-positive anti-bodies may form in the mother's blood and may be transmitted to the child so that it is born with erythroblastosis. The RH-factor can easily be checked as soon as a woman is pregnant; and suitable medical measures can usually be taken to overcome any pernicious influences that may derive from it.

Other genetic factors, however, cannot so easily be overcome in many instances. Couples who have reason to suspect that there is a dangerous hereditary streak in either of their families should go for competent genetic counseling and should, on the basis of this counseling, decide whether it is advisable for them to have children.

Since child-bearing is an exceptionally important responsibility, the more information parents gain in this respect the happier they and their offspring are likely to be (Hammons, 1959; Scheinfeld, 1956).

17.

Birth Control Methods

Eventually, there is bound to come into existence a perfectly safe, foolproof, easy to use method of birth control; but that day is not yet. At present, the proper use of birth control devices, particularly in the case of a woman, is largely a problem of medical instruction and should be worked out by each couple through consultation with a physician (Lehfeldt, 1961b). Consequently, no overly detailed instructions in this regard will be given in this chapter, but merely a serviceable outline of available techniques. There are several major kinds of contraceptive methods available today and these will now be briefly discussed.

Male instruments. The main male instrument of birth control is the condom or sheath (popularly called a "rubber"). This is usually made of rubber or animal skin. Rubber condoms are small sleeve-like jackets which are first rolled up and then rolled onto the penis. They are usually put on the penis when it is erect; but it is also possible, in many instances, to roll them on to the unerect penis and thereby to prepare for intercourse before love play starts, rather than interrupt this play for donning the condom.

Condoms may be tested, to see if any holes exist, by filling them with water or blowing them up like a balloon, to see if any air escapes. It is often advisable to put a little lubricant, such as K-Y surgical jelly or spermicidal jelly, on the inside and outside of the condom before placing it on the penis; otherwise, lack of sensation may result

(Lewin and Gilmore, 1951). It is also advisable to leave a little loose end at the tip of the condom, instead of rolling it tightly on the penis, as rubber condoms may burst if there is no space in which semen may accumulate after ejaculation.

If rubber condoms are of first-class construction, they may often be washed and dried after intercourse, rubbed with talcum powder on both sides, and rerolled and stored for future use. They may then be tested again just prior to re-use.

Condoms made of animal skins are put on when wet, instead of when dry, and are often used repeatedly before disposal. Most men find them less convenient than rubber sheaths but some find them preferable, particularly because they tend to interfere less with penile sensation.

To have maximum contraceptive effectiveness, condoms should normally be used in conjunction with a spermicidal jelly—which may be applied on the outside or inside the tip of the condom and may serve as a lubricant as well. Or else a condom can be used in conjunction with chemical methods, the so-called safe period, or other methods outlined below. Used entirely by itself, it is a reliable but hardly a foolproof method of birth control. It also has the disadvantages of reducing the sensation of many men and their female partners. On the other hand, it has the advantage of prolonging the ejaculation time of some males who usually reach orgasm very quickly.

In using a condom, care should be taken, after ejaculation, to see that it is grasped firmly at the top and that it comes out with the penis. Otherwise, semen may leak over the top of the condom and lead to impregnation.

Female instruments. The main female instrument which is presently employed for contraceptive purposes is the rubber diaphragm, which fits over the entrance to the uterus and blocks the semen from entering the womb.

Plastic or metal caps, which fit over the cervix, are sometimes employed. Intra-cervical pessaries, which are inserted into the cervix itself, and intra-utrerine pessaries, which are inserted into the uterus and left there, are also used. Although once considered dangerous, intrauterine devices have been improved and experimented recently and are now considered to be one of the safest, cheapest and most convenient contraceptives (Tietze, 1962, 1963).

The diaphragm comes in various sizes, to fit differently built women, and therefore should be fitted after gynecological examination by a medical specialist. It is normally used in conjunction with spermicidal jelly or creme, in accordance with medical instructions.

The main advantages of diaphragms are that they are exceptionally safe; offer minimal interference with sex pleasure; and can be put in place before coitus takes place and removed hours after it has occurred, thus eliminating interruption just before or after copulation. On the other hand, some women object to the difficulties involved in inserting their diaphragms and some are so constructed that they cannot use them with safety (Johnson and Masters, 1962).

Plastic or metal caps may be inserted once a month and taken out just before a woman's menstrual period. They have distinct advantages, especially for women who cannot or will not wear a diaphragm; but they may be dislodged by intercourse or other motions, leaving the woman without protection when she thinks she still is protected.

Instead of a diaphragm or a cap, women sometimes employ tampons, sponges, or wads of cotton which can be steeped in contraceptive agents and placed in the vagina prior to intercourse. These instruments, however, are likely to be displaced during coitus and therefore do not constitute a very safe mode of contraception. They also may interfere with intercourse itself.

Women sometimes also douche subsequent to intercourse to wash the semen out of the vagina before it can enter the uterus. Douching, even if done immediately after copulation, may be too late and often does not eliminate all semen. It is a very ineffective contraceptive measure. Douching is also dangerous if done too frequently or performed with caustic, harsh douching agents and should be done only under medical direction.

Chemical methods. There are many kinds of vaginal jellies, pastes, cremes, suppositories, foam tablets, and aerosol foam, on the market today whose purpose, when placed in the vagina, is to kill sperm and block the cervical opening. Most of these chemical agents are effective when used in conjunction with a condom or diaphragm but none are yet recommended as highly when employed alone (Dickinson, 1950; Tietze, 1959a; Guttmacher, 1961).

The so-called safe period or rhythm method. The "safe period" or rhythm method of contraception stems from the now well-known discoveries of Ogino and Knaus that females usually ovulate around the middle of their menstrual cycles and are fertile only for a few days around this time. Theoretically, if they refrain from having coitus from about the eleventh to eighteenth days of a 28-day cycle, they will not become pregnant.

Although there is little doubt that the rhythm method works in general, there is much doubt that it is effective in particular instances. For most women do not menstruate as regularly as they think they do and may have irregular periods because of illness, change of activity, emotional upsets, highly active sex lives, etc. Consequently, the rhythm method may safely be used as a supplementary technique but is not highly reliable in many instances when exclusively employed (Davis, 1963; Hartman, 1962; Nelson, 1963).

Because many women who nurse their children do not menstruate while they are doing so, it is sometimes mistakenly assumed that this nursing time is a "safe period." In point of fact, however, many women ovulate even when they are not menstruating and can conceive while lactating.

Withdrawal. One of the most frequently used methods of contraception is that of withdrawal or coitus interruptus: that is, the male's withdrawing his penis from the vagina just prior to having an ejaculation. This is not a particularly safe method for several reasons: (a) It is possible for the precoital lubricating fluid of the male to contain some sperm and therefore for him to impregnate the female without any ejaculation. (b) It is easy for the male to misjudge his timing and to withdraw his penis after rather than before ejaculation. (c) If the male withdraws successfully but ejaculates, after withdrawal, near the entrance to the vagina, the woman may still become pregnant. (d) If the male who uses withdrawal has intercourse a second time soon after the first, live sperm may remain in his urethra and may impregnate his partner (Clark, 1959c).

Even when it is useful as a birth control method, withdrawal is not recommended since it tends to create too much anxiety, in many instances, in both the male and female who employ it. They are so worried about whether the male will withdraw in time that they do not concentrate effectively on coitus or on the pleasure to be derived from having it. Modified coitus interruptus may be performed by a couple's having intercourse until the wife has her orgasm and then having the husband receive an extracoital orgasm (Robie, 1925). This, too, is contraceptively risky.

Coitus reservatus. Coitus reservatus occurs when a couple has intercourse for a considerable period of time without any orgasm or ejaculation on the part of the male. It is not recommended as a birth control method, as sperm may leak into the male's lubricating fluid, and is not generally recommended as a sex practice, as it may lead to congestion of the prostate gland and seminal ducts. Supposedly, however, it was employed for many years at the Oneida colony in New York during the nineteenth century without adverse results (Ditzion, 1953). *Diana* is a form of coitus reservatus whereby the male derives pleasure from the touch and sight of the nude female form but does not have an orgasm. *Zugassent's discovery* is a variation which involves no orgasm for either the male or the female partner.

Sterilization. If it is necessary that a couple have no more children, either the husband or wife can be sterilized and made absolutely infertile. This is done today by a relatively simple surgical operation which consists of cutting and tying the vas deferens (seminal duct) of the male on both sides; or by a more complicated procedure of tying the fallopian tubes of the female. Once done, sterilization is difficult or impossible to undo and should therefore be performed only after careful consideration (Stone and Stone, 1952; Russell, 1961, Westman, 1959).

Temporary sterilization may also be done by X-ray treatment but is dangerous to future offspring and therefore inadvisable. It may likewise be accomplished by giving a male sufficient amounts of the female hormone, estrogen, or by applying consistent heat to his testes. Large doses of androgens administered to a male may also result in temporary suppression of sperm production. These procedures are rarely to be recommended. But permanent sterilization is a harmless procedure which is advisable in selected cases Russell, 1961; Sanwal, 1958).

Mechanical compression and extrusion. It is possible for some males to stop conception by putting digital pressure on their perineums, where the back part of the urethral tract is located. Such pressure may block ejaculation and result in internal or retrograde ejaculation. Later, the blocked semen may be expelled by urinating.

Females may sometimes, after ejaculation has taken place in the vagina, shake their pelvises, cough, and bear down on their vaginas and cervices, thus forcing mucus and the male ejaculate out of the vagina. Neither the retrograde ejaculation nor the extrusion of semen techniques are recommended as efficient birth control methods.

Oral contraceptives. The most effective birth control measure invented to date is the steroid pill which, when taken regularly for twenty days in a row, will regulate a woman's menstrual periods and render her sterile for as long as she takes it. At the same time, when a woman stops taking the most common forms of this birth control pill, she will usually have increased fertility. Several of the birth control pills which are widely used today create unpleasant side effects in some women, at least for a period of time; but as more research is done in this area, pills that eliminate or minimize these side effects are now beginning to be available. It has so far been found that, when taken by normal women, birth control pills have no proven serious side effects or disadvantages; but it is thought by some gynecologists that, since they have been in use only for a limited period, it is possible (though highly unlikely) that they may eventually affect some women adversely (Guttmacher, 1961).

Abstinence. One of the very best birth control methods, of course, is complete abstinence of both sex partners. But because so few couples can or desire to be abstinent for long periods of time, it is an impractical method for the vast majority of individuals.

Future methods. Several safe, easy, foolproof methods of preventing conception, including a pill that the male will be able to take and that may render him infertile for a year or more at a time, are now being investigated; and it would appear that within the next several years one or more of these methods will be perfected (Lehfeldt, 1961b;

Pincus et al, 1959; Robert Liston, personal communication, 1965). In the meantime, careful use of existing methods (and sometimes of two of them employed simultaneously) should give excellent results.

Although all existing techniques have their distinct disadvantages, it seems far more desirable for most people to accept their limitations realistically than neurotically to rebel against using them and hence get into much more serious difficulties when they wish to avoid having more children. In the last analysis, the effective use of contraceptives, like the effective application of virtually any other sex technique, is a psychological as well as a physiological problem and must be solved by common sense and self-understanding.

Bibliography

Abraham, Karl. *Collected papers*. London: Hogarth, 1950.

Abramson, Harold A. Lysergic acid diethylamide (LSD-25) as an adjunct to psychotherapy with elimination of fear of homosexuality. *J. Psychol.*, 1955, 39, 127-155.

Adams, Clifford R. *An informal preliminary report on some factors relating to sexual responses of certain college wives*. State College, Pa.: Author, 1953. Mimeographed.

Adler, Alfred. The homosexual problem. *Alien & Neurol.*, 1917, 38, 285.

——. *Understanding human nature*. New York: Greenberg, 1927.

——. *The practice and theory of individual psychology*. New York: Harcourt, Brace, 1939a.

——. *Social interest*. New York: Putnam, 1939b.

Allen, Clifford. *The sexual perversions and abnormalities*. London: Oxford, 1949.

——. On the cure of homosexuality. *Int. J. Sexol.*, 1952, 5, 148-150.

Allen, Clifford, Broster, L. R., and others. *The adrenal cortex and intersexuality*. London: Chapman and Hall, 1938.

Allen, E. and others. *Sex and the internal secretions*. Baltimore: Williams & Wilkins, 1939.

Allen, Gordon. Review of O. F. von Verschuer's "Die Genetischen Grundlagen der Sexualkonstitution des Menschen." *Eug. Quart.*, 1956, 3, 238-239.

Anonymous. *The invert and his adjustment*. London: Baillière, Tindall and Cox, 1950.

Ansbacher, Heinz L. Review of Alfred Adler's "La Compensation Psychique de l'Etat d'Inferiorite des Organes suivi de Le Probleme de l'Homosexualite." *J. Individ. Psychol.*, 1958, 14, 191-192.

Ansbacher, Heinz L., and Ansbacher, Rowena R. *The individual psychology of Alfred Adler*. New York: Basic Books, 1956.

Arlington, Norman. Sex in the world of tomorrow. *Mattachine Rev.*, 1958, 4, No. 10, 13-19.

Bach, G. R. *Intensive group psychotherapy.* New York: Ronald, 1954.

Bailey, Derrick S. (Ed.). *Sexual offenders and social punishment.* Westminster: Church of England Moral Welfare Council and Church Information Board, 1956.

Baker, Blanche M. Toward understanding. *One,* 1959, 7, No. 1, 25-26.

Balzac, Honore de. *Physiology of marriage.* New York: Société des Beaux Artes.

Barahal, Hyman S. Testosterone in psychotic male homosexuality. *Psychiat. Quart.,* 1940, 14, 391.

Bauer, Berhard A. *Woman and love.* New York: Dingwall-Rock, 1934.

Beach, Frank A. A review of physiological and psychological studies of sexual behavior in mammals. Physiol. Rev., 1947, 27, 240-307.

———. *Hormones and behavior.* New York: Hoeber, 1948.

———. Characteristics of masculine "sex drive." In Jones, Marshall R., *Nebraska symposium on motivation, 1956.* Lincoln, Neb.: University of Nebraska Press, 1956.

Beigel, Hugo. The meaning of coital postures. *Int. J. Sexol.,* 1953, 6, 136-141.

———. *Encyclopedia of sex education.* New York: Daye, 1952; New York: Ungar, 1962.

———. Abstinence. In Ellis, Albert, and Abarbanel, Albert (Eds.). *Encyclopedia of sexual behavior.* New York: Hawthorn, 1961.

Belafsky, Henry A. Lecture before American College of Obstetrics and Gynecology in Los Angeles, 1958.

Bell, David. Science and Dr. Ellis. *Mattachine Rev.,* 1959, 5, No. 7, 5-7.

Benedek, Therese. *Psychosexual functions in women.* New York: Ronald, 1952.

Benjamin, Harry. An echo of an addendum to "for the sake of morality." *Med. J. & Rec.,* Aug. 5, 1931.

———. Prostitution and venereal disease. *Med. Rev. of Rev.,* Sept., 1935, 5-40; revised 1939a.

———. Sex happiness in marriage. *Med. Rec.,* July 5, 1939b.

———. The sex problem in the armed forces. *Urol. & Cutan. Rev.,* 1939c, 48, 231-244.

——. Prostitution reassessed. *Int. J. Sexol.,* 1951, 4, 54-60; 1951, 5, 37-39.

——. Transsexualism and transvestism. *Amer. J. Psychother.,* 1954, Vol. 7.

——. The treatment of aging. *Senior Citizen,* May, 1958.

——. What is adjustment? *Mattachine Rev.,* 1959, 5, No. 7, 9-11.

Benjamin, Harry, and Ellis, Albert. An objective examination of prostitution. *Int. J. Sexol.,* 1954, 8, 99-105.

Benjamin Harry, and Masters, R. E. L. *Prostitution and Morality.* New York: Julian, 1964.

Berg, Louis, and Street, Robert. *Sex methods and manners.* New York: McBride, 1953.

Bergler, Edmund. *Homosexuality.* New York: Hill & Wang, 1956.

——. *Counterfeit-sex.* New York: Grove, 1961.

Bernard, Jessie, Buchanan, Helen E., and Smith, William. *Dating, mating and marriage.* Cleveland: Allen, 1958.

Best, Winfield, and Jaffe, Frederick. *Simple methods of contraception.* New York: Planned Parenthood Federation of America, 1958.

Bibby, Cyril. *Sex education.* New York: Emerson, 1946.

——. *How life is handed on.* New York: Emerson, 1949.

——. The art of loving. In Ellis, Albert, and Abarbanel, Albert (Eds.). *Encyclopedia of sexual behavior.* New York: Hawthorn, 1961.

Bieber, Irving, et al. *Homosexuality.* New York: Basic Books, 1962.

Blanchard, Phyllis, and Manasses, Carlyn. *New girls for old.* New York: Macauley, 1937.

Blau, S. Venereal diseases. In Ellis, A., and Abarbanel, A. *Encyclopedia of sexual behavior.* New York: Hawthorn, 1961.

Bloch, Iwan. *The sexual life of our time.* New York and London: Rebman, 1908.

Blood, Robert. *Anticipating your marriage.* Glencoe: Free Press, 1955.

Bohm, Ewald. The influence of the vacancy factor versus the sexual need and choice of partner. *Int. J. Sexol.,* 1949, 3, 101-103.

Bonaparte, Marie. *Female sexuality.* London: Imago, 1953.

Bos, C., and Cleghorn, R. A. Psychogenic sterility. *Fertil. & Steril.,* 1958, 9, 84-98.

Boss, M. *Meaning and content of the sexual perversions.* New York: Grune & Stratton, 1949.

Bossard, James H. S., and Boll, Eleanor S. *Why marriages go wrong.* New York: Ronald, 1958.

Bowman, Henry. *Marriage for moderns.* New York: McGraw-Hill, 1957.

Bowman, Karl. Too many sex laws. *Nation,* 1958, pp. 286-289.

Bowman, Karl M., and Engle, Bernice. A psychiatric evaluation of laws on homosexuality. *Amer. J. Psychiat.,* 1956, 112, 577-583.

Branham, V., and Kutash, Samuel (Eds.). *Encyclopedia of criminology.* New York: Philosophical Library, 1949.

Bredtschneider, Wolfgang E. About the prejudice against homosexuality. *Real Life Guide,* 1959, 2, No. 1, 19-25.

Briffault, Robert. *The mothers.* New York: Macmillan, 1929.

———. *Sin and sex.* New York: Macauley, 1931.

British Medical Association. *Homosexuality and prostitution.* London: British Medical Association, 1955.

Bromley, Dorothy D., and Britten, F. H. *Youth and sex.* New York: Harper, 1938.

Brown, Daniel. Transvestism and sex role inversion. In Ellis, Albert, and Abarbanel, Albert (Eds.). *Encyclopedia of sexual behavior.* New York: Hawthorn, 1961.

Brown, Fred, and Kempton, Rudolf T. *Sex questions and answers.* New York: McGraw-Hill, 1950.

Brown, Helen G. *Sex and the single girl.* New York: Geis, 1962.

Brown, Helen G. *Sex and the office.* New York. Geis, 1964.

Brunori, Nicole. *Bestiality in pedagogy and in criminology.* (In Italian) Florence: Macri, 1958.

Buckle, Donald. The treatment of sex offenders. *Int. J. Sexol.,* 1949, 3, 1-8.

Burgess, E. W., and Conttrell, L. S., Jr. *Predicting success and failure in marriage.* New York: Prentice-Hall, 1939.

Burgess, Ernest W., and Wallin, Paul. *Engagement and marriage.* Philadelphia: Lippincott, 1953.

Burton, Maurice. *Animal courtship.* London: Hutchinson, 1953.

Burton, Robert. *Anatomy of melancholy.* New York: Tudor, 1948.

Butterfield, Oliver M. *Love problems of adolescence.* New York: Emerson, 1939.

——. *Sex life in marriage*. New York: Emerson, 1953.

Calderone, Mary (Ed.). *Abortion*. New York: Hoeber, 1958.

Calverton, V. F., and Schmalhausen, S. D. (Eds.). *Sex in civilization*. New York: Macauley, 1929.

——. *The new generation*. New York: Macauley, 1930.

Caprio, Frank S. *The sexually adequate male*. New York: Citadel, 1952.

——. *The sexually adequate female*. New York: Citadel, 1953.

——. *Female homosexuality*. New York: Citadel, 1954.

Carpenter, Edward. *Love's coming of age*. New York: Kennerley, 1911.

——. *Intermediate types*. New York: Kennerley, 1914.

Cauldwell, David. Sex questions answered. *Sexology*, 1958, 24, 738; 1959, 25, 538.

Cavan, Ruth S. *The American family*. New York: Crowell, 1953.

Cesar, Santoro G., and Dubcovsky, J. Esterilidad e infertilidad, y frigidiez. *Med. Argent*, 1957, 44, 2265-2266. *Excerpta Medica*, VIII, 1959, 12, 138-139.

Chambre, A. C. F. *The sexual development of your child*. New York: Lyle Stuart, 1958.

Chesser, Eustace. *Love without fear*. New York: New American Library, 1953.

——. *Sexual behavior, normal and abnormal*. London: Medica Publications; New York: Roy, 1949.

——. *The sexual, marital and family relationships of the English woman*. New York: Roy, 1956.

Chideckel, Maurice. *Female sex perversions*. New York: Eugenics, 1935.

Christensen, Harold T. *Marriage analysis*. New York: Ronald, 1959.

Clark, LeMon. *Emotional adjustment in marriage*. St. Louis: Mosby, 1937.

——. *Sex and you*. Indianapolis: Bobbs-Merrill, 1949.

——. A further report on the virginity of unmarried American women. *Int. J. Sexol.*, 1952, 6, 27-32.

——. A doctor looks at self relief. *Sexology*, 1958a, 24, 785-788.

——. Female sex sensation. *Sexology*, 1958b, 25, 208-212.

——. Newlywed tragedy. *Sexology*, 1958c, 25, 140-144.

——. Treating emotional impotence. *Sexology*, 1959a, 25, 762-767.

———, Overcoming psychological impotence. *Sexology*, 1959b, 25, 698-703.

———. The incomplete sex act. *Sexology*, 1959c, 26, 72-77.

Cleckley, Hervey. *Caricature of love*. New York: Ronald, 1957.

Cole, William Graham, *Sex in Christianity and psychoanalysis*. New York: Oxford, 1955.

Colmeiro-Laforet, C. *Orto y ocaso feminismo*. Buenos Aires: Martinez de Marquia, 1956.

Comfort, Alex. *Sexual behavior in society*. London: Duckworth, 1950.

Cook, Robert C. *Human fertility, the modern dilemma*. New York: Sloane, 1951.

———. (Ed.). *Homosexuality: a cross cultural approach*. New York: Julian, 1956.

———. Paper delivered at the annual meeting of the Mattachine Society, Sept. 8, 1958.

Cory, Donald Webster (pseud.). *The homosexual in America*. New York: Paperback Library, 1963.

Cory, Donald Webster. *The lesbian in America*. New York: Citadel, 1964.

Crawley, Edward. *The mystic rose*. New York: Boni & Liveright, 1927.

Creadick, R. N. Management of homosexuals. *South Med. J.*, 1953. 46, 455-460.

Cross, Harold. Britain's "free love storm." *Sexology*, 1959, 26, 4-15.

Cuber, John F. *Marriage counseling practice*. New York: Appleton, 1948.

Curran, Desmond. Homosexuality. *Practitioner*, 1938, 141, 282.

Curran, Desmond, and Parr, D. Homosexuality: and analysis of 100 male cases seen in private practice. *Brit. Med. J.*, April 6, 1957, 797-801.

Daniels, Anna K. *The mature woman*. New York: Prentice-Hall, 1953.

Danielsson, Bengt. *Love in the South Seas*. New York: Reynal, 1956.

Davis, Katherine B. *Factors in the sex life of 2200 women*. New York: Harper, 1929.

Davis, Kingsley. The sociology of prostitution. *Amer. Sociol. Rev.*, 1937, 2, 744-755.

Davis, M. E. Review of C. Hartman's *Science and the safe period*. *Science*, 1963, 139, 581-582.

Davis, Maxine. *The sexual responsibility of women*. New York: Dial, 1956.

Dean, D. F. *Significant characteristics of the homosexual*. Ph.D. thesis, New York University, 1936.

Dearborn, Lester. Some psychophysical phenomena concerning marital adjustment. *Annals Penn. State Univ. Inst. on Marriage and Home Adjustment*, 1946.

Dearborn, Lester. Masturbation. In Fishbein, Morris, and Burgess, Ernest W. (Eds.). *Successful marriage*. Garden City: Doubleday, 1947a.

———. Extramarital Relations. *Ibid.*, 1947b.

de Beauvoir, Simone. *The second sex*. London: Cape, 1953.

Dell, Floyd. *Love in the machine age*. New York: Farrar and Rinehart, 1930.

Dengrove, Edward. The physiology of impotence. *Sexology*, 1959a, 25, 500-504.

———. Causes of premature ejaculation. *Sexology*, 1959b, 26, 46-51.

de River, Paul. *The sexual criminal*. Springfield, Ill.: Thomas, 1949.

Deutsch, Albert (Ed.). *Sexual habits of American men*. New York: Prentice-Hall, 1948.

Deutsch, Helene. *Psychology of women*. 2 vols. New York: Grune & Stratton, 1944.

Devereux, George. Institutionalized homosexuality of the Mohave Indians. *Human. Biol.*, 1937, 9, 498-527.

———. *Study of abortion in primitive societies*. New York: Julian, 1955.

Dickerson, Roy E. *So youth may know*. New York: Association Press, 1931.

Dickinson, Robert L. *Human sex anatomy*. Baltimore: Williams and Wilkins, 1933.

———. *Techniques of conception control*. Baltimore: Williams and Wilkins, 1950.

Dickinson, R. L., and Beam, L. *A thousand marriages*. Baltimore: Williams and Wilkins, 1931.

———. *The single woman*. Baltimore: Williams and Wilkins, 1934.

Dingwall, Eric. J. *The American woman*. New York: Rinehart, 1957.

Ditzion, Sidney. *Marriage, morals, and sex in America*. New York: Twayne, 1953.

Dollard, John. *Caste and class in a southern town*. New York: Harper, 1949.

Doniger, Simon (Ed.). *Sex and religion today*. New York: Association, 1953.

Dreikurs, Rudolf. *Challenge of marriage*. New York: Duell, Sloane and Pierce, 1948.

Drummond, Isable. *The sex paradox*. New York: Putnam, 1953.

Durand-Wever, Anne-Marie. Influences of the nervous system on the structure and functions of human genital organs. *Int. J. Sexol.*, 1952, 5, 207-211.

Duvall, Evelyn. *Family development*. Philadelphia: Lippincott, 1958.

Duvall, Evelyn, and Hill, Reuben. *When you marry*. New York: Heath, 1952.

Durall, Evelyn, *Love and the facts of life*. New York: Association Press, 1963.

Duvall, Sylvanus. *Men, women and morals*. New York: Association Press, 1952.

Duzet, Louis E. Pros and cons on circumcision. *Sexology*, 1957, 14, 22-27.

Eckert, Ralph. *Sex attitudes in the home*. New York: Association Press, 1956.

Eddy, Sherwood. *Sex and youth*. New York: Doubleday, 1928.

Edwardes, Allen. *The jewel in the lotus*. New York: Julian, 1959.

Edwardes, Allen, and Masters, R. E. L. *The cradle of erotica*. New York: Julian, 1962.

Ehrmann, Winston W. *Premarital dating behavior*. New York: Holt, 1960.

——. Premarital sex relations. In Ellis, Albert, and Abarbanel, Albert (Eds.). *Encyclopedia of sexual behavior*. New York: Hawthorn, 1961.

Elkan, E. The evolution of female orgastic ability. *Int. J. Sexol.*, 1948, 2, 1-13; 1948, 2, 84-92.

Ellis, Albert. The sexual psychology of human hermaphrodites. *Psychosom. Med.*, 1945, 7, 108-125.

——. Application of clinical psychology to sexual disorders. In Brower, Daniel, and Abt, Lawrence A. (Eds.). *Progress in clinical psychology*. New York: Grune & Stratton, 1952a.

——. On the cure of homosexuality. *Int. J. Sexol.*, 1952b, 5, 135-138.

——. Is the vaginal orgasm a myth? In Pillay, A. P. and Ellis, Albert (Eds.). *Sex, society and the individual.* Bombay: International Journal of Sexology, 1953a.

——. Marriage counseling with couples indicating sexual incompatibility. *Marr. Fam. Living*, 1953b, 15, 53-59.

——. (Ed). *Sex life of the American woman and the Kinsey report.* New York: Greenberg, 1954a.

——. Psychosexual and marital problems. In Pennington, L. A., and Berg, Irwin A. (Eds.). *An introduction to clinical psychology.* New York: Ronald, 1954c.

——. Interrogation of sex offenders. *J. Crim. Law,* 1954d. 45, 41-47.

——. *New approaches to psychotherapy techniques.* Brandon, Vermont: Journal of Clinical Psychology, 1955a.

——. Psychotherapy techniques for use with psychotics. *Amer. J. Psychother.*, 1955b, 9, 452-476.

——. A critical evaluation of marriage counseling. *Marr. Fam. Living*, 1956a, 18, 65-71.

——. The effectiveness of psychotherapy with individuals who have severe homosexual problems. *J. Consult. Psychol.*, 1956b, 20, 191-195.

——. *How to live with a neurotic.* New York: Crown, 1957a.

——. Sex problems of couples seen for marriage counseling. *J. Family Welfare,* 1957b, 3, 81-84.

——. Guilt, shame and frigidity. *Quart. Rev. Surg. Obstet. & Gynecol.*, 1959, 16, 259-261.

——. Homosexuality and creativity. *J. Clin. Psychol.*, 1959b, 15, 376-379.

——. Frigidity. In Ellis, Albert, and Abarbanel, Albert (Eds.). *Encyclopedia of sexual behavior.* New York: Hawthorn, 1961.

——. *Reason and emotion in psychotherapy.* New York: Lyle Stuart, 1962a.

——. *The folklore of sex.* New York: Boni, 1951. Rev. ed., New York: Grove Press, 1962b.

——. *If this be sexual heresy . . .* New York: Lyle Stuart, 1963a.

——. *Sex and the single man.* New York: Lyle Stuart, 1963b.

——. *The intelligent woman's guide to man-hunting.* New York: Lyle Stuart, 1963c.

——. *The origins and the development of the incest taboo.* New York: Lyle Stuart, 1963d.

——. *The American sexual tragedy.* Rev. ed. New York: Lyle Stuart, 1962; New York: Grove Press, 1963e.

——. *Sex without guilt.* Rev. ed. New York: Lyle Stuart, 1965; New York: Grove Press, 1965a.

——. *Homosexuality: its causes and cure.* New York: Lyle Stuart, 1965b.

——. *The case for sexual liberty.* Vol. I. Tucson: Seymour Press, 1965c.

Ellis, Albert, and Abarbanel, Albert (Eds.). *The encyclopedia of sexual behavior.* 2 vols. New York: Hawthorn Books, 1961.

Ellis, Albert, and Brancale, Ralph. *The psychology of sex offenders.* Springfield, Illinois: Charles C. Thomas, 1956.

Ellis, Albert, Doorbar, Ruth R., Guze, Henry, and Clark, LeMon. A study of sexual preferences. *Int. J. Sexology,* 1952, 6, 87-88.

Ellis, Albert, Doorbar, Ruth R., and Johnston III, Robert. Characteristics of convicted sex offenders. *J. Soc. Psychol.,* 1954, 40, 3-15.

Ellis, Albert, and Harper, Robert A. *Creative marriage.* New York: Lyle Stuart, 1961a.

——. *A guide to rational living.* Englewood Cliffs, New Jersey: Prentice-Hall, 1961b.

Ellis, Albert, and Sagarin, Edward. *Nymphomania: a study of the oversexed woman.* New York: Gilbert Press-Julian Messner, 1964.

Ellis, Havelock. *Psychology of sex.* New York: Emerson, 1935.

——. *Studies in the psychology of sex.* 4 vols. New York: Random House, 1936.

——. *Sex and marriage.* London: Williams & Norgate, 1952.

Erikson, Erik H. *Childhood and society.* New York: Norton, 1950.

Ernst, Morris L., and Loth, David. *American sexual behavior and the Kinsey report.* New York: Greystone, 1948.

Exner, M. J. *The sexual side of marriage.* New York: Norton, 1932.

Eysenck, H. J. *Uses and abuses of psychology.* London: Penguin, 1953.

Faust, Bernd. Differentialdiagnostische Betrachtung zu verschiedenen Arten habitueller Ipsation im Kindesund Jugendalter. *Prax. Kinderpsychol. Kinderpsychiat.*, 1957, 6, 198-201. *Psychol. Abstr.*, 1958, 33, 175.

Fenichel, O. *Psychoanalytic theory of neurosis.* New York: Norton, 1945.

Feré, Charles S. *Scientific and esoteric studies in sexual degeneration in mankind and in animals.* New York: Anthropological Press, 1932.

Ferenczi, Sandor. *Sex in psychoanalysis.* New York: Basic Books, 1950.

——. *Further contributions to the theory and technique of psychoanalysis.* New York: Basic Books, 1952.

——. *Final contributions to the theory and technique of psychoanalysis.* New York: Basic Books, 1955.

Fielding, William J. *Sex and the love-life.* New York: Dodd, Mead. 1927; New York: Permabooks, 1961.

Finck, Henry T. *Romantic love and personal beauty.* New York: Macmillan, 1887.

Finger, F. W. Sex beliefs and practices among male college students. *J. Abnorm. Soc. Psychol.*, 1947, 42, 57-67.

Fink, Harold Kenneth. *Long Journey.* New York: Julian, 1954.

Fink, Lotte. Premarital sex experiences of girls in Sydney. *Int. J. Sexol.*, 1950, 4, 33-35.

Fishbein, Morris, and Burgess, E. W. (Eds.). *Successful marriage.* New York: Doubleday, 1947.

Fishbein, Morris, and Kennedy, Ruby Jo. *Modern marriage and family living.* New York: Oxford, 1957.

Flugel, J. C. *Psychoanalytic study of the family.* London: Hogarth, 1950.

Folsom, Joseph K. *The family and democratic society.* New York: Harper, 1949.

Forbath, A. (Ed.). *Love and marriage.* New York: Liveright, 1938.

Forberg, F. K. *Manual of classical erotology.* Brussels: Carrington, 1884.

Ford, C. S. *A comparative study of human reproduction.* New Haven: Yale University Press, 1945.

Ford, C. S., and Beach, Frank A. *Patterns of sexual behavior.* New York: Harper, 1951.

Forel, August. *The sexual question.* Brooklyn: Physician's and Surgeon's Book Co., 1922.

Foster, A. W. Treatment of sexual offenders. *Marriage Hyg.,* 1947, 1, 77-80.

Foster, Robert G. *Marriage and family relationships.* New York: Macmillan, 1946.

Frazer, James G. *The golden bough.* London: Macmillan, 1911-1915.

Freud, Anna. Clinical observations on the treatment of manifest male homosexuality. *Psychoanal. Quart.,* 1951, 20, 237-238.

Freud, Sigmund. *Collected papers.* London: Hogarth, 1924-1950.

——. *Basis writings.* New York: Modern Library, 1938.

——. *Outline of psychoanalysis.* New York: Norton, 1949.

Fromm, Erich. *Escape from freedom.* New York: Farrar & Rinehart, 1939.

——. *The art of loving.* New York: Harper, 1956.

Fromme, Allan. *Psychologist looks at love and marriage.* New York: Prentice-Hall, 1950.

Frumkin, Robert. Sexual freedom. In Ellis, Albert, and Abarbanel, Albert (Eds.). *Encyclopedia of sexual behavior.* New York: Hawthorn, 1960.

Gallichan, Walter M. *The great unmarried.* New York: Stokes, 1916.

——. *Human love.* New York: Walden, 1939.

Gebhard, Paul H., Pomeroy, Wardell B., Martin, Clyde E., and Christenson, Cornelia V. *Pregnancy, birth and abortion.* New York: Harper & Hoeber, 1958.

Geddes, D. P., and Curie, E. (Eds.). *About the Kinsey report.* N. Y.: New American Library, 1948.

Gide, André. *Corydon.* London: Secker & Warberg, 1952.

Giedt, F. Harold. Changes in sexual behavior and attitudes following class study of the Kinsey report. *J. Soc. Psychol.,* 1951, 33, 131-141.

Giese, Hans (Ed.). *Human sexology.* (In German). Stuttgart: Ferdeinandtube, 1954, 2 vols.

Ginzburg, Ralph. *An unhurried view of erotica.* New York: Helmsman, 1958.

Glass, S. J., Deuel, H. J., and Wright, C. A. Sex hormone studies in male homosexuality. *Endocr.,* 1940, 26, 590-594.

Glass, S. J., and McKennon, B. J. The hormonal aspects of sex reversal states. *West J. Surg. Obstet.*, 1937, 45, 467.

Glover, Edward. *Technique of psychoanalysis.* New York: International Universities Press, 1955.

Glueck, Bernard C. Psychodynamic patterns in the homosexual sex offender. *Amer J. Psychiat.*, 1956, 112, 584-590.

Glueck, Sheldon, and Glueck, Eleanor. *Five hundred delinquent women.* New York: Knopf, 1934.

Gorer, Geoffrey. *Exploring English character.* New York: Criterion Books, 1955.

Grafenburg, Ernest. The role of the urethra in female orgasm. *Int. J. Sexol.*, 1950, 3, 145-148.

Grant, Vernon. *Psychology of sexual emotion.* New York: Longmans, Green, 1957.

Great Britain, House of Lords. *Homosexual offences and prostitution.* London: Her Majesty's Stationery Office, 1957.

Greenblatt, Bernard R. *A doctor's marital guide for patients.* Chicago: Budlong Press, 1957.

Greenwald, Harold. *The call girl.* New York: Ballantine, 1957.

Greve, Maurice. Sex starvation. *Sexology,* 1957, 14, 10-15.

Groves, Ernest R., and Groves, Gladys H. *The contemporary American family.* Philadelphia: Lippincott, 1947.

Groves, Ernest R., Groves, Gladys H., and Groves, Catherine. *Sex fulfillment in marriage.* New York: Emerson, 1951.

Gurvitz, Milton. Sex offenders in private practice: treatment and outcome. Paper delivered at American Psychological Association annual meeting, Sept. 3, 1957.

Gutheil, Emil. *Handbook of dream analysis.* New York: Liveright, 1950.

Guttmacher, Alan F. *Story of human birth.* New York: New American Library, 1955.

Guttmacher, Alan F., with Best Winfield, and Jaffe Fredericks. *The complete book of birth control.* New York: Ballantine, 1961.

Guyon, Rene. *The ethics of sexual acts.* New York: Knopf, 1934.

——. *Sexual freedom.* New York: Knopf, 1950; Hollywood: France International, 1963.

——. *Human rights and the denial of sexual freedom.* Bangkok: Author, 1951.

Guyot, Jules. *A ritual for married lovers.* Baltimore: Waverly, 1931.

Guze, Henry. Sexual attitudes in the scientific medical literature. *Int. J. Sexol.,* 1951, 5, 97-100.

——. Some bodily and behavioral manifestations of the menstrual cycle. *Int. J. Sexol.,* 1951, 6, 1-14.

——. The anatomy and physiology of sex. In Ellis, Albert, and Abarbanel, Albert (Eds.). *Encyclopedia of sexual behavior.* New York: Hawthorn, 1961.

Hadfield, J. A. The cure of homosexuality. *Brit. Med. J.,* June 7, 1958, 1, 1323-1326.

Haire, Norman. Prostitution: abolition, tolerance or regulation. *Marriage Hyg.,* 1948, 1, 220-228.

——. (Ed.). *Encyclopedia of sex practice.* London: Encyclopedia Press, 1951.

——. (Ed.). *Encyclopedia of sexual knowledge.* London: Encyclopedia Press, 1952.

Hambly, Wilfrid D. Adultery among primitives. *Sexology,* 1959, 25, 562-567.

Hamilton, A. E. *Psychology and "the great God fun."* New York: Julian, 1955.

Hamilton, Eleanor. *Partners in love.* New York: Ziff-Davis, 1961.

Hamilton, G. V. *An introduction to objective psychopathology.* St. Louis: Mosby, 1925.

——. *A research in marriage.* New York: Boni, 1929.

——. Defensive homosexuality. In Robinson, Victor (Ed.). *Encyclopedia sexualis.* New York: Dingwall Rock, 1936.

Hamilton, James B. Treatment of sexual underdevelopment with synthetic male hormone substances. *Endocrin.,* 1937, 21, 649-654.

Hammer, E. F. A psychoanalytic hypothesis concerning sex offenders. *J. Clin. Exper. Psychopath.,* 1957, 18, 177-184.

Hammons, Helen G. (Ed.). *Heredity counseling.* New York: Hoeber, 1959.

Hardenberg, E. W. Psychology of feminine sex experience. *Int. J. Sexol.,* 1949, 2, 224-228.

Harding, T. Swann. The endless war on "vice." *Med. Rec.,* April 20, 1938.

Harper, Fowler (Ed.). *Problems of the family.* Indianapolis: Bobbs-Merrill, 1952.

Harper, Robert A. *Marriage.* New York: Appleton-Century-Crofts, 1949.

———. (Ed.). Premarital sex relations: the facts and the counselor's role in relation to the facts. *Marr. Fam. Living,* 1953, 15, 338-340.

———. Marriage counseling: art or science? *Marr. Fam. Living,* 1951, 13, 164-166.

———. A premarital case: with two years' marital follow-up. *Marr. Fam. Living,* 1952, 14, 133-149.

———. Should marriage counseling become a full-fledged specialty? *Marr. Fam. Living,* 1953, 5, 338-340.

———. Failure in marriage counseling. *Marr. Fam. Living,* 1955, 17, 359-362.

———. Communication problems in marriage and marriage counseling. *Marr. Fam. Living,* 1958, 20, 107-112.

———. Marriage counseling and the mores: a critique. *Marr. Fam. Living,* 1959a, 21, 13-19.

———. Psychological aspects of homosexuality. Paper delivered at the meeting of the society for the Scientific Study of Sex, May 22, 1959b.

———. *Psychoanalysis and psychotherapy: 36 systems.* Englewood Cliffs, N. J.: Prentice-Hall, 1959c.

———. Petting. In Ellis, Albert, and Abarbanel, Albert (Eds.). *Encyclopedia of sexual behavior.* New York: Hawthorn, 1961a.

———. Extramarital sex relations. In *Ibid.,* 1961b.

Harper, Robert A., and Harper, Frances R. Are educators afraid of sex? *Marr. Fam. Living,* 1957, 19, 240-244.

———. Sex education. In Ellis, Albert, and Abarbanel, Albert (Eds.). *Encyclopedia of sexual behavior.* New York: Hawthorn, 1961.

Hartman, Carl. *Science and the safe period.* Baltimore: Williams and Wilkins, 1962.

Healy, William, Bronner, Augusta F., and Bowers, Anna Mae. *Structure and meaning of psychoanalysis.* New York: Knopf, 1953.

Hegeler, Inge, and Hegeler, Sten. *An ABZ of love.* New York: Medical Press, 1963.

Henry, George W. *Sex variants.* New York: Harper, 1941.

———. *All the sexes.* New York: Rinehart, 1955.

Henry, George W., and Gross, Alfred. The homosexual delinquent. *Mental Hyg.,* 1941, 25, 420.

Herrick, E. H. Sex changes in aging. *Sexology*, 1957, 14, 248-253.

Hiltner, Seward. *Sex ethics and the Kinsey report*. New York: Association Press, 1953.

Himelhoch, Jerome, and Fava, Sylvia F. (Eds.). *Sexual behavior in American society*. New York: Norton, 1955.

Himes, Norman E., and Taylor, Donald. *Your marriage*. New York: Rinehart, 1955.

Himwich, Harold E. (Ed.). *Alcoholism—basic aspects and treatment*. Washington: American Association for the Advancement of Science, 1958.

Hirning, J. L., and Hirning, Alma. *Marriage adjustment*. New York: American Book Co., 1956.

Hirsch, Edwin W. *The power to love*. New York: Knopf, 1934; New York: Pyramid, 1962.

——. *How to improve your sexual relations*. Chicago: Zeco, 1951.

——. *Prostate gland disorder*. New York: Greenberg, 1952.

——. *Modern sex life*. New York: New American Library, 1957.

Hirschfeld, Magnus. *Die Homosexualitate des Mannes und des Weibes*. Berlin: Marcus, 1920.

——. Homosexuality. In Robinson, Victor (Ed.). *Encyclopedia sexualis*. New York: Dingwall Rock, 1936.

——. *Sexual anomalies*. New York: Emerson, 1948.

Hobhouse, L. T., Wheeler, G. C., and Ginsberg, M. *The material culture and social institutions of the simpler peoples*. London: 1930.

Hoch, Paul H., and Zubin, Joseph (Eds.). *Psychosexual development in health and disease*. New York: Grune & Stratton, 1949.

Hodann, Max. *Sex life in Europe*. New York: Julian, 1932.

Hohmann, Leslie B., and Schaffner, Bertram. The sex lives of unmarried men. *Amer. J. Soc.*, 1947, 52, 501-507.

Hooker, Evelyn. The adjustment of the male overt homosexual. *J. Proj. Tech.*, 1957, 21, 18-31.

Horney, Karen. *Neurotic personality of our time*. New York: Norton, 1937.

Hotchkiss, Robert. *Etiology and diagnosis in the treatment of infertility in men*. Springfield, Ill.: Thomas, 1952.

Hotep, I. M. (pseud.). *Love and happiness*. New York: Knopf, 1938.

Huhner, Max. *The diagnosis and treatment of sexual disorder in the male and female*. Philadelphia: Davis, 1946.

Huxley, Aldous. *The devils of Loudon*. New York: Harper, 1952.

Iovetz-Tereschenko, N. M. *Friendship love in adolescence*. London: Allen and Unwin, 1936.

Javert, Carl T. Prevention of Habitual abortion. *Mod. Med.*, Jan. 1, 1959.

Johnson, Virginia E., and Masters, William H. Intravaginal contraceptive study. *West. J. Surg. Obstet. & Gynecol.*, 1962, 70, 202-207.

Jones, Ernest. *Essays in applied psychoanalysis*. 2 vols. London: Hogarth, 1951.

——. *The life and works of Sigmund Freud*. New York: Basic Books, 1955-1957.

Jones, Jr., H. W. and Scott, W. W. *Hermaphroditism, genital anomalies and related endocrine disorders*. Baltimore: Williams and Wilkins, 1958.

Joyce, T. Athol, and Thomas, N. W. *Women of all nations*. New York: Metro, 1942.

Jung, C. G. *Two essays on analytical psychology*. New York: Pantheon, 1953.

——. *The practice of psychotherapy*. New York: Pantheon, 1954.

Kahn, Fritz. *Our sex life*. New York: Knopf, 1939.

Kahn, Samuel. *Mentality and homosexuality*. Boston: Meador, 1937.

Kallmann, Franz J. Comparative study on genital aspects of male homosexuality. *J. Nerv. Ment. Dis.*, 1952, 115, 283-298.

Kaplan, Alexander, and Abrams, Morris. Ejaculatory impotence. *J. Urol.*, 1958.

Kardiner, Abram. *Sex and morality*. Indianapolis: Bobbs-Merrill, 1954.

Karpf, Fay. *The psychology and psychotherapy of Otto Rank*. New York: Philosophical Library, 1953.

Karpf, Maurice. Premarital counseling and psychotherapy: two cases. *Marr. Fam. Living*, 1952, 14, 56-75.

——. The effects of prostitution on marital sex adjustment. *Marr. Fam. Living*, 1953, 15, 65-71.

Karpman, Benjamin. *The sexual offender and his offenses*. New York: Julian, 1954.

Katz, Barney. *You can have a better marriage.* New York: American Press, 1956.

Kaufman, J. J., and Goodwin, W. E. Quoted in *Sexology,* 1958, 24, 542.

Kegel, A. H. Sexual functions of the pubococcygeus muscle. *West. J. Surg. Obstet.,* 1952, 60, 521-524.

———. Early genital relaxation. *Obstet. & Gynecol.,* 1956, 8, No. 5.

Kelly, G. L. *Sexual feeling in woman.* Augusta, Ga.: Elkay, 1930.

Kelly, G. Lombard. *Sex manual for those married or about to be.* Augusta, Ga.: Southern Medical Supply Co., 1953.

———. *So you think you're impotent.* Augusta, Ga.: Southern Medical Supply Co., 1957.

———. *A doctor discusses menopause.* Chicago: Budlong Press, 1959.

———. *Sexual feeling in married men and women.* New York: Permabooks, 1961.

Kepner, Jr., James. An examination of the sex theories of Albert Ellis, Ph.D. *One Institute Quarterly: Homophile Studies,* 1959, 2, No. 2, 40-51.

Key, Ellen. *Love and marriage.* New York: Putnam, 1911.

Keys, Ancel, and others. *The biology of human starvation.* Minneapolis: University of Minnesota Press, 1950.

Kinsey, Alfred C. Criteria for a hormonal explanation of the homosexual. *J. Clin. Endrocrinol.,* 1941, 1, 424-428.

Kinsey, A. C., Pomeroy, W. B., and Martin, C. E. *Sexual behavior in the human male.* Philadelphia: Saunders, 1948.

Kinsey, A. C., Pomeroy, W. B., Martin, C. E., and Gebhard, Paul H. Concepts of normality and abnormality in sexual behavior. In Hoch, Paul H., and Zubin, Joseph (Eds.). *Psychosexual development in health and disease.* New York: Grune & Stratton, 1949.

———. *Sexual behavior in the human female.* Philadelphia: Saunders, 1953.

Kirkendall, Lester A. *Sex adjustment of young men.* New York: Harper, 1940.

———. Toward a clarification of the concept of male sex drive. *Marr. Fam. Living,* 1958, 20, 367-372.

———. Sex worries of teenage boys. *Sexology,* 1959, 25, 360-365.

——. Sex drive. In Ellis, Albert, and Abarbanel, Albert (Eds.). *Encyclopedia of sexual behavior*. New York: Hawthorne, 1961a.

——. *Premarital intercourse and interpersonal relationships*. New York: Julian, 1961b.

Kirkpatrick, Clifford. *The family*. New York: Ronald, 1956.

Kirkpatrick, Clifford, and Kanin, Eugene. Male sex aggression on a university campus. *Amer. Sociol. Rev.*, 1957, 22, 52-58.

Kisch, E. H. *The sexual life of woman*. New York: Allied Book Co., 1926.

Kleegman, Sophia J. Frigidity, *Quart. Rev. Surg. Obstet. & Gynecol.*, 1959, 16, 243-248.

Kling, Esther B., and Kling, Samuel G. *For better or worse*. New York: Holt, 1947.

——. *How to win and hold a mate*. New York: Permabooks, 1957.

——. Sexual behavior and the law. New York: Geis, 1965.

Kling, Samuel G., and Kling, Esther B. *The marriage reader*. New York: Vanguard, 1947.

Klumbies, G., and Kleinsorge, H. Circulatory dangers and prophylaxis during orgasm. *Int. J. Sexol.*, 1950, 4, 61-66.

Knight, M. M., Peters, I. L., and Blanchard, Phyllis. *Taboo and genetics*. New York: Moffat, Yard, 1920.

Knight, Robert. Functional disturbances in the sexual life of women. *Bull. Menninger Clin.*, 1943, 7, 25-35.

Koos, Earl L. *Marriage*. New York: Holt, 1953.

Krafft-Ebing, R. von. *Psychopathia sexualis*. Brooklyn: Physician's and Surgeon's Book Co., 1922.

Krantz, K. E. Innervation of the human vulva and vagina. *Obstet. & Gynecol.* Oct. 1958.

Krich, A. M. *The homosexuals*. New York: Citadel, 1954.

Kroger, W. S., and Freed, S. C. *Psychosomatic gynecology*. Philadelphia: Saunders, 1951.

Kronhausen, Eberhard W., and Kronhausen, Phyllis C. Sweden: modern sex pioneer. *Candida*, 1959a, 1, No. 3, 11, 47-49.

——. *Pornography and the law*. New York: Ballantine Books, 1959b.

Kronhausen, Phyllis C., and Kronhausen, Eberhard W. *The Sexually responsive woman*. New York: Grove, 1964.

Kupperman, Herbert S. Frigidity: endocrinological aspects.

Quart. Rev. Surg. Gynecol. & Obstet., 1959, 16, 254-257.

——. Sex hormones. In Ellis, Albert, and Abarbanel, Albert (Eds.). *Encyclopedia of sexual behavior.* New York: Hawthorn, 1961.

LaBarre, Weston. *The human animal.* Chicago: University of Chicago, 1955.

Laidlaw, Robert W. A clinical approach to homosexuality. *Marr. Fam. Living,* 1952, 14, 39-46.

Lampe, E. H., and Masters, W. H. Problems of male fertility. *Fertil. & Steril.,* 1956, 7, 123-127.

Landis, Carney, and others. *Sex in development.* New York: Hoeber, 1940.

Landis, Carney, and Bolles, M. M. *Personality and sexuality of the physically handicapped woman.* New York: Hoeber, 1942.

Landis, Judson, and Landis, Mary G. *Readings in marriage and the family.* New York: Prentice-Hall, 1952.

Landis, Paul. *Making the most of marriage.* New York: Appleton-Century-Crofts, 1955.

Lang, Theodore. Studies in the genetic determination of homosexuality. *J. Nerv. Ment. Dis.,* 1940, 192, 55.

Langdon-Davies, John. *Sex, sin and sanctity.* London: Gollancz, 1954.

Lanval, Marc. *Inquiry into the intimate lives of women.* New York: Cadillac, 1950a.

——. *Les vicissitudes de la vie sexuelle.* Bruxelles: Le Laurier, 1950b.

——. *Sexualité.* Bruxelles: Laurier, 1951.

Lastrucci, Carlo. The dynamics of sexual motivation. *Marr. Hyg.,* 1947, 1, 65-69.

Laubscher, B. J. F. *Sex, custom, and psychopathology.* New York: McBride, 1938.

Lawrence, D. H. *Sex, literature and censorship.* New York: Twayne, 1953.

Lazarsfeld, Sofie, and Kadis, Asya. "Change of life"—end of life? *J. Indiv. Psychol.,* 1958, 14, 167-170.

Lehfeldt, Hans. Artificial insemination. In Ellis, Albert, and Abarbanel, Albert (Eds.). *Encyclopedia of sexual behavior.* New York: Hawthorn, 1961a.

——. Contraception. In *Ibid.,* 1961b.

Lehfeldt, Hans, and Ellis, Albert (Eds.). *Aspects of female sexuality.* Monograph of the Society for the Scientific

Study of Sex. *Quart. Rev. Surg. Obstet. & Gynecol.*, 1959, 16, 217-263.

LeMasters, E. E. *Modern courtship and marriage.* New York: Macmillan, 1957.

Lerner, Max. *America as a civilization.* New York: Simon & Schuster, 1958.

Leuba, C. *Ethics in sex conduct.* New York: Association Press, 1948.

Levie, L. H. Disturbances in male potency. *Int. J. Sexol.*, 1951, 4, 138-142.

Levine, Lena. *Modern book of marriage.* New York: Bartholomew, 1957.

Levine, Maurice. *Psychotherapy in medical practice.* New York: Macmillan, 1955.

Levy, John, and Munroe, Ruth. *The happy family.* New York: Knopf, 1938.

Lewandowski, Herbert. *Ferne Länder—fremde Sitten.* Stuttgart: Gunther, 1958.

Lewin, S. A., and Gilmore, John. *Sex wthout fear.* New York: Medical Research Press, 1951.

Lewinsky, H. Features from a case of homosexuality. *Psychoanal. Quart.*, 1952, 21, 344-354.

Licht, Hans. *Sexual life in ancient Greece.* London: Routledge, 1932.

Lindsey, Ben, and Evans, W. *Revolt of modern youth.* New York: Boni & Liveright, 1925.

——. *Companionate marriage.* New York: Garden City, 1929.

Linton, Ralph. *Study of man.* New York: Appleton-Century, 1936.

Liswood, Rebecca. *A marriage doctor speaks her mind.* New York: Dutton, 1961.

Locke, Harvey. *Predicting adjustment in marriage.* New York: Holt, 1951.

Loewenstein, J. *Treatment of impotence with special reference to mechanotherapy.* London: Hamilton, 1947.

London, Louis S. Analysis of a homosexual neurosis. *Urol. & Cutan. Rev.*, 1933, 37, 93.

——. *Mental therapy.* New York: Liveright, 1937.

London, Louis S., and Caprio, Frank S. *Sexual deviations.* Washington: Linacre, 1950.

Long, H. W. (pseud. for Smith, William H.) *Sane sex life and sane sex living.* New York: Eugenics, 1922.

Loras, Olivier. Honeymoon shock. *Sexology,* 1957, 14, 4-9.

Lucka, Emil. *Evolution of love.* London: Allen & Unwin, 1922.

Ludovici, Anthony M. *Man: an indictment.* New York: Dutton, no date.

———. The martyrdom of man in sex. *Marriage Hyg.,* 1947, 1, 21-26.

Lundberg, Ferdinand, and Farnham, Marynia. *Modern woman: the lost sex.* New York: Harper, 1947.

Lynd, R. S., and Lynd, H. M. *Middletown.* New York: Harcourt, 1929.

———. *Middletown in transition.* New York: Harcourt, 1937.

Lyon, Phyllis. Male and female: there is a difference. *Ladder,* 1959, 3, No. 10, 5-9.

MacDougald, Duncan. Aphrodisiacs. In Ellis, Albert, and Abarbanel, Albert (Eds.). *Encyclopedia of sexual behavior.* New York: Hawthorn, 1961.

Mace, David. *Marriage: the art of lasting happiness.* London: Hodder & Stoughton, 1945.

———. *Marriage counseling.* London: Churchill, 1948.

———. *Success in marriage.* New York: Abingdon, 1958.

———. The case for chastity. In Ellis, Albert, and Abarbanel, Albert (Eds.). *Encyclopedia of sexual behavior.* New York: Hawthorn, 1961.

Maclay, D. T. Boys who commit sexual misdemeanors. *Brit. Med. J.,* Jan. 16, 1960, 1, 186-190.

Maddock, L. Perilous pedestal. *Candida,* 1959, 1, No. 3., 21.

———. *Single and pregnant.* Hollywood: Genell, 1962.

Magoun, F. Alexander. *Love and marriage.* New York: Harper, 1948.

Malchow, C. W. *The sexual life.* St. Louis: Mosby, 1923.

Malinowski, B. *The sexual life of savages in northwestern Melanesia.* New York: Halcyon House, 1929.

Malla, K. *Ananga ranga.* New York: Medical Press, 1964.

Mantegazza, Paolo. *The sexual relations of mankind.* New York: Eugenics, 1935.

———. *The physiology of love.* New York: Eugenics, 1936.

Maranon, G. *Evolution of sex and intersexual conditions.* London: Allen & Unwin, 1932.

Maslow, A. H. Self-esteem (dominance-feeling) and sexuality in women. *J. Soc. Psychol.,* 1942, 16, 259-294.

———. *Motivation and personality.* New York: Harper, 1955.

Masters, William H. Rationale of sex steroid replacement in the "neutral gender." *J. Amer. Geriatrics Soc.,* 1955, 3, 389-395.

———. Infertility—a family unit problem. *Minn. Med.,* 1957a, 40, 842-846.

———. Sex steroid influence on the aging process. *Amer. J. Obstet. Gynecol.,* 1957b, 74, 733-746.

———. Menopause and thereafter. *Minn. Med.,* 1958, 41, 1-4.

Masters, William H., and Johnson, Virginia. The anatomy of female orgasm. In Ellis, Albert, and Abarbanel, Albert (Eds.). *Encyclopedia of sexual behavior.* New York: Hawthorn, 1961.

Masters, William H., and Johnson, Virginia. The sexual response cycle of the human female. III. The clitoris: anatomic and clinical considerations. *West. J. Surg. Obstet. & Gynecol.,* 1962, 270, 248-257.

Masters, William H., and Ballew, John W. The third sex. *Geriatrics,* 1955, 10, 1-4.

Masters, William H., Maze, Laurence E., and Gilpatrick, Thomas P. Etiological approach to habitual abortion. *Amer. J. Obstet. Gynecol.,* 1957, 73, 1022-1032.

Mauer, D., and Vogel, V. *Narcotics and narcotics addiction.* Springfield, Ill.: Thomas, 1954.

Maurois, André. *The art of being happily married.* New York: Harper, 1953.

Maxey, Wallace de Ortega. *Man is a sexual being.* San Francisco: Fabian, 1959.

May, Geoffrey. *Social control of sex expression.* New York: Morrow, 1931.

McPartland, John. *Sex in our changing world.* New York: Rinehart, 1947.

McReynolds, David. The gay underground—a reply to Mr. Krim. *Village Voice,* March 25, 1959.

Mead, Margaret. *From the south seas.* New York: Morrow, 1939.

———. *Male and female.* New York: Morrow, 1949.

Meagher, J. F. W., and Jelliffe, S. E. *A study of masturbation and the psychosexual life.* Baltimore: Williams & Wilkins, 1936.

Mehta, Rustam J. *Scientific curiosities of sex life.* Bombay: Taraporevala, 1938.

Menninger, Karl. *The human mind.* New York: Knopf, 1948.

Mercer, J. D. (pseud.). *They walk in shadow*. New York: Comet, 1959.

Meyer, Johann. *Sexual life in ancient India*. New York: Barnes and Noble, 1953.

Michelet, M. J. *Love*. New York: Rudd & Carleton, 1859.

Michigan, State of. *Report of the Governor's Study Commission on the deviated criminal sex offender*. Lansing: State of Michigan, 1951.

Mills, W. G., and Cameron, J. Lyle. Papers on hysterectomy and marital relations. *Brit. Med. J.*, Jan. 31, 1959.

Milne, Lorus J., and Milne, Margery J. *Mating instinct*. Boston: Little, Brown, 1954.

Moll, Albert. *Sexual life of the child*. New York: Macmillan, 1912.

——. *Perversion of the sex instinct*. New York: Julian, 1931.

Money, John. Hermaphroditism. In Ellis, Albert, and Abarbanel, Albert (Eds.). *Encyclopedia of sexual behavior*. New York: Hawthorn, 1961.

Money-Kyrle, Roger E. *Development of the sexual impulses*. London: Kegan, Paul, 1932.

Montagu, M. F. Ashley. *Adolescent sterility*. Springfield, Ill.: Thomas, 1946.

——. *The meaning of love*. New York: Julian, 1953.

Moore, K. L. Sex reversal in the newborn. *Lancet*, 1959, 1, 217.

Mowrer, O. H. Modern woman and the Harvard Report. *Proc. Inst. Child Res.*, 1947, 14, 43-51.

Mozes, Eugene B. The technique of wooing. *Sexology*, 1959a, 25, 756-760.

——. Married virgins. *Sexology*, 1959b, 25, 412-418.

——. Treating organic impotence. *Sexology*, 1959c, 25, 568-573.

——. Dangers of self-induced abortion. *Sexology*, 1959d, 25, 704-709.

Mudd, Emily H. *Practice of marriage counseling*. New York: Association Press, 1951.

Mudd, Emily H., Stone, Abraham, Karpf, Maurice, and Nelson, Janet F. *Marriage counseling: a casebook*. New York: Association Press, 1958.

Mudd, Emily H., and Krich, Aron M. (Eds.). *Man and wife*. New York: Norton, 1957.

Mullahy, Patrick. *Oedipus: myth and complex*. New York: Hermitage, 1948.

Munroe, Ruth. *Schools of psychoanalytic thought.* New York: Dryden, 1955.

Murdoch, George P. *Social structure.* New York: Macmillan, 1949.

Neal, Lee Roy. The sexual criminal. *Sexology,* 1959, 26, 40-44.

Nedoma, K. Homosexuality in sexological practice. *Int. J. Sexol.,* 1951, 4, 219-224.

Nefzawi, Mohammed al. *Perfumed garden.* Paris: Librairie Astra, no date.

Neugebauer, F. L. von. *Hermaphroditus bein Menschen.* Leipzig: Klinkhardt, 1908.

Nelson, Warren G. The physiology of reproduction. *Marr. Fam. Living,* 1963, 25, 74-80.

Neustadt, Rudolf, and Myerson, Abraham. Quantitative sex hormone studies in homosexuality. *Amer. J. Psychiat.,* 1940, 97, 524.

Neville-Rolfe, Sybil. *Sex in social life.* New York: Norton, 1950.

Newman, Horatio H. Twins and sex. In Robinson, Victor (Ed.). *Encyclopedia sexualis.* New York: Dingwall Rock, 1936.

Niemoeller, Adolph F. *American encyclopedia of sex.* New York: Panurge Press, 1935.

Nimkoff, Meyer F. *Marriage and the family.* Boston: Houghton Mifflin, 1947.

Nystrom, Anton. *Natural laws of sexual life.* St. Louis: Mosby, 1919.

Nyswander, Marie. *The drug addict as a patient.* New York: International Universities Press, 1958.

Oliven, John F. *Sexual hygiene and pathology.* Philadelphia Lippincott, 1955.

Olsen, Arthur R. *Readings on marriage and family relations.* Harrisburg: Stackpole, 1953.

Olsen, Henry. *Sexual adjustment in marriage.* London: Allen & Unwin, 1954.

Overzier, O. Chromosomatic sex in transvestitism. *Dtsch. Med. Wschr.,* 1958, 83, 181. *Excerpta Medica,* VIII, 1959, 12, 139.

Ovid. *Art of love.* New York: Putnam, 1929.

Parmelee, Maurice. *Sexual freedom in modern society.* Unpublished manuscript.

Parshley, H. M. *Science of human reproduction*. New York: Norton, 1933.

Parsons, Talcott, and Bales, Robert F. *Family, socialization and interaction process*. Glencoe, Ill.: Free Press, 1955.

Peck, M. W., and Wells, F. L. On the psycho-sexuality of college graduate men. *Ment. Hyg.*, 1923, 7, 697-714.

———. Further studies in the psycho-sexuality of college graduate men. *Ment. Hyg.*, 1925, 9, 502-520.

Peer, Lyndon A. Paper delivered at American Society of Plastic and Reconstructive Surgery. *Sci. Newsletter*, Nov. 1, 1958.

Phillips, E. Lakin. *Psychotherapy*. Englewood Cliffs, N. J.: Prentice-Hall, 1956.

Piers, Gerhart, and Singer, Milton B. *Shame and guilt*. Springfield, Ill.: Thomas, 1953.

Pillay, A. P. *The art of love and sane sex living*. Bombay: Taraporevala, 1948.

———. Common sense therapy of male sex disorders. *Int. J. Sexol.*, 1950, 4, 19-22.

Pillay, A. P., and Ellis, Albert (Eds.). *Sex, society and the individual*. Bombay: International Journal of Sexology, 1953.

Pilpel, Harriet F., and Zavin, Theodora. *Your marriage and the law*. New York: Rinehart, 1952.

Pincus, Gregory, and others. Effectiveness of an oral contraceptive. *Science*, 1959, 130, 81-83.

Ploscowe, Morris. *Sex and the law*. New York: Prentice-Hall, 1951.

Podolsky, Edward. *Sex today in wedded life*. New York: Simone, 1942.

———. (Ed.). *Encyclopedia of aberrations*. New York: Philosophical Library, 1953.

Poe, J. S. Successful treatment of a forty-year-old passive homosexual. *Psychoanal. Rev.*, 1952, 29, 23-36.

Pollens, Bertram. *The sex criminal*. New York: Macauley, 1938.

Pomeroy, Wardell B. Paper delivered at the annual meeting of the Mattachine Society, Sept. 8, 1958.

Popenoe, Paul. *Marriage: before and after*. New York: Funk, 1943.

———. *Modern marriage*. New York: Macmillan, 1953.

———. *Sexual inadequacy of the male*. Los Angeles: American Institute of Family Relations, 1946.

Porterfield, Austin L., and Salley, H. Ellison. Current folkways of sexual behavior. *Amer. J. Sociol.*, 1946, 52, 209-216.

Praz, Mario. *The romantic agony*. New York: Oxford, 1951.

Radzinowicz, L. (Ed.). *Sexual offences*. London: Macmillan, 1957.

Ramsey, Glenn V. *Factors in the sex life of 291 boys*. Madison, N. J.: Author, 1950.

Rank, Otto. *Will therapy and truth and reality*. New York: Knopf, 1950.

Reevy, William R. Sex in adolescence. In Ellis, Albert, and Abarbanel, Albert (Eds.). *Encyclopedia of sexual behavior*. New York: Hawthorn, 1961.

Reich, Wilhelm. *The sexual revolution*. New York: Orgone Institute Press, 1945.

———. *The function of the orgasm*. New York: Orgone Institute Press, 1942.

Reik, Theodor. *Of love and lust*. New York: Farrar, Straus, 1958.

———. *Masochism in modern man*. New York: Farrar and Rinehart, 1941.

Reiss, Iral. *Premarital sexual standards in America*. Glencoe: Free Press, 1960.

Rice, Thurman. *Sex, marriage and family*. Philadelphia: Lippincott, 1946.

Rickles, N. K. *Exhibitionism*. Philadelphia: Lippincott, 1950.

Riedman, Sarah R. Heightening sexual satisfaction. *Sexology*, 1957, 13, 768-773.

Robertiello, C. *Voyage from lesbos*. New York: Citadel, 1959.

Robie, W. F. *The art of love*. Ithaca, N. Y.: Rational Life Press, 1925.

———. *Rational sex ethics*. Ithaca, N. Y.: Rational Life Press, 1927.

Robinson, Marie N. *The power of sexual surrender*. New York: New American Library, 1962.

Robinson, Victor (Ed.). *Encyclopedia sexualis*. New York: Dingwall-Rock, 1936.

Robinson, Victor. *Morals in wartime*. New York: Publishers Foundation, 1943.

Robinson, William J. *Treatment of sexual impotence*. New York: Critic and Guide, 1915.

———. *Woman: her sex and love life*. New York: Eugenics, 1929.

———. (Ed.). *Sexual continence*. New York: Eugenics, 1930.

——. (Ed.). *Sexual truths*. New York: Eugenics, 1937.

Robinson, William J., and others. *Sex morality*. New York: Critic and Guide, 1912.

Rockwood, L. D., and Ford, M. E. N. *Youth, marriage and parenthood*. New York: Wiley, 1945.

Rogers, Carl R. *Client-centered therapy*. Boston: Houghton, Mifflin, 1951.

Rongy, A. J. *Abortion*. New York: Vanguard, 1933.

Rosanoff, Aaron J. *Manual of psychiatry*. New York: Wiley, 1938.

Rosen, Harold (Ed.). *Therapeutic abortion*. New York: Julian, 1954.

Rosen, James A. *Fertility in men and women*. New York: McCann, 1952.

Ross, Robert T. Measures of the sex behavior of college males compared with Kinsey's results. *J. Abnorm. Soc. Psychol.*, 1950, 45, 753-755.

Rougelot, R. Painful coitus. *Sexology*, 1958, 25, 276-281.

Rubin, Alan, and Bobbott, David. Impotence and diabetes mellitus. *J. Amer. Med. Assoc.*, Oct. 4, 1958.

Rubin, Isadore. Progress report on birth control pills. *Sexology*, 1958, 25, 218-220.

——. Illegal abortion. *Sexology*, 1959a, 25, 348-353.

——. The sordid business of sex. *Sexology*, 1959b, 25, 768-772.

——. Homosexual frameup. *Sexology*, 1959c, 26, 4-9.

Rubinstein, J. Psychotherapeutic aspects of male homosexuality. *Brit. J. Med. Psychol.*, 1958, 31, 74-78.

Russell, Bertrand. *Marriage and morals*. New York: Liveright, 1929.

Russell, Murray. Sterilization. In Ellis, Albert, and Abarbanel, Albert (Eds.). *Encyclopedia of Sexual Behavior*. New York: Hawthorn, 1961.

Rutgers, J. *The sexual life*. New York: Cadillac, 1940.

Sadler, W. S., and Sadler, L. K. *Living a sane sex life*. Chicago: Wilcox and Follett, 1944.

Safier, Benno, and others. *A psychiatric approach to the treatment of promiscuity*. New York: American Social Hygiene Association, 1949.

Salzman, Leon. Premature ejaculation. *Int. J. Sexol.*, 1954, 8, 69-76.

Sanders, Jacob. Homosexual twins. In Robinson, Victor (Ed.). *Encyclopedia sexualis*. New York: Dingwall Rock, 1936.

Sanger, Margaret. *Happiness in marriage*. New York: Brentanos, 1928.

Sanger, William W. *History of prostitution*. New York: Medical Publishing Co., 1921.

Sanwal, H. Socio-economic indications for permanent conception control. *J. Fam. Welfare*, 1958, 5, 27-37.

Schapera, I. *Married life in an African tribe*. New York: Sheridan, 1941.

Scheinfeld, Amram. *Women and men*. London: Chatto and Windus, 1947.

———. *Human heredity handbook*. Philadelphia: Lippincott, 1956.

Schilder, Paul. *Goals and desires of man*. New York: Columbia University Press, 1942.

Schreiner, Olive. *Woman and labour*. London: Allen, 1911.

Scott, George R., and Garland, Peter. *Sex and its mysteries*. Westport, Conn.: Associated Booksellers, 1955.

Secor, H. W. Alcohol and sex. *Sexology*, 1958, 24, 644-666.

———. Sex frustration. *Sexology*, 1959, 25, 480-483.

Seward, Georgene. *Sex and the social order*. New York: McGraw-Hill, 1946.

Shentoub, S. A. De quelques problemes dans l'homosexualité masculine active. *Rev. Franc Psychanalyse*, 1957, 21, 485-534. *Excerpta Medica*, VIII, 1959, 12, 958.

Sherwin, Robert Veit. *Sex and the statutory law*. New York: Oceana Publications, 1949.

———. Some legal aspects of homosexuality. *Int. J. Sexol.*, 1950, 4, 22-26.

———. Sex expression and the law. I. The law of rape. *Int. J. Sexol.*, 1951a, 4, 206-210.

———. Sex expression and the law. II. Sodomy: a medico-legal enigma. *Int. J. Sexol.*, 1951b, 5, 3-13.

———. Prostitution: a study of law and disorder. *Int. J. Sexol.*, 1952, 5, 201-205.

Shuttleworth, Frank. A biosocial and developmental theory of male and female sexuality. *Marr. Fam. Living*, 1959, 21, 163-170.

Skidmore, Rex A., and Cannon, Anthon S. *Building your marriage*. New York: Harper, 1958.

Slater, Elliott, and Woodside, Moya. *Patterns of marriage*. London: Cassell, 1951.

Sorokin, Pitirim. *The ways and power of love*. Boston: Beacon, 1954.

——. *The American sex revolution.* Boston: Sargent, 1956.

Spitz, René A. Autoerotism. *Psychoanalytic study of the child.* 1949, 3-4, 85-120.

——. Authority and masturbation. *Psychoanal. Quart.,* 1952, 21, 490-527.

Steinach, E. *Sex and life.* New York: Viking, 1940.

Stekel, Wilhelm. *Peculiarities of behavior.* New York: Liveright, 1924.

——. *Frigidity in women.* New York: Liveright, 1926.

——. *Sadism and masochism.* New York: Liveright, 1929.

——. *Sexual aberrations.* New York: Liveright, 1930.

——. *The homosexual neurosis.* New York: Physician's and Surgeon's Book Co., 1934.

——. *Bisexual love.* New York: Emerson, 1944.

——. *Autoerotism.* New York: Liveright, 1950.

Stokes, Walter R. *Modern pattern for marriage.* New York: Rinehart, 1948.

Stokes, Walter R., and Mace, David R. Premarital sexual behavior. *Marr. Fam. Living,* 1953, 15, 234-249.

Stone, C. P. Sex drive. In Allen, E. (Ed.). *Sex and internal secretions.* Baltimore: Williams & Wilkins, 1939.

Stone, Hannah M., and Stone, Abraham S. *A marriage manual.* New York: Simon and Schuster, 1952.

Stopes, Marie. *Married love.* London: Hogarth, 1952.

Storr, Anthony. The psychopathology of fetishism and transvestitism. *J. Analyt. Psychol.,* 1957, 2, 153-166.

Strain, Frances B. *Love at the threshold.* New York: Appleton-Century, 1939.

Strakosch, F. M. *Factors in the sex life of 400 psychopathic women.* Utica, N. Y.: State Hospital Press, 1934.

Strecker, Edward A. *Their mothers' sons.* Philadelphia: Lippincott, 1951.

Sullivan, Harry Stack. *Conceptions of modern psychiatry.* Washington: William Alanson White Foundation, 1947.

——. *The psychiatric interview.* New York: Norton, 1954.

Sulloway, Alvah W. *Birth control and the Catholic doctrine.* Boston: Beacon, 1959.

Suttie, Ian. *The origins of love and hate.* New York: Julian, 1952.

Swartz, Marc. Sexuality and aggression on romanum Truk. *Amer. Anthropol.,* 1958, 60, 467-486.

Swyer, G. I. M. Endocrine malfunctioning and homosexuality. *Practitioner,* 1957.

Talmey, Bernard S. *Love*. New York: Practioners Publishers, 1919.

Tappan, Paul W. *The habitual sex offender*. Trenton, N. J.: State of New Jersey, 1950.

Taylor, G. Rattray. *Sex in history*. London: Thames & Hudson, 1953; New York: Ballantine, 1962.

Taylor, William S. A. critique of sublimation in males. *Genet. Psychol. Monogr.*, 1933, 13, 1-115.

Tenenbaum, Joseph. *The riddle of sex*. New York: Pioneer, 1935.

Terman, Lewis M. *Psychological factors in marital happiness*. New York: McGraw-Hill, 1938.

———. Correlates of orgasm adequacy in a group of 556 wives. *J. Psychol.*, 1951, 32, 115-172.

Terman, Lewis M., and Miles, Catherine C. *Sex and personality*. New York: McGraw-Hill, 1936.

Thoma, Helmut. Mannlicher transvestitsmus und das verlangen nach geschlectsumwandlung. *Psyche*, 1957, 11, 81-124. *Psychol. Abstr.*, 1958, 32, 510.

Thomas, P. *Kama kalpa*. Bombay: 1953.

Thorne, Frederick C. *Principles of personality counseling*. Brandon, Vermont: Journal of Clinical Psychology, 1950.

Thornton, Henry, and Thornton, Freda. *How to achieve sex happiness in marriage*. New York: Vanguard, 1939.

Tietze, Christopher. *The clinical effectiveness of contraceptive methods*. New York: National Committee on Maternal Health, 1959a.

———. Legal abortion in Scandinavia. *Quart. Rev. Surg. Obstet. & Gynecol.*, 1959, 16, 227-234.

———. The use-effectiveness of contraceptive methods. *Res. Family Planning*, 1962, 357-369.

———. Intra-uterine contraceptive rings. *Excerpta Medica Internat. Cong.* Series 54, 1963.

Unwin, J. D. *Sexual regulations and human behavior*. London: Williams and Norgate, 1933.

———. *Sex and culture*. London: Oxford, 1934.

Vaerting, Mathilde, and Vaerting, Mathias. *The dominant sex*. New York: Doran, 1923.

Van de Velde, T. H. *Ideal marriage*. New York: Covici Friede, 1926.

Van Emde Boas, C. Group therapy of anorgastic women. *Int. J. Sexol.*, 1950, 4, 1-6.

——. *Abortus provocatus*. Amsterdam: Netherlands Vereniging Voor Sexuelle Servorming, 1952.

Vatsyayana. *The kama sutra*. Paris: Librarie Astra, no date.

Vincent, Clark. Hidden causes of frigidity. *Sexology*, 1957, 14, 180-185.

——. *Readings in marriage counseling*. New York: Crowell, 1956a.

——. Social and interpersonal sources of symptomatic frigidity. *Marr. Fam. Living*, 1956b, 18, 355-360.

Vincent, L. Toward an enlightened society. *Mattachine Rev.*, 1961, 7, 12-14.

Vollmer, August. *The police and modern society*. Los Angeles: University of California Press, 1936.

Von Urban, Rudolf. *Sex perfection and marital happiness*. New York: Dial, 1949.

Walker, Kenneth. *Physiology of sex*. New York: Penguin, 1946.

——. *Marriage*. London: Secter & Warburg, 1951.

Walker, Kenneth, and Strauss, E. B. *Sexual disorders in the male*. Baltimore: Williams & Wilkins, 1952.

Wall, O. A. *Sex and sex worship*. St. Louis: Mosby, 1932.

Waller, Willard, and Hill, Reuben. *The family*. New York: Dryden, 1954.

Weininger, Otto. *Sex and character*. New York: Putnam, 1906.

Weiss, Charles. Routine non-ritual circumcision in infancy. *Clin. Pediatrics*, 1964, 3, 560-563.

West, Donald J. *The other man*. New York: Morrow, 1955.

Westermarck, Edward. *The origin and development of the moral ideas*. London: Macmillan, 1917.

——. *The history of human marriage*. New York: Macmillan, 1922.

Westman, Axel. Effects of sterilization. *Sexology*, 1959, 25, 376-381.

Westwood, Gordon. *Society and the homosexual*. New York: Dutton, 1953.

——. *A minority*. New York: Longmans, 1960.

Wettley, Annemarie. Imaginary sex "disease." *Sexology*, 1959, 25, 778-784.

Wexberg, Erwin, *Psychology of sex*. New York: Blue Ribbon, 1931.

Wile, Ira S. (Ed.). *Sex life of the unmarried adult*. New York: Vanguard, 1934.

Williamson, Paul. Baffling sex parasite. *Sexology*, 1958, 24, 480-484.

Willoughby, Raymond R. *Sexuality in the second decade.* Washington: Society for Research in Child Development, 1937.

Winch, Robert F. *The modern family.* New York: Holt, 1952.

Winch, Robert F., and McGinnis, Robert (Ed.). *Selected studies in marriage and the family.* New York: Holt, 1953.

Windsor, Edward. *Hindu art of love.* New York: Falstaff, 1937.

Witschi, Emil. Sex deviations, inversions and parabiosis. In Allen Edgar (Ed.). *Sex and internal secretions.* Baltimore: Williams and Wilkins, 1932.

———. Studies on sex deferentiation and sex determination in amphibians. *J. Exp. Zool.,* 1937, 75, 313.

Witschi, Emil, and Mengert, W. F. Endocrine studies on human hermaphrodites and their bearing on the interpretation of homosexuality. *J. Clin. Endocrin.,* 1942, 2, 279-286.

Wittels, F. *Critique of love.* New York: Macauley, 1929.

Wolman, Benjamin. Sexual development in Israel adolescents. *Amer. J. Psychother.,* 1951, 5, 531-539.

Wood, Robert. Sex life in ancient civilizations. In Ellis, Albert, and Abarbanel, Albert (Eds.). *Encyclopedia of sexual behavior.* New York: Hawthorn, 1961a.

———. Sexual reform movements. In *Ibid.,* 1961b.

Woodside, Moya. Orgasm capacity among 200 English working class wives. *Int. J. Sexol.,* 1948, 1, 133-137.

Wright, Clifford A. Endocrine aspects of homosexuality. *Med. Rec.,* 1935, 142, 407-410.

———. Further studies of endocrine aspects of homosexuality. *Med. Rec.,* 1938, 147, 449-452.

———. Results of endocrine treatment in a controlled group of homosexual men. *Med. Rec.,* 1941, 154, 60-61.

Wright, Helena. *Sex fulfillment in married women.* London: Williams and Norgate, 1949a.

———. A contribution to the orgasm problem in women. *Int. J. Sexol.,* 1949b, 3, 8-12.

Wylie, Philip. *An essay on morals.* New York: Rinehart, 1947.

Yerkes, R. M. Sexual behavior in the chimpanzee. *Human Biol.,* 1939, 11, 78-111.

Young, Kimball. *Isn't one wife enough?* New York: Holt, 1954.

Young, W. C. Observations and experiments on mating behavior in female mammals. *Quart. Rev. Biol.,* 1941, 135-156; 311-355.

Young, Wayland. *Etos denied.* New York: Grove, 1964.

Zimmerman, Carle C., and Cervantes, Lucius F. *Marriage and the family.* Chicago: Regnery, 1956.

Zuckermann, S. *The social life of monkeys and apes.* London: Kegan, Paul, 1932.

California sexual deviation research, January 1953. California: Assembly of the State of California, 1953.

California sexual deviation research, March 1954. California: Assembly of the State of California, 1954.

The homosexual in our society. San Francisco: Pan Graphics Press, 1958.

Report of the committee on homosexual offenses and prostitution. (Wolfenden report). London: Her Majesty's Stationery Office, 1957.

Report of the Church Assembly. London, 1958.

Report on study of 102 sex offenders at Sing Sing prison. Albany: State of New York, 1950.

Index

R

Ramsey, Glenn V., 30, 32
Rank, Otto, 157
Rational psychotherapy
  and retarding orgasm, 156
  illustrative cases, 158-160
  methods of, 158
  techniques of, 161
Rear entry position, 110-112
  advantages, 111-112
  disadvantages, 112
  variations, 110-111
Reevy, William R., 36
Reik, Theodor, 44
Reproductive system, 16-18
  condition of health of, 16
RH blood types, 228-229
Rhythm method, birth control, 233
Rickles, N. K., 191
Riedman, Sarah, 142
Robertiello, C., 196
Robie, W. F., 126, 234
Robinson, William J., 113, 182
Rockwood, L. D., 36
Rogers, Carl R., 157
Rongy, A. J., 226
Rosanoff, Aaron J., 182
Rosen, Harold, 226
Rosen, James A., 220
Rougelot, R., 124
Rubin, A., 117
Rubin, Isadore, 200, 202, 226, 235
Rubinstein, J., 196
Russell, Bertrand, 39
Russell, Murray, 234
Russell, Rhoda Winter, 49

S

Sadism, 191
Safe period, birth control, 233
Salzman, Leon, 118
Sanders, Jacob, 182
Sanwal, H., 235
Satyriasis, 208
Schaffner, Bertram, 37

Scheinfeld, Amram, 25, 229
Schilder, Paul, 183
Scott, W. W., 211, 212
Secor, H. W., 35
Self-arousal, 65
Self-confidence in sexual arousal, 46-47
Self-defloration, 76
Self-stimulation (see Masturbation)
Self worth and sex competence, 82-84
Sensory organs, 15
Sensuality and sexuality, 16
Seward, Georgene, 29
Sex and Censorship, 140
Sex competence and self worth, 82-84
Sex determination of unborn child, 227-228
Sex dreams (see Dreams, sexual)
Sex excitement (see Arousal, sexual)
Sex murder, 192
Sex offenders
  prostitution, 202-204
    defined, 203
    reasons for male patronization, 203
  types of, 201
Sex offenses, laws against, 201-204
Sex organs, (see also Genitals)
  and location of pubic hair, 21
  female, 18-22
    and hormones, 21
    cervix, 20
    clitoris, 19
      caressing techniques, 58-59
      circumcision of, 19
      contact with during coitus, 95-96
    Fallopian tubes, 22
    glands of Bartholin, 20
    labia majora, 19
    labia minora, 19